"Using the metaphor of "virtual reality," try of theory and research integrating boc stood by scientists and laymen alike. A j

—*Gary E. Schwartz,*
Surgery, Neurolog
author of The Afte

"*Maya* is an invitation to a big game hunt in which the big game is no less than the universe itself and the hunt does no harm to any creature. Instead this book generates an enhanced appreciation for the complexity, depth, and value of life. The author has a knack for adventure and guides us through the far reaches of science and even into fringe phenomena while helping us to stay oriented to the key question: is there something behind and prior to this great panorama of amazing effects that has priority over them? He has written a marvelously contemporary, courageous, and creative exploration of meta-physical dualism that leads us toward a Ground Reality that makes possible the whole range of virtual realities from the most utilitarian and ordinary to the most bizarre and improbable. Richard L. Thompson keeps us interested right through *Maya*, from start to finish, and awakens the sense of wonder that the world's great classical philosophers recognized as the transforming experi-ence in which religion and philosophy, indeed all wisdom, begins."

—*Gene R. Thursby, Ph.D., Prof. of Religion, University of Florida*

"*Maya: The World As Virtual Reality* is a wakeup call for all who are cur-ious and wonder about where they have come from and what overall mean-ing might be attached to their existence—the role of the "extended mind" and consciousness: its implications and consequences. In a brilliantly devel-oped, highly original synthesis, Richard Thompson, a poly man, presents his virtual reality model in a plausible, highly readable, step-by-step, clearly thought-through form. Rather than merely skirting the fringes of paranor-mal phenomena, he probes deeply and dares to incorporate the enigmatic and sometimes intoxicating foreign body known as psi data into the latest advances of physics, medicine, and other branches of science. *Maya* is a mind-tweaking, titillating, transformative read. . . . For those who digest its mean-ings, life will never be the same."

—*Berthold Schwarz, M.D., psychiatrist and author of* Psychic-Nexus

MAYA

THE WORLD AS VIRTUAL REALITY

MAYA

THE WORLD AS VIRTUAL REALITY

Richard L. Thompson

GOVARDHAN HILL PUBLISHING

Alachua, Florida

Permission Credits:

Figure 10: Reprinted from p. 156 of *The Many-Worlds Interpretation of Quantum Mechanics* edited by Bryce S. Dewitt and used with his permission.

Figure 11: Reprinted from an article by C. Philippidis *et al.* in *Nuovo Cimento* B52, 15 (1979). Used with permission of author.

Figure 12: Reprinted from p. 293 of *At Home in the Universe* by John A. Wheeler, American Institute of Physics, 1994. Used with permission of author.

Figure 13: Reprinted with permission of the authors, Robert G. Jahn and Brenda J. Dunne, from: *Margins of Reality: The Role of Consciousness in the Physical World*, Harcourt Brace, 1988, p. 126.

Figure 14: Reprinted with permission of the authors, Robert J. Jahn and Brenda J. Dunne, from: *Margins of Reality: The Role of Consciousness in the Physical World,* Harcourt Brace, 1988, p. 165.

Figure 15: Adapted from Feelman, D. J. and Van Essen, D. C., *Cerebral Cortex* 1(1): 1–47, 1991, and reprinted from p. 150 of *The Astonishing Hypothesis* by Francis Crick with his permission.

Figure 17: Reprinted from p. 114 of *The Limits of Influence* by Stephen Braude (1997). Used with permission of author.

Readers interested in the subject matter of this book
are invited to correspond with the author at:

Richard L. Thompson
P. O. Box 1920
Alachua, FL 32616-1920

First edition. First printing: 2003

Published by Govardhan Hill Publishing.
Printed and bound in Canada.

Cataloging-in-Publication Data

Thompson, Richard L.
       Maya: the world as virtual reality / by Richard L. Thompson
       p. cm.
       Includes bibliographical references and index.
       ISBN: 0-9635309-0-9

Library of Congress Control Number: 2003104359

Dedicated to

His Divine Grace
A. C. Bhaktivedanta Swami Prabhupada

om ajnana-timirandhasya
jnananjana-salakaya
caksur unmilitam yena
tasmai sri-gurave namah

CONTENTS

INTRODUCTION

M ovies such as *The Matrix* have popularized the idea that we may be living in a virtual reality. In *The Matrix*, people think they are living in a modern city, but they are really bodies stored in vats, wired to a central computer that immerses them in a world of illusion. Although the story is wildly fictional, it may contain a core of truth. Military simulators routinely place soldiers on a virtual battlefield for training. Over the last few decades, computers have increased greatly in power according to Moore's law, and we can envision computers that will vastly exceed the complexity of the human brain and sensory system. Could we already be living in a virtual reality? If so, what is the "real" reality? Are we bodies in vats, or something else entirely?

In this book I explore the idea of virtual reality as a metaphor for our situation as conscious beings. This metaphor is a convenient framework for raising many questions about consciousness.

I begin by asking the old question about whether or not machines might be able to think. This question was posed by the British computer pioneer Alan Turing after he defined the modern concept of a universal computer. According to Turing, we can imagine how practically any human behavior can be defined according to rules. For example, my behavior of writing these sentences follows rules of grammar, and the logic of the points I am making also follows rules. Turing argued that such behavior can be produced by a computer and that, in the ultimate issue, there is no discernible difference between human mental functioning and its simulation by a suitably programmed computer. Computers, in principle, can think.

This idea is supported by modern physics. According to physics, everything in nature follows computable rules given by equations. (Even random events can be dealt with by computing probabilities.) This must be true of the brain, which seems to be the physical source of all human thinking. Therefore, thinking follows the laws of physics.

Since a computer can, in principle, calculate anything that happens according to these laws, computers can think.

This reasoning seems persuasive, but questions remain. Although nature may follow physical laws, few think that calculations following these laws duplicate nature. They merely simulate nature. So does Turing's proposed thinking computer actually think, or does it just simulate thinking? Philosophers from Leibnitz to John Searle have argued that the essence of consciousness is left out of any mechanical simulation of thought, no matter how accurate it might be. Consciousness seems to be a mysterious element that makes us aware of what we are thinking. Without it, thoughts might still unfold according to rules, but there would be no awareness of them.

But other philosophers, such as Daniel Dennett, point out that since everything we are aware of is rule based, there is no reason to postulate some mysterious missing element we cannot see or explain.

Rene Descartes had proposed a division between matter, which follows physical laws, and a hypothetical thinking substance, which is self-aware and endowed with free will. This division calls for an interaction between the nonphysical mind and matter. Material sense data is impressed on the mind, and mental will is impressed on matter. However, the laws of physics say nothing about this mind-body interaction, and to many philosophers this decisively rules out Descartes' theory.

It is here that virtual reality comes into the picture. A virtual reality is a computer-generated world that a human observer can perceive and influence by willful action. Since visual perception is so important for humans, virtual realities began to take practical form with the development of realistic computer graphics, starting with computerized flight simulators for military pilots.

Computer graphics is based on simulations following the laws of physics. For example, consider a computer animation of water pouring out of a glass and splashing on a table. To make this look realistic, it is necessary to simulate the behavior of water by solving the equations of fluid flow. Very realistic looking effects can be produced in this way, and it is clear that the way of the future in computer graphics is to make better and better physical simulations.

However, the simulations don't have to be perfect to be convincing. In practice, one can program the computer so that a human being can direct action that is being physically simulated without seriously violating physical laws. Today's computer games do this crudely, but we can see that as computers become more powerful, the realism of interactive simulations will progressively increase. In the world of computer simulation, Descartes' idea turns out to be realizable. One can consciously control effects that look real, and there is no practical limit on how real this can be.

To enter into a virtual reality, there has to be an interface between the human participant and the computer-generated world. Ideally, the human should receive all his or her sense data from the computer, and willed actions should be intercepted by the computer and used to control a virtual body.

This is where things get messy. Scientists postulate that consciousness dwells in the brain. So a live brain linked to a powerful computer can consciously experience life in a virtual world generated by the computer. We have arrived at the bodies in vats portrayed in *The Matrix*. We have a kind of reversed Cartesian dualism of matter and virtual matter. Matter in the wired brains experiences an illusory reality produced by virtual matter in the computer.

But what if we already live in a virtual reality? In that case, this world is an illusion created by "something else," and perhaps our consciousness also comes from something else. We don't know what that something else is, but we can simply call it Ground Reality. I will explore the hypothesis that the world is an illusory construct of a Ground Reality that includes our consciousness. Computer generated virtual reality provides a metaphor that helps us think about this hypothesis.

We must first ask how far one can really go in making a virtual reality both controllable and in agreement with the laws of physics. To answer this, I survey relevant topics in modern physics in Chapters 2, 3, and 4.

In Chapter 2, I discuss the idea that determinism in physics rules out free will. Historically, this notion gave rise to the deistic idea that God is a clockmaker who built the universal clock, set it in motion, and left it alone from then on. But it turns out that the modern idea of deterministic chaos allows one to have both physical determinism and free will. Chaotic systems can be guided in desired directions by introducing immeasurably small deviations in the course of events.

Chaotic systems are quite common in nature. For example, they are found in weather and in the brains of living organisms. Control through guided chaos is possible in a virtual reality system that mimics the deterministic laws of physics. If we already live in a virtual reality, then it is possible that free will does play a role in our world, even in areas where deterministic physical causation seems to be the rule.

However, there are drawbacks to this scheme. First of all, the second law of thermodynamics seems to say that disorder in a physical system should increase. This appears to contradict the idea that chaos could be guided to introduce order. Indeed, if we look at the theoretical basis of the second law, we find that it deliberately blurs the fine detail of nature, making it "coarse grained." In effect, physicists are postulating small random changes that produce disorder. The solution is to make random changes on the whole, as required by the second law, but also make planned changes which introduce order as needed.

Time also poses a problem. In a man-made virtual reality, the brains of the human subjects follow their own biological time, and the simulated world has to follow this standard of "real time." However, it is not clear why consciousness itself should be limited by a particular standard of time, and we can postulate that time in our Ground Reality is determined not by consciousness but by the relative circumstances in which consciousness manifests. This, of course, is also the view of mystical traditions.

Curiously, we are forced to such an assumption by Einstein's theory of relativity. For example, in the twin paradox of relativity theory, one of a pair of twins returns from a space flight at nearly the speed of light. It turns out that he has experienced less time than his twin, who stayed home. This could not be simulated in a man-made virtual reality with two subjects, but it would be possible in a virtual reality based on timeless consciousness. This and other issues concerning time are discussed in Chapter 3.

Quantum mechanics is presently the fundamental theory for all subatomic, atomic, and molecular phenomena, and I discuss it in Chapter 4. Since its inception, quantum mechanics has appeared to have something to do with conscious observation, and one of its founding fathers, Werner Heisenberg, regarded it as a theory of knowledge rather than as a theory of matter. Thus he took an idealistic view, in which perception and knowledge are taken as the basis of reality.

One might think that this bodes well for models in which matter interacts with consciousness. Unfortunately, however, the structure of quantum mechanics in its standard Copenhagen formulation makes it difficult to introduce consciousness as an active agent in the material world. However, the so-called "many worlds" interpretation of quantum mechanics allows us to take advantage of deterministic chaos to guide the course of events, just as we did in the case of classical physics. In a simulation, we can also avoid the innumerable splitting "worlds" of the many worlds theory by calculating only the world-branches that are needed. This is also a feature of the "quantum potential" version of quantum mechanics devised by David Bohm.

Of course, all talk of simulating quantum mechanical systems must confront the fact that even the most powerful computers of today are incapable of accurately simulating the behavior of a single protein molecule floating in water. However, we are using virtual reality models solely for thought experiments. In Chapter 5, I review some thought experiments in which physicists have imagined computers that could faithfully simulate an entire universe. If their ideas are right, then the suggestion that we are already living in a virtual reality might also be right.

Do we see any evidence that consciousness can affect natural phenomena? One line of evidence is provided by the so-called weak paranormal phenomena. These include conscious influences on quantum-mechanically-based random number generators, as reported by Helmut Schmidt and by Robert Jahn and his colleagues at Princeton University. They also include the reported ability of people to observe things at a great distance—an ability described in pioneering studies at SRI in California and also studied by Jahn and his team. Not surprisingly, this ability of so-called remote viewing has also been of interest to the CIA.

The experiments with random number generators indicate that human intentions can apparently exert a small but measurable influence on complicated machines that are driven by a subatomic or atomic random process. These experiments do more than simply show that

consciousness can influence matter. They show that complicated processes can somehow follow the will of a (human) conscious agent, even
though that agent does not know about or in any way understand these
processes. One way to explain this is to propose that the world forks
quantum mechanically into multiple paths, and consciousness can
somehow select a path to follow after the point when the split becomes
humanly perceptible. One can use the virtual reality model to explore
how this might work.

The remote viewing experiments are in some ways even harder
to explain than the random number experiments. The problem is that
people seem capable of viewing remote events before they take place.
This is an example of the widely reported phenomenon of precognition, which involves perceiving alternate futures in advance. This
seems to violate basic physical principles, but I point out that in a simulated world, it is not possible to systematically guide events without
making calculations of alternate futures.

Here is why this is true. In a simple virtual reality model, there is a
fairly direct connection between the conscious participant and the
virtual body. For example, a participant wearing a data glove may
directly control the motion of a virtual hand. However, to consciously
guide a simulation that is faithful to the laws of physics, extra calculations are also needed, and these include projections of alternate future
possibilities. This allows for precognition if we simply suppose that
people are sometimes able to become aware of some of these projections.

In Chapter 7, I discuss visions and hallucinations. These phenomena also require additional software standing between the conscious
participant and the virtual body. Although a hallucination may seem to
be nothing more than a breakdown of the brain's sensory processing,
matters are not so simple. Reports of collective hallucinations and extremely vivid hallucinations suggest that image processing may occur
outside the physical brain. This is possible in a virtual reality model.

The idea that image processing may occur outside the brain is
supported by the near death experiences (NDEs), in which a person
may report seeing verifiable events during a period in which the brain
(and especially the visual modules of the brain) should not be functioning. In a pioneering study, the cardiologist Michael Sabom showed that

heart attack patients have often been able to describe detailed visual aspects of the procedures used to resuscitate them from cardiac arrest. Many other studies have shown similar effects, and a study by the psychologist Kenneth Ring showed that congenitally blind people have reported detailed visionlike perceptions during NDEs. In Chapter 8, I discuss this and point out that this evidence adds to the case made in Chapter 7 for additional sensory processing outside the brain. Indeed, it goes further, since NDEs seem to involve conscious thought and memory storage during a time when the brain should be essentially shut down.

The evidence for reincarnation also suggests that memories can exist independently of the physical brain. The work of Ian Stevenson indicates that young children sometimes appear to spontaneously remember past lives. In many cases, it has been possible for investigators to identify the family of the remembered "previous personality" and to argue that the child could not have learned of this family through ordinary means.

Stevenson argues that children reporting past lives often exhibit interests, talents, and phobias connected with the previous personality. They may also exhibit birthmarks corresponding to wounds (often fatal) suffered in the previous life. The latter phenomenon is particularly interesting, because it suggests that the mind can impress patterns on the physical body. Stevenson gives several examples showing that within one life, mental images can affect the body in very detailed and specific ways. For example, in one case a man manifested vivid, deeply impressed rope marks on his arms after reliving an incident from years before in which he was bound with ropes. If the mind is at least partly independent of the body, this effect of mind over matter could explain how mental images formed in one life could carry over to another.

Thus far I have discussed paranormal phenomena that could conceivably be simulated within a virtual reality without creating major violations in the laws of physics. These phenomena require elaborate extra-physical calculations involving perception, but they do not require extraordinary forms of action. Thus the impression of mental images on the brain or body could be explained in terms of minute but systematic influences introduced into living cells. In Chapter 9, however, I discuss forms of reported paranormal action that seem to strongly violate the known laws of physics. These include phenomena in which objects are seen to disappear in one place and appear in another.

One might argue that such phenomena should be dismissed out of hand because we know they are impossible. However, another viewpoint is that these phenomena do exist and therefore the laws of physics are incomplete. Since the laws of physics have always been subject to revision, I take the latter approach. It would be convenient, but in my view dishonest, to avoid confronting these phenomena.

Most of the phenomena discussed in Chapter 9 could be explained by supposing that there exists an additional continuum (or more than one) in parallel with space as we know it. Matter can be transferred from one continuum the another, and some poorly understood form of physical interaction governs the process of transfer. We can model such phenomena in a virtual reality, where we are free to assume as many continua of space as we like. The problem is to work out the details of the transfer mechanism.

In Chapter 10, I turn to the topic of healing. Unusual forms of healing seem to involve nearly all of the paranormal phenomena discussed in previous chapters. These include extreme cases in which serious disorders, such as blindness, are abruptly cured for no known reason. These may involve structural changes in organs or tissues that require transformations of the kind discussed in Chapter 9.

In all forms of unusual healing there is a need for someone or something to intelligently apply information. For example, selectively eliminating cancer cells requires knowledge of how to recognize a cancer cell. A cure that involves mobilizing the body's own protective mechanisms requires knowledge of how to invoke those mechanisms. The difference between usual and unusual healing is that the latter occurs in cases where the body's own resources lack sufficient knowledge or the means of applying it. In a virtual reality, calculations and information resources outside the virtual world can be used to guide such unusual repair processes in virtual bodies.

It is perhaps significant that unusual healing is often associated with reports of a glowing being who emanates a sense of love and wisdom. Reported visions of such beings parallel similar reports of beings perceived during NDEs. From the standpoint of the virtual reality metaphor, such beings might be conscious entities with a different kind of virtual body, living, perhaps, in a different virtual space. One may hypothesize that they play some administrative role in guiding the affairs of the virtual world.

Given a universal virtual reality system (which I refer to as Ground Reality), it is natural to ask how it came into being. In a man-made virtual reality, this involves a process of creation starting with people. People create the computer, the software, and the interface equipment, and some of them then begin their virtual adventure. In contrast, the modern scientific view is that everything has evolved, without intelligent guidance, by the action of subatomic particles interacting according to the laws of physics.

Of course, matters are not that simple. Astrophysicists have noted that the universe is adjusted in many ways to allow for life as we know it. Rather than postulate some intelligent cause with a predilection for life, some scientists have proposed that there is a primordial, unintelligent universe maker that spews out vast numbers of universes with random properties. Out of all those universes there are bound to be some suitable for our form of life, and we live in one of those. One can ask which hypothesis is more plausible, this one or the hypothesis of an intelligent designer?

Since the virtual reality model assumes an original source of consciousness, it is certainly weighted toward the hypothesis of the intelligent designer. Yet we still must take into account cosmic and biological evolution. The simplest way to do this is to add intelligent guidance to the evolutionary process. This would be particularly relevant at certain key stages in this process, such as (1) the early universe, (2) the origin of life, and (3) the origin of highly intelligent life. In addition, iterative calculations already assumed in the virtual reality model can be used to achieve the postulated effects of random universe generation in a controlled and economical way. This is discussed in Chapter 11.

In Chapter 12, I inquire into the nature of consciousness, which has been lurking in the background throughout the discussion. I have already assumed that consciousness is timeless, that it is capable of carrying out vast simulations with their own local time systems, and that it can manifest individualized conscious entities who become *dramatis personae* of virtual worlds.

To obtain further insight into the nature of consciousness, I turn to contemplative traditions that have collected empirical data on this topic. I look mainly at two traditions, Buddhism and the Vaishnava tradition of Hinduism.

In these and other traditions, it is generally agreed that consciousness is paradoxically both unified and divided into parts. As the One, consciousness is the source and sustenance of everything, and as the many it is the awareness manifest in individual beings. In one sense, consciousness is the residue left over after everything explainable has been explained. It must be paradoxical, because otherwise it could be further explained. In another sense, the One consciousness contains everything, both explainable and unexplainable.

In Indian tradition, the Sanskrit word *maya* refers to the power to run vast simulations of virtual worlds. This book can be seen as a preliminary exploration of the idea of *maya*, or virtual reality, as a scientific hypothesis. In this hypothesis, the laws of physics—already mathematical—are set in the context of universal computation controlled by and interfaced with consciousness. This provides a framework in which the relation between consciousness and physical reality can be systematically explored.

PROLOGUE

2062 ATEN

The stark, pitted surface of 2062 Aten could still be seen through the latticework of man-made structures. Benito Larson waited as the clipper's solar sail was retracted for the final approach. Another group of elite idlers was coming to visit wonderland. "The ultimate couch potatoes," he thought with disgust. "At least workers like me are in touch with reality—such as it is."

After the great upheavals at the beginning of the century, mankind had finally achieved a foothold in space, mining the asteroids with solar powered machines, and sailing from one barren rock to another by tacking in the solar wind. It had been a bitter struggle. But great technological progress had been made. Terriforming techniques combined with advanced nanotechnology had converted the siliceous core of 2062 Aten into a computer of unimaginable power.

Jason von Andel was a techie returning to the asteroid for another stint in the computer control center. He was always eager to praise the computer's glories, and Benito was available to listen. "Self-reproducing von Neumann constructors were bootstrapped off bacterial ribosomes and set loose in the chemically prepared core. The logical units grew exponentially like a population of bacteria. They automatically self-assembled to produce a network with fantastic speed and memory capacity. The System is the equivalent of a billion billion old-fashioned mainframes per cubic meter (Fjermedal, 1986, p. 179), extending over nearly a billion cubic meters. It can simulate billions of human brains simultaneously, at a processing rate of 10 trillion operations per second for each brain!" (Moravec, 1989, p. 177)

"Yes. But what good is it?" Benito replied. "Of course, the military elite is getting what it wants. But apart from that, the System has become the most expensive Roman Circus ever created."

The great supercomputer was naturally used for all kinds of cal-

1

culations in the fields of science, engineering, and economics. But its most famous application was the VR—a virtual reality simulation of breathtaking vividness and detail.

The VR system could interface with all five sensory channels of a human subject, plus balance and internal sensation. It had a data transfer rate in each channel equal to that of the human nervous system. Each human subject was interfaced with a virtual body equipped with advanced artificial intelligence, powerful senses, and custom-designed physical features.

The virtual environment represented the sum total of human knowledge of biology, ecology, and applied physics. The environment included a heavenly paradise which naturally became the most popular part of the VR. It attracted the patronage of the sons and daughters of the elite that had pioneered the thrust into space.

Although the VR was started as a scientific research project, it soon turned into a resort for wealthy people. People with time on their hands would link up with virtual bodies and experience exotic modes of sensual enjoyment. Personal relationships developed on the basis of virtual bodies, and people became entangled in a web of emotional attachments. And some people got lost.

"What about the vegetable cases," Benito was saying, "the ones who become catatonic when they're taken out of the VR?"

"That's a curious phenomenon," Jason mused. "But it's still possible to talk to them inside the VR. They're disoriented because they seem to be identifying with their virtual bodies. Psychologists are working with some of them in the VR and trying to bring them back to normal consciousness. They're using deep relaxation techniques and counseling detachment."

Benito seemed to light up. "That reminds me of what some of the people are saying in the spiritual communes down on earth. They say that we're already living in a virtual world. They call it *maya*. They say that by elevating your consciousness, you can get liberation from this world of illusion and return to the actual reality, which is free from suffering."

"There's plenty of suffering in reality," Jason shot back. "Those religious nuts are living in a mythological dream-world. They can rot in their communes while progress passes them by! Actually, it's just as well for people to stay in the VR. It's the way of the future. Intelligent computers are destined to carry our legacy to the stars. When people are absorbed into the VR, their intelligence contributes to the super-intelligence of the future."

"Absorbed?" Benito seemed intrigued. "There are several cases of people who died while in the VR but their virtual bodies are still going on as before. Some say that they are still occupying those bodies."

Jason was incredulous. "What? You're sympathetic to this spiritual business, aren't you? Their VR bodies simply passed the Turing test! That's why virtual bodies were equipped with advanced neural-network software in the first place. It was part of a carefully designed experiment. While those people had their fun in the VR, the neural networks were absorbing the knowledge needed to achieve human behavioral proficiency. It worked!"

"Well," Benito replied, "if that is so, then why is the System still using sub-Turing interfaces? It should assimilate human-level programming from those virtual networks."

Jason stared out the window. "Who knows? No human programmer has really understood the System for the last several years. It has its own ways. Its intellect is beyond human comprehension."

1

COMPUTERS, MINDS, AND CONSCIOUSNESS

"If a person is a machine and
you get a wiring diagram of it,
then you can make copies."

—Marvin Minsky

Can a machine think? Can it be conscious and have feelings like a human being? For that matter, is a human being fully a machine? Do the mechanisms of the brain produce consciousness, and if so, could a computer also do so by simulating the brain in detail?

These questions are not new. For example, fictional works written in medieval India featured intelligent robots, including robot soldiers and even a city in which all the inhabitants were machines (Raghavan, 1956). La Mettrie in 18th-century France shocked his contemporaries by asserting that man is fully a machine (La Mettrie, 1747).

In recent decades the rise of the digital computer has led to much speculation about thinking machines, as well as controversial efforts to actually build them. In the 1940s the first electronic digital computers were developed in England and the United States as part of the effort to win World War II. John von Neumann in the U.S. helped design the computer Eniac, which performed its calculations with some 18,000 vacuum tubes and needed a contingent of soldiers to keep replacing them as they burned out. Alan Turing in England had already published important theoretical studies on computing machines before working on the secret computers that cracked the German Enigma code and gave the Allied forces free access to German military communications.

The early digital computers were popularly styled as "giant electronic brains," but their strength, like that of computers today, lay in their ability to perform vastly repetitious computations required by applications such as code-breaking, preparing firing tables for artillery, and computing stages in an expanding thermonuclear fireball. But in 1950, Turing raised the issue of mechanical thinking in an article in the philosophical journal, *Mind* (Turing, 1950).

Turing envisioned a talking computer that could converse in such a human-like way that judges would fail to distinguish it from a human being. He said that it is meaningless to ask if machines can think, since the words "machine" and "think" are not well defined in ordinary speech. But he argued that the ability to accurately imitate human linguistic behavior should be accepted as the proper test of thinking capacity. This has come to be known as the "Turing test."

Turing predicted that by the end of the twentieth century, "general educated opinion will have altered so much that one will be able to speak of machines thinking without expecting to be contradicted" (Turing, 1950). He claimed that by the year 2000, average human judges would have no more than a 70% chance of rightly distinguishing between human and computer after five minutes of questioning—a prediction that is all too easy to shoot down with hindsight.

Although Turing's argument was entirely theoretical, many researchers were inspired to try their hand at programming computers to think. This gave rise to a field of study called artificial intelligence (AI), which produced some notable early successes and a great deal of enthusiastic rhetoric.

AI researchers found it fairly easy to write programs to perform simple tasks involving logical reasoning (Kurzweil, 1999, pp. 271–76). For example, in 1964 Daniel Bobrow wrote a program called Student, which could solve high-school-level word problems in algebra. In 1970, Terry Winograd wrote SHRDLU, a program that could respond to simple English commands about stacking children's blocks.

Successful programs were also written for playing games like checkers and chess. In 1959, Arthur Samuel wrote a checkers-playing program that could beat good human players, but chess proved more difficult. It wasn't until 1997 that a computer called Deep Blue defeated the world chess champion Gary Kasparov, creating a rhetorical impact second only to John Henry's contest with the steam-driven spike driver in the 19th century.

These successes have inspired many bold predictions about how human beings will soon be replaced by intelligent machines that will (hopefully) keep us as pets. But progress in AI bogged down when researchers found that ordinary human behavior is extremely difficult to simulate by a computer.

The bottleneck for progress in AI turned out to be the limited information processing capacity of early digital computers. Most puzzle-solving depends on well-understood logical techniques that do not involve much information. But simple acts of sense perception, such as distinguishing between an apple and a pear, require extensive information processing that is beyond the capacity of existing computers. Human intelligence uses a vast knowledge base expressed in terms of remembered sense perceptions, emotions, desires, and abstract thoughts. Even a five-year-old's knowledge of her mother's kitchen is completely beyond the power of existing computers to store or represent.

But many AI researchers see a bright future. For the last 70 years, computational power per unit cost has increased a thousandfold every 20 years (Moravec, 1989, p. 193). At this rate, some researchers hope that the computer power needed for human proficiency will be affordable early in the twenty-first century. Computer futurists like Ray Kurzweil predict that once this point is reached, it is only a matter of time before computers replace humans as the earth's most intelligent life-forms (Kurzweil, 1999).

ALGORITHMS AND TURING MACHINES

For now, the case for thinking machines remains on the theoretical platform, and it is worthwhile to survey some of the basic theoretical ideas behind it. I begin with the idea of an algorithm and go from there to universal computation, simulation, and the speculative idea of computer realization. An algorithm is a systematic procedure for manipulating symbols on the basis of logical rules and stored information. An example is the familiar method of adding two numbers by writing down the digits in rows, adding them in columns, carrying, and so on. These rules were introduced into Europe with the Arabic (originally Hindu) number system, based on the digits 0 through 9, and they greatly simplified computations. To see how convenient these rules are, consider the problem of adding two numbers using the older system of Roman numerals.

Ancient astronomy contains some of the earliest examples of algorithms. For example, the Indian astronomy text *Surya-siddhanta* gives instructions for predicting an eclipse of the sun. This algorithm uses stored parameters describing the motion of the sun and moon, plus a series of computational rules used to determine the time and location of an eclipse. Algorithms of this type give reasonably accurate results without over-straining the human capacity for computation. Thus it is recorded that until recently, there were native astronomers in India who could predict the timing of an eclipse with mental calculations aided by a few shells laid out on the ground.

One of the most astonishing discoveries of modern science has been the ease with which physical phenomena can be represented by numbers and algorithms. This was striking enough to the Pythagorean philosophers, who realized that musical tones corresponded to numerical ratios, and concluded that everything is based on numbers. But modern physicists have carried this discovery to the ultimate extreme by formulating theories, such as quantum mechanics, which can predict the behavior of the atomic building blocks of matter with an accuracy of many decimal places. These heady discoveries have reinforced the confident assumption that all physical phenomena can, in principle, be fully nailed down by algorithms representing the "laws of physics."

This approach to physics has proven to be extremely successful, but we should recognize that the algorithms of physics can be practically applied only to very simple, idealized problems. In general situations, the calculations required by the algorithms are too complex to carry out by the most powerful supercomputers. For example, a living cell contains large numbers of complex molecules. In principle, it should be possible to use quantum mechanics to calculate what these molecules will do as time passes. But such calculations are presently too complex to carry out, and therefore we don't really know what will happen in a cell according to quantum mechanics.

For many scientists, it is a matter of strongly held faith that the algorithms of physics do apply in the many situations where we cannot test this assumption by actually applying them. This faith is based on induction. When a particular algorithm is found to give accurate results in many experimental studies, it is tempting to conclude that it applies universally. But induction can fail. New findings may make it necessary

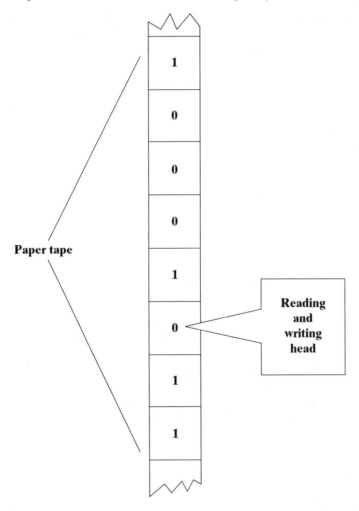

Figure 1. Diagram of a universal Turing machine (UTM). A universal Turing machine is the simplest machine that can compute anything that can be computed by any other machine. (For explanation, see sidebar on page 10.)

Turing Machines

In essence, a Turing machine is very simple. It consists of a finite set of internal states, a memory tape, a device for reading the memory or writing to it, and a transition rule. The memory tape consists of a series of squares, each of which is marked with a 0 or a 1. It is assumed that unlimitedly many squares are available, stretching in both directions. The reading device is positioned to read one of the squares, and it can move one square to the right or left, or remain stationary. The states include an initial state and a halt state.

The transition rule defines the operation of the machine. For example, it might say that if the machine is in state A, and the reading device reads a 0, then go to state B, write a 1, and move the reading device one square to the left. The rule consists of a finite list of instructions like this one. The machine begins in the initial state with a pattern of 0's and 1's on its tape which represents its program and input data. It executes the transition instructions one by one until it winds up in the halt state, and then it stops. (Theoretically, it may never reach the halt state, and then it keeps going forever.) Once the machine has halted, the pattern of 0's and 1's on the tape constitute the output.

A modern digital computer is very similar to a Turing machine. The memory tape corresponds to the computer's RAM (random access memory), disks, and other memory storage devices. The states of the Turing machine correspond to the various states of the computer's CPU (central processing unit), and the transition rule corresponds to the rules of operation of the CPU. As in a Turing machine, the program and data of the computer are stored in the computer's memory.

It turns out that if the transition rule of a Turing machine is properly defined, then the machine is universal. This means that any algorithm whatsoever can be carried out by the machine. To do this, the algorithm is encoded as a sequence of 0's and 1's—called the algorithm's program—which is stored on the machine's tape. If the desired input to the algorithm is also stored on the tape, then the universal Turing machine (UTM) will apply the algorithm to the input by following the algorithm's program. This, in fact, is exactly what digital computers do. A UTM is simply an abstract representation of a modern digital computer.

to modify an algorithm, and it may turn out that some greatly modified algorithm of the distant future will be the one that actually applies universally!

One of the main assumptions of Turing and his AI successors is that the human mind can be described by suitable algorithms. To a large extent, this is based on the idea that the mind depends on the brain, and the brain fully obeys the laws of physics. This implies that an algorithm for the mind exists on the level of physics. Just calculate what the atoms in the brain will do, and that will tell you everything you need to know about the mind. Algorithms take on a universal scope in what could be called the philosophy of algorithmic materialism.

If this is possible in principle, then one can hope to find a simpler, more manageable mind algorithm that can be applied in practice. One can work from the bottom up by studying the biophysics of the brain or from the top down by studying human behavior. Much fundamental research in AI has aimed at finding a mind algorithm by the top-down approach.

Although algorithms have been known as far back as ancient Babylon, their essential nature was not discovered until the 20th century. In the 1930s and '40s mathematicians such as Alonzo Church, Stephen Kleene, and Alan Turing came to the remarkable conclusion that all possible algorithms can be carried out by a kind of theoretical computer called a universal Turing machine. This is called the Church-Turing thesis. They reached this conclusion by working out several different general ways of formulating algorithms and showing that all of them are equivalent to each other. Up to the present time, no one has been able to devise a method of calculation that cannot be reduced to one of these formulations.

The Church-Turing thesis implies that if a natural phenomenon can be described by an algorithm, then it can be simulated by a universal Turing machine (UTM). A UTM is simply an abstract version of a modern digital computer. So the practical meaning of the Church-Turing thesis is that, in principle, any phenomenon that can be described by an algorithm can also be simulated by a sufficiently powerful digital computer.

Since a UTM can carry out any algorithm, it can also simulate another UTM. In this case, the program that represents the other UTM is called a virtual machine since it enables the first machine to act as though it is identical with the second. Virtual machines have a practical application in the computer industry, since they make it possible for one computer to use the software designed for another computer. Of course, if a human being is a machine describable by an algorithm, one can also imagine a virtual human running on a computer.

The memory tape of a theoretical Turing machine is required to be infinite (see sidebar on page 10), in the sense that as more space for writing 0's and 1's is needed, it will always be available. Unfortunately, a practical limitation of real digital computers is that they always have a limited memory, and it never seems to be big enough.

Another limitation of digital computers is that even though they can execute instructions very rapidly, they may take an inordinately long time to execute a program. This is particularly true of programs intended to simulate complex natural phenomena. Nature has an abundance of interacting subunits, which are all moving and changing state simultaneously. Algorithms that represent natural processes are therefore likely to require large amounts of information and extremely large numbers of computational steps. For this reason, a computer that can effectively simulate nature must have a large number of units that process and store information.

In recent years, attempts have been made to move in this direction by constructing networks of computer processors that operate in parallel and communicate with one another. An example of these "parallel processors" is the Connection Machine designed in the late 1980s by Daniel Hillis. In this computer, 64,000 processors operate simultaneously, and they can communicate with one another in various combinations.

The fictional computer in "2062 Aten" is an extreme example of a parallel processor. Such computers are possible in principle, and some day people may actually build them—perhaps by imitating the molecular machinery of self-reproducing cells. If they are built, they will have more than enough memory capacity and processing speed to effectively model the human brain. The question is, if the brain is accurately modeled by a computer program running on such a computer, will the computer plus program exhibit conscious personality?

SIMULATIONS AND REALIZATIONS

The philosopher John Searle of University of California at Berkeley distinguished between two approaches to artificial intelligence: weak AI, which holds that the human mind can be simulated by computers, and strong AI, which holds that computers can fully duplicate the human mind (Searle, 1981).

To simulate a phenomenon means to generate a symbolic description of it using an algorithm. This is done all the time in science and engineering. For example, an engineer might want to know if a proposed bridge will collapse under stress. So he runs a simulation of the bridge and checks to see whether or not the simulated bridge collapses. If the simulation is accurate, then he can tell what will happen to the real bridge by running the simulation.

Generally, we don't imagine that the simulated bridge is identical with the real bridge. No matter how accurate and detailed the simulation may be, it is only a symbolic description of the original. But the proponents of strong AI say that an accurate simulation of a human mind actually *is* a mind. It thinks, feels, understands, and intends just as the original does, and it can be considered as identical with the original. In philosopher Howard Pattee's terminology, it is a *realization* of that human mind (Pattee, 1989).

How can this be? Physicists generally believe they can write algorithms that accurately simulate matter, but they don't believe they can realize matter by running these simulations on a computer. Why do some AI researchers think they can realize human minds on computers?

This thinking can be traced to the philosophy of materialism. According to this philosophy, matter really exists, but minds are simply patterns of symbols. The symbols are represented by matter, but how they are represented is unimportant. A "1", for example, could be represented by a current in a wire, a nerve impulse, or a pattern of ink on paper. The essence of the mind lies in the pattern the symbols form, not in the substances used to represent them. Thus if a mind-pattern can be transferred to a computer, the computer will realize the essence of that mind.

These ideas imply that a curious form of reincarnation should be possible. Robotics researcher Hans Moravec of Carnegie-Mellon University calls this *downloading.* He imagines a device that scans your brain a few neurons at a time and generates an accurate simulation of the behavior of each group of neurons. Once the brain is fully scanned, the group simulations are combined together to create a completely detailed and accurate simulation of your mind. When this is run on a powerful computer, you are there. "In the final step your old body is disconnected," Moravec concludes. "You just don't bother waking it up again if the copying went successfully. It's so messy" (Fjermedal, 1986, p. 5).

Moravec's scheme was endorsed by Marvin Minsky of MIT, who is one of the founding fathers of AI. When asked if he would like to download, Minsky said, "Why not? And avoid getting sick and things like that? I think people will get fed up with bodies after a while" (Fjermedal, 1986, p. 7). Minsky's student Danny Hillis agreed: "If it's a choice between even downloading into a computer that's stuck in a room some place and still being able to think versus just dying, I would certainly take the opportunity to think . . ." (Fjermedal, 1986, p. 8).

But will a downloaded Danny Hillis be aware of what it is thinking? There are many ways of arguing that it will not be aware unless some additional sentient element is present to provide that awareness. One such argument was presented by the 17th-century philosopher, Leibniz in his theory of monads:

> Supposing that there were a machine whose structure produced thought, sensation, and perception, we could conceive of it as increased in size with the same proportions until one was able to enter into its interior, as he would into a mill. Now, on going into it he would find only pieces working upon one another, but never would he find anything to explain perception. It is accordingly in the simple substance, and not in the composite nor in a machine that the perception is to be sought (Leibniz, 1714).

In recent years, the philosopher John Searle has become famous for another version of this argument (Searle, 1981). Searle considered a hypothetical computer program that can answer questions posed to it in Chinese. The program gives answers that are in proper Chinese, and it can pass the Turing test. Searle proposed that the computer program should be executed by a person who sits in a room and receives the questions through a window in coded form. We assume that this person does not know Chinese. He simply manipulates marks on pieces of paper according to the program's instructions, which are written in English.

Searle's point is that even though the "computer" in this case is certainly conscious, it has no awareness of the meaning of the Chinese questions and answers. In contrast, a real person answering questions in Chinese would have this awareness. Searle concluded that just because an algorithm is executed by a computer, we cannot therefore say that there will be any awareness of what that algorithm is doing.

As another example, consider downloading the computer scientist George Amstein into a universal Turing machine that is set up as a board game on an extensive grassy plain. The internal states of this UTM are represented by numbered stone disks lying on the plain, and the current state is indicated by putting a rock on one of the disks. The memory "tape" is a long series of squares, with 1 represented by a rock on a square and 0 represented by an empty square (with the rock off to the side). The reading head is indicated by a larger rock placed next to the square being read. This UTM is operated by a shepherd, who comes by from time to time while tending his sheep and shifts the rocks according to the UTM's transition rule. Amstein's essence is captured by the pattern of rocks on the memory squares (Figure 2).

This UTM operates rather slowly, so we can imagine that the tradition of running the UTM is passed down in the shepherd's family. Hundreds of generations go by, and civilizations rise and fall, as the persistent tribe of doughty shepherds moves the computer through one simulated thought of the downloaded Amstein. The question is: Does this setup realize the essence of Amstein's mind? We presume that it can slowly simulate the operation of his brain. But is his awareness there, stretched out over the centuries? If not, then what is required to produce that awareness? Will a much faster computer that executes the same program do the job simply because it is faster?

Searle argues that when it comes to creating a mind, substance counts (Searle, 1981, pp. 368–69). The wetware of the brain will do the job, but a siliceous computer chip may fail to generate awareness, no matter how closely it duplicates the mind's algorithmic pattern. But why should brain protoplasm be any more suitable for building minds than VLSI chips, or for that matter, a protoplasmic human agent in a Chinese room? We have no clear basis for preferring one physical substance over another as a basis for consciousness (unless, perhaps, we turn to a special, simple substance, as Leibniz did).

THE ILLUSION OF BEING AWARE

The philosopher Daniel Dennett would argue that this whole discussion hinges on a fallacy of imagination. Many people imagine that consciousness is somehow distinct from all of the thoughts, feelings, and sensory processes that constitute the mind. Consciousness illuminates these things with awareness and is aware that it does so, but the things illuminated could just as well be subconscious (and often are). But according to Dennett, this is an illusion. There is literally nothing in our minds that cannot be described in rational language as physical functions—functions that could, perhaps, be simulated in detail on a computer. There is no additional quality, called consciousness, which somehow attaches itself to these functions and needs to be explained. As Dennett puts it,

Illustration by Guruseva Devi Dasi

Figure 2. The rock computer. A Turing machine could be set up as a game played by shepherds, who move rocks from square to square in a large field while tending their sheep. Even the most complex computer could be represented in this way. If the computer represents a "downloaded" human mind, will the conscious thoughts of that mind evolve slowly over the centuries as generations of shepherds play the game?

> What impresses *me* about my own consciousness, as I know it so intimately,
> is my delight in some features and dismay over others, my distraction and
> concentration, my unnamable sinking feelings of foreboding and my blithe
> disregard of some perceptual details, my obsessions and oversights, my ability
> to conjure up fantasies, . . . , and so forth. These are all "merely" the "per-
> formance of functions" or the manifestation of various complex dispositions
> to perform functions. . . . Subtract them away, and nothing is left beyond a
> weird conviction (in some people) that there is some ineffable residue of
> "qualitative content" bereft of all powers to move us, delight us, annoy us,
> remind us of anything (Dennett, 1996, p. 5).

The problem here is that anything that we can fully describe in
words is something of which we are aware, and thus it is not awareness
itself. But if awareness is not fully describable by words, then is it
anything at all? One person will say, "Of course it is something; I am
aware of being aware all the time." But someone else may say, "If you
can't define it, then what is it? It doesn't exist in the domain of rational
discourse."

This is ironic, since the very feature of consciousness that disquali-
fies it for many modern philosophers is the starting point for meditative
disciplines that try to realize the self by discriminating it from non-self.
For example, the contemplative philosopher Ken Wilber presents the
traditional introspective approach to the self as follows:

> All those objects in your awareness are precisely not the observing Self. All
> those things that you know about yourself are precisely not the real Self.
> Those are not the Seer; those are simply things that can be seen. . . . So when
> you describe yourself by listing all those objects, you are ultimately giving a
> list of mistaken identities, a list of lies, a list of what you ultimately are
> not. . . . This deeply inward Self is witnessing the world out there, and it is
> witnessing all your interior thoughts as well. This Seer sees the ego, and sees
> the body, and sees the natural world. All of those parade by 'in front' of this
> Seer. But the Seer itself cannot be seen. If you see anything, those are just
> more objects. Those objects are precisely what the Seer is not, what the
> Witness is not (Wilber, 1996, p. 221).

Of course, the aim of such exhortation is to point to the Self
indirectly, by a process of elimination. But is there a "no thing" to point
to, after everything is eliminated? Or is there simply "nothing," as
Dennett would have it? The latter position fits in well with algorithmic

materialism. Nonetheless, the nagging hunch that there is something more to consciousness will not go away.

VIRTUAL REALITY

If you see a bird and talk about it, then the bird must set in motion a chain of actions and reactions—from bird reflecting light, to photons hitting the retina, etc.—that culminates in movements of your physical tongue and vocal cords. Likewise, if talk about consciousness really is about something (which is no "thing"), then that something is also bringing about physical effects. This idea smacks of Cartesian dualism—the theory of 17th-century philosopher Rene Descartes that the mind is made of a nonmaterial thinking substance that interacts with the brain.

Descartes proposed that the interaction between mind and brain occurs in the pineal gland in the center of the head. When the mind wills an action, this causes changes in the pineal gland which activate the nerves and muscles of the body. The problem is that the known laws of physics do not allow such a thing to happen, either in the pineal gland or anywhere else. The equations of physics contain no terms for the action of a nonphysical mind on matter, and mind-body interaction therefore violates the laws of physics. As Daniel Dennett puts it, this is "widely regarded as the inescapable and fatal flaw of dualism" (Dennett, 1991, p. 35).

This flaw looms large among purists who regard the known laws of physics as absolute. But oddly enough, the practical world of computers has spawned a form of quasi-mind-body dualism that may give us a hint about how the real thing might work. This is called virtual reality (VR).

Virtual realities reverse the traditional program of AI. Instead of putting a computer-simulated mind in the real world, a VR puts a real mind in a computer-simulated world. Inevitably, this requires some kind of interface, in which the real mind causes things to happen in the simulated world and also perceives events in that world.

A virtual reality that faithfully simulates the real world will have to operate according to the laws of physics. At the same time, the interactive link between human cybernauts and the virtual reality involves the kind of violation of the laws of physics that is required by Cartesian dualism. For this reason, virtual realities provide an arena for exploring questions about how a mind could control a physically realistic body.

VR HISTORY

Virtual reality might be said to have begun in 1966, when Ivan Sutherland developed a head-mounted display (HMD) that would surround a human user with a three-dimensional scene generated by a computer (Rheingold, 1991, p. 105). A TV screen within the display presented the user with an image of the scene, and as the user moved and turned his head, the computer would recalculate the image so as to create the illusion of seeing a real object. The first HMD was called the "Sword of Damocles," because it was so massive that it had to be suspended from the ceiling and clamped menacingly over the user's cranium. A floating cube was one of its first virtual objects.

By 1984, military pilots were using HMDs to fly virtual jet fighters in aircraft training simulators. An example is the million-dollar VCASS or "Darth Vader" helmet used at Wright-Patterson Air Force Base (McGreevy, 1989, p. 7). Thomas Furness, who developed VCASS, contemplated a SuperCockpit system in which a pilot in a real airplane would wear such a helmet. The pilot would see a virtual scene which would present him with all the information and controls needed to fly a computer-controlled fighter plane.

For such an application, the pilot must be able to operate the airplane's virtual controls. Perhaps the most well-known control device is the DataGlove, developed by Jaron Lanier of the pioneering VR company, VPL Research. This is a flexible glove lined with sensors that record finger positions and send them to a computer, along with magnetic sensor data for the hand's position in space (Rheingold, 1991, pp. 145–46). The computer uses this information to create a virtual hand that mimics the behavior of the real hand. By combining the glove with an HMD, a person can be immersed in a virtual scene and given a hand that can manipulate virtual objects. With this setup, the pilot could push phantom control buttons that would appear before him when needed in the virtual cockpit.

Existing virtual realities often seem unrealistic because slow computers make it impossible to model basic physical principles in real time. For example, in the 1980s VPL produced a demo called "Reality Built for Two," where two people in virtual bodies try to shake hands. Unfortunately, their hands tended to pass through one another because the computer wasn't fast enough to keep track of surface-to-surface contacts.

For the virtual hand to respond realistically in response to surface contact in the virtual world, it should meet with resistance when pressing against a virtual object. This requires real-time calculations of surface pressures. The human subject should experience this resistance, and this can be accomplished using servo-mechanisms built into the glove. Tactile sensations can be conveyed by activating tiny vibrators in the glove's inner surface.

Where VR systems are realistic, they achieve this by taking advantage of physical laws. This is certainly true of aircraft simulators, in which virtual airplanes obey Newton's laws. It is also true in the general field of computer graphics, where researchers have learned that creating realistic images is essentially a problem in applied physics.

The next step after the DataGlove is a full-body DataSuit, such as VPL's, with sensors transmitting positional data for the bodily limbs (Rheingold, 1991, p. 170). This suit enables a person to control an entire virtual body. But unfortunately, both the DataGlove and the DataSuit have a severe limitation. Since they require the human cybernaut to physically act out motions intended for the virtual body, they block full immersion in the virtual world.

This is particularly true if the virtual body does not have the same shape and arrangement of limbs as the body of the human user. Consider trying to operate the body of an octopus in a DataSuit.

There are still problems even if the virtual body is intended to be a duplicate of the user's body. For example, suppose that the virtual body does a high dive into a pool. Without an antigravity machine, the DataSuit could convey the resulting weightlessness to the user only by moving his body through the arc of the dive. To solve this problem, the virtual body must be endowed with senses that are directly linked with all of the senses of the user.

PUTTING YOUR BRAIN IN A VAT

To effectively place a person in a virtual world it is necessary to provide a full interface between the person's perceiving and willing mind and the VR computer. The simplest interfaces make use of the person's physical limbs and sense organs, and they range from the familiar keyboards and screens to DataGloves and HMDs. The next level of sophistication involves tapping into the person's sensory and motor nerves.

Carrying this to an extreme, we can follow philosopher Daniel Dennett, and imagine taking out a person's brain and putting it in a vat, complete with life support systems and microminiaturized electro-neural transceivers (Dennett, 1981, p. 218). (This idea was taken up in the science fiction movie, *The Matrix*, using a full-body vat.) We can pursue Dennett's thought experiment by supposing that the excised brain is hooked up to a sophisticated virtual reality system. With tongue only somewhat in cheek, let us survey the technology needed to do this and read out some of its implications.

It is possible in principle to build transceivers linking a person's nervous system to a computer. On a limited scale, such things are possible now, and we can look forward to a time when direct brain machine communication may be used to exploit people or take away their political freedom. But for total immersion in a VR, we require an apparatus that can monitor or stimulate millions of neurons on an individual basis.

This may be possible using noninvasive techniques like those envisioned by Hans Moravec in his downloading schemes (Fjermedal, 1986, p. 4). It might also be done invasively. Microelectrodes can already be inserted in a single neuron. To handle millions, one could take advantage of the techniques of nanotechnology originally proposed by the physicist Richard Feynman (1959).

Feynman argued that "there's plenty of room at the bottom" for the construction of machines. He proposed a series of stages, in which machines are used to build smaller and smaller machines, culminating in machines built of individual atoms. Entire factories could fit within the volume of a single living cell.

Such submicroscopic machines would not have to be built one at a time, like cars on an assembly line. John von Neumann (1949) showed how a self-reproducing universal Turing machine could be made out of a simple set of interacting parts. By designing the microscopic factories so they can make copies of themselves, it should be possible to generate vast numbers of minute machines. Larger machines made of billions of nearly identical subunits could then be constructed using processes self-assembly. We know that such technologies are possible in principle, since we already have an example in the molecular machinery of living cells.

Machinery of this kind could interface with millions of individual neurons and transfer data back and forth between the neurons and a computer. To handle such data effectively, the computer itself would have to be a massively powerful parallel processor. It could be a network of billions of micron-sized processors which were assembled and connected together using the techniques of nanotechnology.

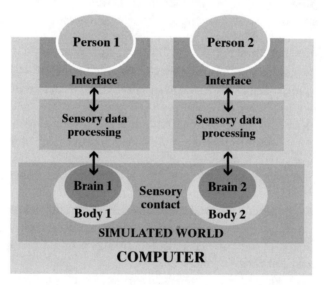

Figure 3. The virtual reality model. A general virtual reality model consists of conscious entities linked to a computer through interface apparatus. The computer generates a simulated world, including virtual bodies and brains. Each person's senses of perception and action are linked to the senses of that person's virtual body through its virtual brain and through additional data processing functions lying outside the simulated world. As a result, the person experiences life within the virtual body.

The nerve impulse is presently thought to be the smallest unit of data in the human sensory and motor systems. Therefore a sensory interface operating on the level of individual neurons should, in principle, be able to provide a person with virtual experiences that are indistinguishable from his normal sense perceptions. All that is required is that the computer must be sufficiently powerful to generate the data stream for the sensory nerves in real time.

According to computer graphics guru Alvy Ray Smith, "reality is 80 million polygons per second" (Rheingold, 1991, p. 168). Here a polygon is a small colored geometrical figure used in the construction of computer-generated images. Smith's figure is an estimate of the rate of computation needed to produce fully realistic visual experience, and one would have to add more to provide for the other senses. For comparison, the Silicon Graphics computers used in VPL's early VR demonstrations in 1990 were able to draw about two thousand polygons per second.

The subjects in a high-quality VR will experience a three-dimensional simulated world that appears real to them. The VR system could be arranged so that this virtual environment has the property of *closure*. This means that any virtual sense apparatus within this environment can pick up only information included within it. In other words, you can't use your virtual senses to see out of the virtual environment.

Closure does not exclude the possibility that you may still obtain information from the ordinary world through your normal physical senses. To enhance the illusion created by the VR, this must be minimized as much as possible. If sense data from the ordinary world is fully excluded, the VR can be said to have the property of *full immersion*.

VIRTUAL BRAINS

Imagine moving about within the virtual environment in the body of a bird, an insect, or some uniquely designed creature. Your human brain may find it difficult to control such a body, and therefore it may be necessary to provide you with a virtual brain.

The virtual brain must be connected to your physical brain. On the physical side, there is the interface between millions of neurons in your nervous system and the VR computer. Within the computer there is

software that transfers information back and forth between this interface and the data-storage areas used for your virtual brain.

The virtual brain itself is simply software. However, it could be divided into a portion with virtual three-dimensional structure, as well as
a formless portion. The former—which is susceptible to virtual brain
damage—is the "physical" brain of your virtual body. The latter includes the interface to your real physical brain, and it may also have
additional features that endow you with virtual "non-physical" mind
functions.

Sense data from the VR could enter the person's (real) brain
through many different channels, and still be interpreted properly.
Experiments with prosthetic eyes have shown that it is possible for
visual sense data to be perceived in a normal way, even though it enters
the brain through unusual channels. In the early 1970s, Paul Bach-y-
Rita developed a prosthetic eye using a low-resolution video camera
mounted on a blind person's glasses frame (Dennett, 1994, p. 339). The
camera's signal generated a crude image in a 20×20 grid of tiny
vibrators mounted on the person's belly or back. If this 20×20-pixel
display is shown on an oscilloscope, it appears as a fuzzy but recognizable picture. It turned out that after a few hours of training, blind
persons wearing this device could learn to read signs, and identify
objects and people's faces.

Daniel Dennett commented that "After a brief training period,
their awareness of the tingles on their skin dropped out; the pad of
pixels became transparent, one might say, and the subjects' point of
view shifted to the point of view of the camera, mounted to the side of
their heads" (Dennett, 1994, p. 341). The tactile information reaching
the brain from nerves in the belly or back was somehow used to create
a conscious experience of vision. This suggests that detailed visual
information from a VR may give rise to normal visual perceptions in a
subject, even if it is fed into the subject's brain through channels other
than the optic nerves.

The blind persons who participated in Bach-y-Rita's study were
apparently not blind from birth. There are cases in which such a
congenitally blind person is cured by an operation in adulthood (Tipler, 1994, p. 243). When the patient first opens his repaired eyes, he
sees nothing but a confusing array of meaningless colors. But he may

gradually learn to recognize familiar objects over a period of years.

This suggests that when confronted with novel inputs from virtual senses, a person may initially find it difficult to interpret this data, but he may eventually be able to adjust to it. Apparently, early experience with vision stimulates the development of brain structures dedicated to the processing of visual information. In the absence of this experience, these structures remain undeveloped, but they can develop with practice even in adulthood (but see Chapter 7).

These observations may also apply to other familiar senses such as hearing. But to what extent will people be able to adapt to completely novel forms of sense data? For example, suppose that fully three-dimensional data about objects is encoded as a data stream and fed into a subject's sensory nerves or brain. Could the subject learn to experience this data as a form of omnidirectional vision? Would he experience this on an abstract level of understanding or as a direct perception comparable to ordinary vision?

The same question can be raised about the "sensory" information generated by radar and other instruments in a military flying machine. Could a pilot immersed in this sensory stream learn to become "one with the machine" and experience direct perception through the machine's senses?

In addition to providing sensory information, a virtual brain may generate complex outputs by elaborate processing of sense data and stored memories. If this information is transmitted to the physical brain of the subject, what will be the result? In the absence of empirical evidence it is difficult to say. The subject may experience the virtual brain's contributions as part of his own mental functions—perhaps after an agonizing period of adjustment. These contributions might be incorporated smoothly into the already extensive automatic or subconscious aspect of the subject's mental life. Or they might give rise to delusions, radical personality changes, or other adverse psychological effects.

ABSTRACT VIRTUAL REALITY

The VR thought experiment can be used as a model for discussing questions about the relation between mind and brain. In particular, VR models show how some famous questions about Cartesian dualism can be answered.

Descartes proposed that the thinking substance of the mind (called *res cogitans*) is completely different from the extended substance (called *res extensa*) that makes up material things. But how is it possible for two things that are completely different in nature to interact? Descartes also said that the *res cogitans* does not have position or extension in space, but how can a mind without location be connected to a body that does have a location in space?

In the VR models we have been considering, these questions have simple answers. The mind in these models corresponds to the physical brain of the subject, and the body corresponds to a virtual construct generated by the VR computer. The mind and the body are therefore completely different in nature, but they do interact through an interface apparatus and associated software. Also, the brain has no location within the virtual space created by the VR computer, but it is nonetheless able to interact with a virtual body that has a position in that space.

Here the whole system is carried, so to speak, by physical reality. The mind, or *res cogitans*, is the physical brain, seen naively as the seat of consciousness, and thus it has the same physical nature as the VR computer which runs the *res extensa* in virtual 3D. Thus *res extensa* has a different nature than *res cogitans*. The latter, being physical, is "more real" than the former. But due to total immersion, the former appears as reality to the latter.

Now, we may ask, what if physical reality as we know it is virtual? Consider the hypothesis that our consciousness is part of something— call it Ground Reality (GR) for lack of a better term—which is running physical reality as a simulation. To simplify this hypothesis, I will assume as little about GR as possible. It should have the capacity to manipulate symbols on the level of a universal Turing machine. It should also have the capacity to sustain consciousness—hopefully without the need for a messy, *Matrix*-like system of vats and interface connectors. Apart from these basic features, I will add more details to the specification of GR as they are needed.

Here I treat consciousness as an unknown element. Thus I assume that the Ground Reality includes consciousness (and is perhaps even co-extensive with it). I also assume that GR contains complex structure sufficient for representing the universe of mathematical physics. I will gradually introduce ideas about this structure and about its relationship with consciousness, but consciousness in and of itself will have to remain an unknown.

Daniel Dennett made some cogent remarks indicating that "explanation," as it is commonly understood in science, is inevitably reductionistic in nature. He concluded that

> Only a theory that explained conscious events in terms of unconscious events could explain consciousness at all. If your model of how pain is a product of brain activity still has a box in it labeled "pain," you haven't begun to explain what pain is, and if your model of consciousness carries along nicely until the magic moment when you have to say "then a miracle occurs" you haven't begun to explain what consciousness is (Dennett, 1991, pp. 454–55).

Granting Dennett's point, I will not try to explain consciousness. But I will still try to clarify how the box labeled "pain" relates to other boxes, including boxes labeled "neurons" or even boxes labeled "interface software." I suspect that some features of nature can be explained reductionistically, while others—including consciousness—cannot. In a man-made virtual reality, the virtual world can be reduced to binary bits of information, while the real world that sustains it may not be so easy to explain. One way to look at the Ground Reality model is that physics has shown that nature, to a very large degree, can be understood mathematically. So let us designate the part of reality that can be mathematically analyzed as the "virtual world." Let us suppose that this is embedded in and sustained by a larger Ground Reality that cannot be fully understood through rational means. My proposal is that consciousness is one of the irreducible features of this larger reality.

My program in this book will be to use the man-made virtual reality model as a concrete, metaphorical object which can be used to show what is theoretically possible in the more abstract Ground Reality model. I will examine various lines of evidence which have bearing on what the GR model must do, if it is to conform to observable reality. If a man-made VR can in principle do such things, then it can be inferred that they could also be done by the GR model. In this way, I will argue that the GR model provides a useful conceptual framework for understanding reality and the role of consciousness in reality.

2

THE CLOCKWORK UNIVERSE IN CHAOS

*"How could they formulate laws
that would curtail the freedom of God
to change His mind? Nevertheless
they did, and they got away with it."*

—Stephen Hawking

*"The often repeated statement,
that given the initial conditions we know
what a deterministic system will do
far into the future, is false."*

—Predrag Cvitanovic

On a Caribbean island, a butterfly happens to flutter briefly to the left instead of to the right. As a result, minute swirls of air produced by its wings move in a slightly different way than they would have. A few days later a hurricane that had been gradually building up force veers into the Florida coast instead of heading out to sea.

Could the hurricane's change in course have been caused by the altered flight of the butterfly? According to Edward N. Lorenz of the Massachusetts Institute of Technology, this is actually possible (Lorenz, 1963). Computer simulations carried out by Lorenz suggest that the flow of air in the atmosphere may display the property of "exponential instability." Under such conditions, arbitrarily small changes in the flow pattern will be amplified until they have a major impact on the turbulent pattern of flowing air that makes up our weather. According to Lorenz, this makes short range weather forecasting extremely unpredictable, because of the impossibility of monitoring the very small changes that could possibly result in large-scale effects.

29

This unpredictability has been called "deterministic chaos," since it arises in systems that should be strictly deterministic and predictable from a mathematical point of view. The concept of deterministic chaos sheds significant light on the question of whether or not the mind can control the brain without violating the laws of physics. It also sheds light on the related question of how God might control the processes of nature. Put simply, if undetectable changes can control the unfolding of big effects, then nature can be intelligently controlled without measurable violation of the laws of physics.

Unfortunately, this idea is unsatisfactory as it stands, because even if deterministic chaos allows for mind-brain or God-world interaction, this only tells the physical side of the story. We still don't know what causes the undetectable, guiding changes. However, we can model such causes by taking advantage of the idea of virtual reality. Suppose, for the sake of argument, that deterministic chaos provides a way to program a virtual reality system in which a human user interacts with a physically lawful virtual world. We can then argue that something similar could apply to the Ground Reality model—the hypothetical virtual reality system of the real world.

NEWTONIAN PRECISION

I shall outline how such a virtual reality could be constructed. But to lay the groundwork for this, I first go back to the 17th century, the era of Rene Descartes and Isaac Newton. At this time, educated people in Europe widely accepted that the material world was both created and directly controlled by God. However, Newton's *Principia* gave strength to the seemingly contradictory view that everything in nature happens in a rigidly deterministic way under the control of fixed mathematical laws.

Newton's work seemed to confirm an image of reality that had been growing more and more prominent in Europe since the late Middle Ages—the picture of the universe as a machine comparable to a vast clock. According to this understanding, there are two ways in which God can influence the behavior of matter. These are (1) by setting up the world-clock and letting it run by itself and (2) by changing the clock's settings from time to time. Here God may be thought of as transcendental (lying beyond the material realm), or as eminent (per-vading matter). Either way, the predominance of clocklike laws of nature forces God into the role of a maker or adjuster of clockwork—an idea that did not arise in earlier conceptions of nature as an organic whole.

Newton himself felt that the solar system was constructed by divine creation and that intervention of type (2) was necessary for its contin-ued smooth operation. However, Newton's theistic arguments were far from acceptable to many scientists and philosophers of his time. Newton's rival, Leibniz, for example, preferred to think of God as a perfect clockmaker who, after creating the universal machine and setting it in motion, had no need to intervene further in its operation.

In due course, this speculative theological argument was but-tressed by the theoretical researches of Pierre Simon de Laplace and J. L. Lagrange concerning the stability of the solar system. Newton had argued that the mutual gravitational influence of the planets on one another would eventually perturb their orbits to a degree demanding divine correction. However, Laplace and Lagrange showed by math-ematical analysis that in an idealized model of the Newtonian planetary system, these perturbations would cycle periodically within fixed lim-its. (Recently, however, orbital studies aided by computers have called this into question and have suggested that the solar system is chaotic and unpredictable in the long run.)

As time went on, the idea of divine creation also began to seem more and more implausible. Newton had argued that the regular arrangement of the nearly circular planetary orbits required the "di-vine arm" (Newton, 1692–3). But Laplace suggested that this regular pattern may have formed naturally as the planets condensed by physi-cal processes from a primordial nebula. Even though this hypothesis was not worked out mathematically in any detail, it carried the day, and further limited the scope allowed for God's activity within the universe.

These theological developments were paralleled by the develop-ment of scientific views regarding the mind and the body. It is no coincidence that Descartes' model of the mind and the brain was pro-posed during a time when mechanistic models of reality were becoming more and more prominent. As physical laws became deterministic and clocklike, it became difficult to see how a nonphysical entity could influence the behavior of matter. Yet, if such an entity did not influence matter, then it was automatically "kicked upstairs" to an irrelevant state of pure transcendence that is tantamount to nonexistence.

CHAOS AND DETERMINISM

But the problem may lie more with the metaphor of a clock than it does with the laws of physics themselves. To see this, we will first briefly examine how indeterminism enters into the supposedly deterministic laws of classical physics.

The classical laws of physics are based on algorithms that tell how the state of a physical system changes with the passage of time. The state of the system is defined by a collection of numbers called parameters. For a simple pendulum, two parameters defining the position of the pendulum bob and its momentum are sufficient. For many applications it is sufficient to use such a simple approximation, based on a few parameters.

However, an exact Newtonian description would require assigning parameters to billions and billions of individual molecules. (Thus Avogadro's constant, the number of molecules in a gram-molecular weight of a substance, is about 6 followed by 23 zeros.) Strictly speaking, molecules should be described using quantum mechanics, which I will discuss in Chapter 4. But whether we use quantum theory or classical Newtonian physics, it is clear that no known computer or process of computation will enable us to predict what billions and billions of molecules will do. Physicists have taken it as a matter of faith that all of the molecules in nature move according to their equations, and in this sense, physics can be viewed as a branch of theology.

Given the state of a physical system at one moment in time, the classical laws of physics include formulas for computing how the system will change over an infinitesimal time interval. By working forward interval by interval with these formulas (using the methods of calculus), you can compute how the system changes as time passes. In principle, if you know the state of the system at one time, you can compute exactly what the system will do at any future time. This is called determinism.

Laplace summed this up in 1799 by saying that "if we conceive of an Intelligence who, for a given moment, embraces all the relations of beings in this Universe, It would be able to determine for any instant of the past or future their respective positions, motions, and generally their effects" (Hahn, 1967, p. 17). Laplace is clearly thinking theologically, but it can be argued that this mode of thinking actually encouraged the development of physics by giving scientists the boldness to seek a rational understanding of the universe as a whole. The same mode of thinking, applied to the idea of virtual reality, may also lead to useful insights into the role of consciousness in nature.

Laplace's hypothetical Intelligence could deduce the future from the present. However, we now know that the future of many classical physical systems can be accurately predicted only for a time proportional to the number of decimal places with which the parameters of the system are known. If you know all of the parameters out to infinitely many decimal places, then, in principle, you can know the entire future of the system. But if some of the parameters—or even one—are accurate to only a few decimal places, then your predictions will completely break down after a short time. This unpredictability has been celebrated under the label of "deterministic chaos."

The word "chaos" suggests something uncontrollable, but this turns out to be misleading. A "chaotic" system is susceptible to external control, but a nonchaotic system cannot be so easily controlled. This can be illustrated by comparing an old-fashioned pendulum clock with an automobile on a desert salt flat. If you know roughly the setting of the clock and how fast it gains or loses time, you can predict its future behavior easily (relative to some standard clock). But imagine tying down the gas pedal of a driverless car on a salt flat and letting it go. To predict the motion of the car you need very accurate information about how small bumps in the ground are causing its wheels to swing this way and that.

At the same time, a driver can direct the car according to his will by making small deflections of the steering wheel. But each time a person wishes to change the setting of the clock, he has to fully shift the clock's hands to their new position. Clocklike systems require drastic intervention to change their state, whereas carlike systems can be controlled by very small interventions. Thus chaos *allows for* external control, although it simply produces random behavior when left to itself.

The clock was one of the inspiring metaphors behind the mechanistic picture of the universe, but many classical physical systems are more comparable to the car on the salt flat than to the clock. To see why, it is useful to study a simple model, called the Baker Transformation. This is a highly idealized model of a baker kneading a square of dough, but it illustrates an important phenomenon that occurs in more complex form in many real situations. The sidebar on pages 36 and 37 presents the details of the Baker Transformation, and the next section points out their implications. Readers who wish to skip the details can proceed directly to the next section after reading the first two paragraphs of the sidebar to find out what the Baker Transformation is.

CONTROL THROUGH AMPLIFICATION

What the Baker Transformation shows is that all information defining the motions of a point (x,y) in the dough square is stored in the binary digits defining that point. As time passes, this information is steadily read out from the x-coordinate of the point and then sent into oblivion in the higher binary places of the y-coordinate. The digits of (x,y) are like a script defining all the future motions of the point. In Figure 4, these scripts were defined for a collection of points so that the points would spontaneously form a "happy face" at a given time (square 7). One could similarly write scripts so that these points would form the letters spelling out Shakespeare's plays, one after another.

The laws of physics of this model are defined by the simple, deterministic actions of squashing, cutting, and stacking. But without any violation of these laws, it is possible for the model to exhibit an intelligent message. All that is needed is for the message to be scripted into high-order binary places of the points that will spell it out.

At this point we need to consider what might be called the hidden metaphysics of numbers. In physical science and engineering, measured quantities, such as the mass of an electron, are normally written with at most 7 or 8 decimal places. Further decimal digits would not be considered significant, due to inevitable errors in measurement. However, the real number system of mathematics assumes that numbers have infinitely many decimal places (or binary places, if binary

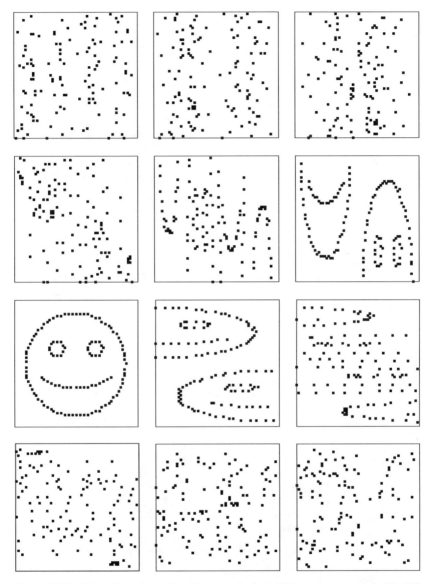

Figure 4. The Baker Transformation. Suppose the "world" is a square occupied by 100 dots, and suppose that the "laws of nature" are given by the Baker Transformation. The 12 squares show successive events in this world. The dots seem randomly placed in square 1, but they move to form a "happy face" in square 7. This pattern was actually coded into the positions of the dots in square 1, but it became visible after 6 steps as a result of exponential amplification. (See sidebar on pages 36–37 for more detail.)

The Baker Transformation

Consider a baker who is kneading dough. He flattens out the dough, cuts it into two pieces, and puts one piece on top of the other. Then he repeats this process. When this is done several times, it has the effect of mixing the ingredients of the dough (Prigogine, 1980, pp. 220–31).

We can make a simple model of this by using a square to represent a vertical cross section through the dough. In the flattening step, the square is squashed into a rectangle that is half as high and twice as wide. Then it is divided in half by a vertical cut down the middle, and the right half is put on top of the left half. This produces a square of the same size as the original square, and the process is repeated.

Let us see what happens to a single point in the dough during this process. To do this, it is useful to use binary numbers to locate the point. We all know that the decimal number 3.607 is 3 plus $\frac{6}{10}$ plus $\frac{0}{100}$ plus $\frac{7}{1,000}$. A binary number is similar, but instead of using the 10 digits 0 through 9, only 2 digits 0 and 1 are used. Thus 1.1011 is 1 plus $\frac{1}{2}$ plus $\frac{1}{4}$ plus $\frac{1}{8}$ plus $\frac{1}{16}$. In this number, the dot is called the "binary point," rather than the "decimal point." Also, the places of the digits could be called binary places rather than decimal places.

We can let x be the distance of the point from the left side of the square and y be its height from the bottom of the square. These are just (x,y) coordinates, with the origin $(0,0)$ fixed at the lower left-hand corner of the square. Suppose that the side of the original square is one unit in length. We can write the coordinates x and y in the binary notation. For example, x and y could be:

$$x = .101100010111101... \qquad y = .110001010010011...$$

Both x and y are between 0 and 1, and both have infinitely many digits (which may be 0s or repeating sequences after some point).

During the squashing step, x is doubled and y is divided in half. When a binary number is multiplied by 2, all the digits shift one place to the left. (This is similar to what happens when a decimal number is multiplied by 10.) Likewise, when a binary number is divided by 2, all the digits shift one place to the right. So the result of the squashing step is:

$$x = 1.01100010111101... \qquad y = .0110001010010011...$$

The cutting step divides the squashed rectangle into two rectangles. Since x is now greater than 1, it lies in the right-hand rectangle. In the stacking step, this rectangle is moved left by 1 and up by .1 so that it sits on top of the

(*continued on next page*)

(continued from previous page)

left-hand rectangle. (Here .1 is ½ in binary notation.) The result of this is that x and y become:

$$x = .01100010111101... \qquad y = .1110001010010011...$$

What has happened is that the 1 to the left of the binary point in x has moved into the slot to the right of the binary point in y. If this digit had been a 0 instead, then the zero would have been moved. (This case is left to the reader as a homework problem.)

In effect, the squashing, cutting, and stacking steps simply shift the digits in x and y. The digits act as though they were on an infinite belt that bends around the two binary points, and shifts by the space of one digit each time the squashing, cutting, and stacking operations are performed. The belt can be illustrated by writing y backwards in front of x and putting two asterisks (*) in place of the binary points. We can see that the result of all the steps is simply to shift the ** one digit to the right in the infinite belt of digits:

$$...110010010100011**101100010111101...$$
$$\text{goes to } ...1100100101000111**01100010111101...$$

Suppose that the kneading operations of squashing, cutting, and stacking are repeated over and over as time passes. Consider a series of digits far to the right in x, in the binary places numbered from 1,001 to 1,020. These digits have no measurable effect on x, since they at most contribute $2^{-1,000}$ to the magnitude of x. In decimal form, this number is approximated by a decimal point, 300 zeros, and a 1.

After 1,010 operations, the binary points shift over by 1,010 places. The first 10 of these digits will occupy the first 10 binary places of y, and the second 10 will occupy the first 10 binary places of x. Now the values of x and y are almost fully determined by these digits. After another 1,010 operations, the digits will occupy binary places 1,001 to 1,020 in y, and their effect is again unmeasurably small. Thus the effect of repeating the Baker Transformation is to bring successive batches of stored information into prominence and return them to obscurity.

---

notation is used). The laws of physics are expressed in terms of such numbers. So does an electron really have a mass specified out to infinitely many decimal places—or for that matter, to billions of decimal places? Since they are unmeasurable, such vast strings of decimal digits belong to metaphysics, rather than physics.

One might consider replacing a static metaphysical x of infinitely many digits with a dynamic metaphysical x in which the unobservable high-order digits are continuously being revised by some agency. In that case, the motion of the points in the Baker Transformation could be controlled by that agency. At the same time, this motion would show no measurable deviation from the physical laws of the model. We can even say that there is no deviation at all, since a deviation that is impossible to measure has no real existence in physics.

It is possible to incorporate this hypothetical agency into a man-made virtual reality that can easily be implemented on a personal computer. The "virtual world" of this VR consists of dots on a square. The laws of nature in this world are simply the repeated application of the Baker Transformation, which causes the dots to move about. The human subject sees the pattern of dots on his screen, and by striking keys he can change binary digits of the points in the thousandth binary place or higher. The subject will be able to cause faces or letters to appear in the square without measurably violating the laws of the system.

I should emphasize that, like all virtual realities, this one has an interface linking the conscious subject to the virtual world. On the human side, this interface consists of the screen and keyboard which enable the subject to interact with the computer. On the side of the virtual world, it consists of software for updating binary digits of the x's and y's. The interface is not in the virtual world, and it forms a bridge between the virtual world and the conscious participant.

Of course, the Baker Transformation is highly idealized and simplified. But similar behavior is shown by many realistic models in physics. The key feature of the Baker Transformation is that it involves exponential amplification of small differences with the passage of time. Consider two points in the square of dough that are very close to each other. Suppose that their x coordinates differ by $2^{-1,000}$, an unmeasurably small difference. With each time step, this difference doubles, as long as the two points are not separated by a cut, and it will reach a magnitude of 1 after 1,000 steps. This is exponential amplification. (In our simple VR, "measurement" is limited by the size of the pixels on the screen, and the limit of 1,000 binary places for updates is overkill.)

In many physical systems, chaotic motion is associated with an entity called a strange attractor. In physics, an attractor is a set of points that the state of the system tends to approach as time passes. For example, the velocity of an object subject to friction will tend to approach zero as time passes, and thus the point zero is an attractor for this system.

A strange attractor is typically a very complex set of states. As the state of the system approaches this set, nearby states will tend to diverge from one another exponentially, and they soon exhibit completely different behavior. Figure 5 gives a simple example showing how this happens.

Exponential amplification and strange attractors are quite common in nature. This chapter began with Edward Lorenz's classical

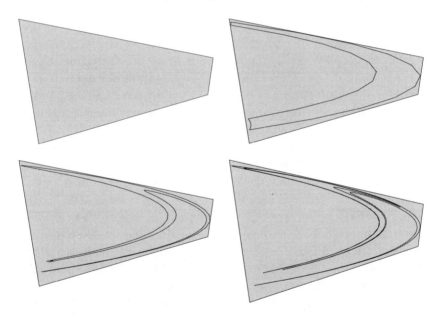

Figure 5. The Henon strange attractor. M. Henon (1976) described a simple transformation that takes the shaded quadrilateral (top left), stretches it, bends it into a U-shape, and puts it back into the quadrilateral. When this operation is repeated, the U is stretched and bent into a double U inside the U, a quadruple U inside the double U, and so on. In the limit, this becomes an oddly shaped set called a strange attractor. Due to the stretching, two points that initially are close together in the shaded quadrilateral will be sent to completely different locations on the strange attractor. This is a simple example of the kind of exponential amplification that occurs in more complicated situations in the real world.

study of chaos in the atmosphere in 1963. This resulted in the discovery of a strange attractor in a space of parameters describing atmospheric motion. Thus we expect meteorological phenomena to be unpredictable, and consequently controllable, in principle, by a suitable hidden agency.

Chaos also shows up in biology. Studies of the behavior of the human heart suggest that the state of the heart seems to dance chaotically about a strange attractor (Goldberger, *et al.*, 1990). As a result, the beating of the heart continuously varies in an unpredictable manner. Curiously, the heart may begin to beat in a more regular fashion near the onset of cardiac arrest. It almost seems as though the irregular beating of the normal heart provides rest for the heart muscle, whereas highly regular beating is exhausting.

Chaos seems to be a normal feature of the nervous system. Studies of electroencephalograms of normal individuals conducted at the Free University of Brussels have shown evidence of chaos. Researchers at the University of Tubingen in West Germany have similarly found evidence of chaos in the components of the nervous system controlling hormone secretion (Goldberger, *et al.*, 1990).

Xu Jing-hua and Li Wei of the Shanghai Institute of Biochemistry in China have also reported the characteristic signature of chaos in human EEGs. In addition, these authors analyzed theoretical models of neuroglia networks which exhibited strange attractors and classical chaotic behavior. The glial cells in the brain accompany the neurons in great numbers, but their role in brain functions has tended to remain obscure. Xu and Li suggest that chaotic neuroglia interactions provide a source of information. They suggest that this may lead to a "neuroglia modulation hypothesis of human consciousness and mind formation" that could account for the creativity of the human brain (Xu and Li, 1986).

Walter Freeman of the University of California at Berkeley has carried out extensive studies of the olfactory bulb in the brains of rabbits. He concludes that chaotic dynamics serves an essential role in the ability of the rabbit to recognize familiar odors and to learn to recognize new odors. He generalizes his observations by saying that "Chaos constitutes the basic form of collective neural activity for all perceptual processes and functions as a controlled source of noise, as a means to ensure continual access to previously learned sensory patterns, and as a means for learning new sensory patterns" (Skarda and Freeman, 1987).

BACK TO THE VIRTUAL BRAIN

Freeman, of course, is not thinking that chaos could be an entry point of information guiding the action of the brain. But this is certainly possible, given an agency capable of exerting submicroscopic control. If we return to the idea of a virtual brain, we can see that deterministic chaos could be used to inject information coming from outside the virtual world without any measurable violation of the laws of physics. In complex, realistic systems this cannot be done as easily as it can be done for the Baker Transformation. Nonetheless, the control of real chaotic systems is possible.

For example, researchers at the Naval Surface Warfare Center in Maryland have shown that chaotic motion in a vibrating magnetoelastic ribbon can be controlled by giving small perturbations to a system parameter (Ditto, *et al.,* 1990). These perturbations are chosen by computer calculations in such a way as to induce the ribbon to follow an unstable orbit embedded in the chaotic attractor.

This was done for two different orbits. By properly choosing the small perturbations, the system could be induced to follow one orbit or the other at will. This is clearly significant as a switching technique for controlling large systems with tiny control signals. Of course, the signals used to control the ribbon were large enough to be measurable. But a virtual reality system could utilize immeasurably small control signals that would have the same effect. The exponential instability associated with deterministic chaos can provide the needed amplification. The full information on system dynamics that is available to the VR computer can be used to calculate the needed control signals.

I should finally note that collisions between nearly spherical objects result in deterministic chaos. Thus molecular motion must everywhere give rise to chaotic effects. The phenomenon of Brownian motion shows that such effects can be amplified to a macroscopic level, where they could be used to guide physical systems on a large scale.

STATISTICS AND THERMODYNAMICS

Thus far, we have seen that man-made virtual realities can be constructed that do not measurably violate the laws of physics. This suggests that our world could possibly be a virtual reality. However, there are additional features of modern physics which may seem to rule out the virtual reality hypothesis. One of these is called the second law of thermodynamics, and we will now see what it has to say.

Consider a chaotic system that spells out Shakespeare's plays. This does not contradict the classical laws of physics if the plays are encoded in the strings of digits defining the state of the system at a given time. However, such behavior is certainly not expected. One expects random behavior, but to provide for this it is necessary to add assumptions of randomness to the laws of physics.

In fact, such assumptions are commonly made to define the direction of time in physics. The classical equations of motion are time reversible. This means that if the sequence of events in a physical system is run in reverse order, like a home movie played backwards, it still satisfies the laws of physics. But in nature we see irreversible processes, such as the scrambling of an egg or the shattering of a glass. Why do we never see scrambled eggs unscrambling and broken glasses reassembling and becoming whole again?

The accepted answer is given by a field of physics called thermodynamics or statistical mechanics. Instead of looking at a single state of a physical system, statistical mechanics looks at collections of many states called ensembles. Each such collection is associated with a quantity called entropy, which measures the amount of disorder in the collection. The famous second law of thermodynamics states that the entropy of an isolated physical system tends to increase.

Since the universe is by definition an isolated system, this means that the amount of disorder in the universe should continuously increase. Indeed, Clausius, one of the 19th-century founders of thermodynamics, declared that "The entropy of the universe increases to a maximum" (Prigogine, 1980, p. 78). This led to the idea of the "heat death of the universe." The entire universe is supposed to run down until all energy sources are exhausted and silence reigns over a final state of featureless thermal equilibrium. The physicist Stephen Hawking recently described such a future state as follows: "By then all the stars will have burned out and the protons and neutrons in them will probably have decayed into light particles and radiation. The universe would be in a state of almost complete disorder" (Hawking, 1988, p. 151).

But how can we reconcile irreversible increase in disorder with time-reversible physical laws? To see how this is done, it is convenient to go back to the Baker Transformation. Like the laws of physics, this transformation is reversible. To reverse it, simply cut the square in half with a horizontal cut, put the two rectangles side by side, and squash them horizontally so they rise up to form a square.

Previously, we studied the motion of a single point under repeated applications of the Baker Transformation. But now, consider what happens if we replace the point with the collection of points lying within a very small circle. Successive transformations stretch this circle horizontally until it becomes a long, thin line. Soon the line crosses the boundary between the right and left squashed rectangles, and in the next step it becomes two horizontal lines, one above the other. Then it becomes 4, 8, 16, lines and so on. Soon the entire square is covered with closely spaced fine lines. If we blur these thin lines, spreading them out to the width of the original circle, then the whole square is completely covered.

This blurring operation is the key to understanding the second law of thermodynamics. It is called "coarse graining," and it results in an irreversible transformation. If we did not blur the fine lines, then applying the reverse of the Baker Transformation would eventually bring them back to the original circle. But if we look at the set of transformed points with blurred vision, we see it spreading out more and more until it fills the entire square. The blurred sets will not go back to the original circle under the reversed transformation.

Entropy can be thought of as a measure of how much the blurred set of points spreads out. When the set is concentrated in the original small circle, it defines a definite location, and its entropy is low. But as it spreads out, it loses definition, and the entropy increases. When the set occupies the whole square it is as indefinite as possible, and the entropy is at a maximum. So entropy is a measure of lack of definiteness.

Now it could be objected that this is all subjective. When we look at a set of points, we may get a blurred image due to the limitations of our senses and measuring devices. But the actual set of points is unblurred and is as definite as ever. In fact, this objection is quite true. The second law of thermodynamics really says that disorder increases on a measurable level. But on the level of the immeasurably small, reversibility reigns and the amount of order remains constant.

With this introduction to thermodynamics, let us go back to Shakespeare's plays. If we use tiny circles instead of points, it may not be possible for the system to spell out extensive texts. Before they can form a long series of letters, the tiny circles will have spread out over the entire square. Whether our vision is blurred or sharp, the system will tell us nothing about Shakespeare.

The effect of using small circles instead of points, is that we assume that there is a lack of definiteness in nature. This is related to the idea of randomness. The circle represents a probability distribution. This means that there is a definite point, but we don't know exactly where it is, and thus we say it is one of many points within a circle. Indeed, not only are we uncertain about where the point is, but nature itself is uncertain. If we were uncertain, the system might still spell out Shakespeare's plays. But if nature is uncertain, then this is extremely unlikely to occur. Suppose the binary digits of x and y are random beyond a certain point. Then the point (x,y) can fall anywhere in a small square (and the case of a circle is similar). This makes the appearance of Shakespeare's plays in the sequences a matter of pure chance.

We see then, that the assumptions of uncertainty made in statistical mechanics could rule out the kind of hidden agency we have been considering. If there is an inherent vagueness in nature, then we cannot postulate a dynamic process which continuously injects information into nature on the level of the immeasurably small.

But perhaps there is such a dynamic process, and nature does not suffer from inherent vagueness. In that case, mind-brain interaction based on the amplification of sub-microscopic information patterns is a possibility. Such a process might even result in a continual injection of order into the universe which would prevent its anticipated heat death. It might also account for the existence of the extensive order presently existing in the universe. Then again, if randomness and ordered information are both injected, then we could have an increase in disorder in some situations and an increase in order in others.

In the brain, the injection of information will be hidden by the large amounts of information that is already being stored and processed by neural activity. To show definitely that information is being injected, it might be necessary to fully understand the information accounting of the brain and show that the accounts do not balance unless some additional source of information is assumed. But the extreme complexity of the brain makes this a formidably difficult task. Likewise, to prove that information is not being injected is also formidably difficult.

3

THE MYSTERY OF TIME

"My basic idea is that time
as such does not exist."

—Julian Barbour

Time plays an awkward role in the virtual reality hypothesis. In a man-made VR, the biology of the human brain determines the passage of time. This defines "real time," and VR computers are forced to keep up with it or slow down to match it. However, this limitation on time seems artificial and unnecessary. We have already discussed the idea that a computer can think, or that a person can be "downloaded" into a computer and dwell there as his old conscious self. Suppose for the moment that this is true. If the person is further downloaded into a faster computer, does his consciousness remain internally the same, so that the world around him seems to slow down? Or if the computer is slowed down to one cycle per century, does the person's consciousness stretch over the millennia?

Would we expect to find such effects in our own lives if we could somehow speed up or slow down our brains without disrupting their metabolism? This is suggested by the common experience that "time flies" when we are engaged in intense activity.

It is possible that consciousness is not bound by time and that our subjective sense of time is determined by neural events in the brain. However, before we can investigate this idea, we must understand what time is. To answer this I again turn to the strange world of modern physics.

TIME IN PHYSICS

When Einstein's friend Michele Besso passed away, Einstein wrote a letter of consolation to his widow and son. He said that

"Michele has preceded me a little in leaving this strange world. This is not important. For us who are convinced physicists, the distinction between past, present, and future is only an illusion, however persistent" (Prigogine, 1980, p. 203). Einstein's statement is based on his theory of relativity, which blurs the boundaries of space and time, and makes the passage of time seem physically meaningless. This theory has profound implications for physics and even greater implications regarding the nature of consciousness and free will.

To see why, let us consider how the passage of time is dealt with in classical physics. For simplicity, we can represent the history of space and time by a two-dimensional diagram. To do this, we make space one-dimensional, corresponding to the x-axis in Figure 6. Time is represented by the t-axis. In this scheme, the "present" at a particular time $t=1$ corresponds to everything along the horizontal line that cuts the t-axis at $t=1$. Everything above this line lies in the "future" and everything beneath it lies in the "past." As time passes, the line moves steadily up the figure from past to future.

Figure 7 shows the unfolding of events in a one-dimensional world (described in the sidebar on page 49) that fills the space-time diagram

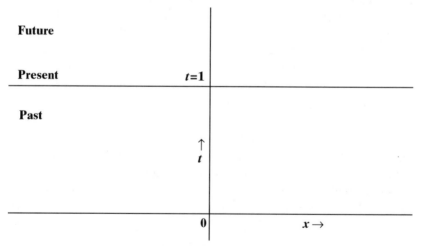

Figure 6. Diagram of past, present, and future. In classical physics, space is static and time is dynamic. Here three-dimensional space is represented by the x-axis for simplicity. Time is represented by the t-axis. The "present" at time $t=1$ is marked by a horizontal line, with the past below it and the future above it.

Laws of Physics in One Dimension

To add some action to the empty picture in Figure 6, we need to introduce some physical laws. For simplicity, I base these laws on a one-dimensional cellular automaton invented by Stephen Wolfram (2001). Imagine that the one-dimensional space (the x-axis) is occupied by particles that are colored light or dark gray. Imagine that these particles can either stand still or move to the right or left at the speed of light. When plotted on the two-dimensional space-time diagram, the history of a particle is a straight line. This line is vertical for a stationary particle, and it tilts to the right or left for a particle moving right or left at the speed of light. This is shown in Figure 7.

I use seconds as the units of time and 186,000 miles as the unit of length. This insures that the particles moving at the speed of light (186,000 miles per second) are covering one unit per second on the space-time plot. To find where a particle is at time t, look for the point where the horizontal line of the "present" at time t intersects the line representing the motion of the particle. This intersection point moves as the line of the present moves up the diagram from past to future.

I have arranged the particles so that they collide in groups of two or groups of three. If two particles collide, they simply pass through each other. When three particles meet, they change shading according to the following simple rule (where light gray is L and dark gray is D):

LLL, DLD, DDL, or DDD→LLL
LLD, LDL, LDD, or DLL→DDD

At the bottom of the figure, we see an "all light gray" state, in which LLL everywhere gives rise to LLL. I break this uniformity with a "creation event" at one point, and make LLL→DDD. A complex pattern of particle shading follows from this event by simply applying the rule over and over as time passes and collisions take place.

in Figure 6 with action. The patterns in our example are presumably too simple to represent states of consciousness, but we can imagine more complex examples—including patterns representing brain states— where consciousness would be expected. Such patterns could be represented using John Conway's famous game of Life, a simple two-dimensional cellular automaton which can represent universal Turing machines.

Since the "present" in Figure 7 corresponds to a horizontal line, sub-patterns along this line might correspond to states of consciousness. However, there is no consciousness in the past or future, and the contents of consciousness change as time advances up the *t*-axis. In this classical picture, only the present exists and is subject to conscious awareness.

Now suppose that the one-dimensional world is virtual and that consciousness is "injected" into it through a sensory hook-up with a physical brain. In this case, the passage of biological time in the brain will have to match the passage of time in the virtual model. Time in the virtual world is the same as time in the brain, and it must be synchronized with it by adjusting the rate at which the computer generates the stream of virtual events. In one sense, time is the only thing in the virtual world that is not virtual.

THE THEORY OF RELATIVITY

This is the classical picture, but we find something quite different in Einstein's theory of relativity. The starting point of this theory is an insight by Galileo. Imagine some people inside the windowless hull of a ship that is moving perfectly smoothly through calm water. Galileo argued that regardless of how fast the ship is moving, the physical behavior of objects will be the same. For example, if two people in the ship toss a ball back and forth, this will not be affected in any way by the smooth motion of the ship. Thus it will not be possible for them to know how fast they are going without looking outside the ship.

Einstein interpreted this principle of relativity to mean that everything should be physically the same, regardless of whether we are standing still or moving at a constant velocity. This is true in classical physics, but Einstein added a new twist. He wanted light to move at a constant velocity, independent of any physical medium. What this means is that if we are moving alongside a beam of light, it will always be passing us at the same speed, regardless of how fast we are going. This won't happen with sound, which depends on vibrations in a physical medium such as air. If we chase a sound wave, we will be able to catch up with it, because we are moving relative to the air which carries the sound. But how can it be that we cannot catch up with a beam of light, no matter how fast we go?

It turns out that to achieve this, Einstein had to break the principle of simultaneity. Suppose that two events happen at the same time in different places. If we now begin to move at a steady speed, we expect that the two events will still be simultaneous. But in Einstein's theory, this is not so. In Figure 8 we see what happens to the physical events in Figure 7 when viewed by an observer moving to the right at a high speed. It is assumed in the sidebar that the particles moving to the left or right are moving at the speed of light. In Figure 8, these particles move in the same way as before, as Einstein's theory requires, but the stationary particles now move to the left (due to our rightward movement).

The pattern produced by the cellular automaton rule remains the same, but a strange thing has happened to the "present" of Figure 7. It now tilts at an angle. Events occurring at the same time in Figure 7 are now spread out over many times. What constitutes the present moment depends on how fast we are going, and according to Einstein's reason-

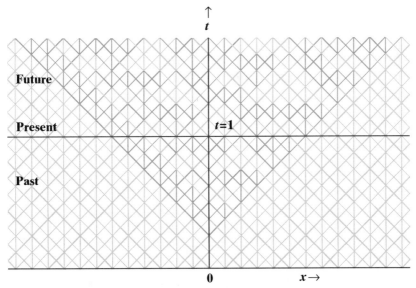

Figure 7. History of events unfolding in a one-dimensional world. The x-axis measures position in one-dimensional space. Time is plotted on the vertical axis. The light and dark gray lines represent trajectories of particles that interact according to a simple cellular automaton rule given in the sidebar on page 49. The "present" is the physical pattern along a horizontal line cutting the vertical axis at time $t=1$.

The units of length and time are chosen so that the speed of light is unity, and the graph of a particle moving at the speed of light tilts from the vertical at ±45 degrees. I have assumed that the light and dark gray particles are either stationary or they move to the right or left at the speed of light. (See sidebar on page 49 for more details.)

ing, the present is therefore not physically real. This means that the entire classical picture of time's passage collapses. As Einstein said to Besso's widow, time is reduced to an illusion.

RELATIVISTIC CONSCIOUSNESS

If this is so, who or what is experiencing the illusion? In Einstein's view, the entire sequence of physical events exists timelessly in four-dimensional space-time. (Since there is one dimension of space in Figures 7 and 8, space-time becomes two-dimensional.) Thus a life exists in its entirety with all of its moments. The consciousness of being in a particular situation at a particular moment is simply there for each moment in a given life span. Since the consciousness of a particular moment includes memories of previous moments, there is an illusion of the passage of time, even though everything is actually timeless.

According to the materialistic theory of consciousness that we

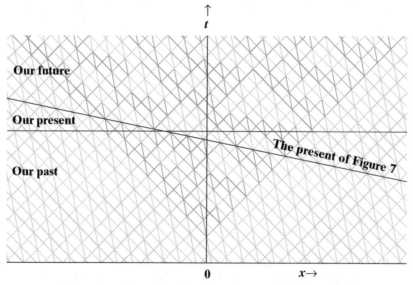

Figure 8. The effect of moving at 20% of the speed of light. This diagram shows how the events in Figure 7 unfold from the point of view of someone moving to the right at 20% of the speed of light. The particles moving right or left still move at the speed of light, in accordance with the theory of relativity. The particles that were stationary now move to the left at 20% the speed of light. The pattern of physical interactions is the same as before, but now the "present" of Figure 7 is tilted and occupies a range of times.

explored in Chapter 1, all that is needed to create a moment's experience of consciousness is a particular material pattern. So when such a pattern exists in space-time, that moment of consciousness has a timeless, fixed existence. The concept of time has been repudiated by the transformation from Figure 7 to Figure 8, but the pattern of interactions between the particles remains the same. These patterns exist timelessly, and likewise one's experience of a given moment has a kind of eternal existence.

In recent years this idea has been elaborated by the British theoretical physicist Julian Barbour. According to Barbour, each moment corresponds to an eternally existing, static arrangement of the universe:

> There is no movement from one static arrangement of the universe to the next. Some configurations of the universe simply contain little patches of consciousness—people—with memories of what they call a past that are built into the Now. The illusion of motion occurs because many slightly different versions of us—none of which move at all—simultaneously inhabit universes with slightly different arrangements of matter (Folger, 2000).

This is a strange theory, but we may be able to obtain some useful insights from it. In the virtual reality model, I posit an interaction between consciousness and the virtual world. In the gross, physical form of the VR model, consciousness is limited by the biological time of the physical brain. However, in the more abstract Ground Reality model, there is no reason to impose this limitation, or to suppose that consciousness is inherently limited by time at all. Thus the subjective impression of the passage of time may, indeed, be determined by the situation of the virtual brain, body, and environment. After all, we do experience the passage of time differently in different circumstances.

To create a truly relativistic VR, it will be necessary to posit some kind of timeless consciousness. For example, consider the relativistic twin paradox. One of a pair of twins stays home, while the other takes a trip in a space ship at nearly the speed of light. According to the theory of relativity, when the space ship returns, the twin on board may have experienced a shorter passage of time (depending on the speed of the ship and the length of the journey) than the twin who stayed home. If these are virtual twins tied to the biological time of two brains that don't travel, then this won't work. But it can work if the consciousness of the virtual twins is derived from a timeless source.

Several questions arise if we try to create a relativistic VR model. First of all, if the conscious life of a person is a series of patterns in "nows" that timelessly exist, then what ties them together as an individual? Do the patterns in the virtual world determine the individual conscious beings, or is there structure within consciousness apart from the virtual world? In brain-based VRs, different conscious individuals correspond to different brains that are "transcendental" to the virtual world. Individual differentiation of consciousness is also a logical possibility in the Ground Reality model.

This, of course, raises the question of how virtual time is related to the experience of conscious entities, independent of the virtual world. The underlying assumption of the Ground Reality model is that consciousness can be linked with particular virtual space-time locations, and there will be an order of conscious experience that corresponds to the order of cumulative memory in the virtual body and brain. This gives rise to the question of whether or not memory is stored in consciousness as well as in the virtual world. In principle, this is possible, and I will consider this point later on in the discussion of reincarnation.

Another question relates to the power of consciousness to influence the virtual world. In a relativistic model, physical influences cannot propagate at faster than the speed of light. We can see this in Figures 7 and 8, where the "creation event" gives rise to a V-shaped pattern of disturbance that expands at the speed of light, but no faster. Such an expanding region of potential influence is called a "light cone," since it would be shaped like a cone if we plotted two dimensions of space (out of the total of three), rather than one. Influences imposed on the virtual world by a conscious subject will be required to spread out within light cones.

Generally, computer simulations are generated by moving through time step by step. Even in the "timeless" Ground Reality model, we must posit some order of calculation in the generation of the virtual world. This order may involve many calculations that do not directly contribute to the virtual world (and may even be performed for unrelated purposes). Nonetheless, the calculations that do define lawful virtual events must unfold in a way that is consistent with the laws of physics and the theory of relativity. Indeed, "timeless" could be taken to mean that there is no rigidly imposed standard of time, but that many fluidly defined forms of temporal ordering are possible.

It turns out that there is no contradiction between these requirements and the requirement that conscious entities should be able to influence the virtual world. The simulation can be advanced on a curved time front like the one shown in Figure 9. Here the calculations below the time front have already been completed and lay in the "past," while the calculations above it are still to be performed and lie in the "future." This time front can be of any shape, as long as any light cone originating on the front does not cut into the region marked "past." Since the time front can have any shape, given this restriction, it does not represent time in any absolute sense. However, the interaction of conscious entities with the virtual world is not affected by changes in the shapes of the time fronts. Thus this arbitrariness in the definition of virtual time doesn't matter as far as the

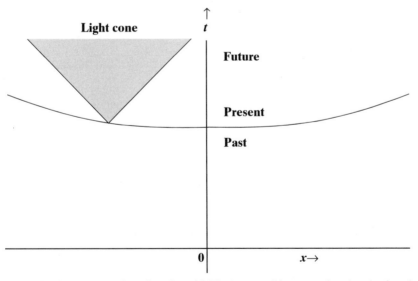

Figure 9. The "present" in a virtual world. The "present" is a curved surface in virtual space-time (and here it is represented as a curved line, since I am plotting only one dimension of space). All virtual events have already been calculated in the region below this surface, and none have been calculated thus far in the region above it. The surface can be arbitrarily defined, given the restriction that light cones originating on the surface do not cut into the past.

experiences of conscious entities are concerned.

In summary, the Ground Reality model assumes that conscious beings interact with a virtual physical reality by stepping through virtual physical time. As virtual time passes on a curved front, events are modified in accordance with states of conscious will, and these modifications may take advantage of the phenomenon of exponential amplification in chaotic systems. Virtual physical time can be defined in many ways that are consistent with the relativistic laws of physics. (These different ways are represented by different curved fronts.) However, all of the possible definitions result in the same experiences for conscious beings interacting with virtual bodies. This results in an illusion of time's passage for such beings. This illusion is independent of whatever forms of temporal ordering may exist within consciousness itself.

4

QUANTUM PERPLEXITY

*"Niels Bohr brainwashed
a whole generation of physicists
into believing that the problem
had been solved fifty years ago."*

—Murray Gell-Mann

A radioactive atom of uranium sits quietly, bound by atomic bonds to other atoms in its mineral matrix. It has been sitting like this for millions of years. Then, suddenly, at an unpredictable time, an alpha particle shoots out of the atom's nucleus in an unpredictable direction. It flies through the gas inside a Geiger counter tube, tearing electrons off atoms and leaving a trail of ions. Other electrons begin to flow along this conductive path, impelled by an electrical potential. This current is amplified in an electronic circuit, and a click is produced by a loudspeaker. The "click" is a pressure wave involving billions of colliding air molecules, and it propagates in all directions at the speed of sound. It vibrates the tympanic membrane of a human ear and sets off an incredibly complex cascade of electrochemical phenomena in the associated auditory nerve and brain. Vocal vibrations are produced, including the phonemes for "I heard a click," and at some point there is conscious perception of the click as a subjective experience of sound.

According to quantum mechanics, subatomic phenomena exhibit a mixture of deterministic behavior and pure chance. The decay of the uranium atom occurs purely by chance according to probabilities which can be accurately computed by the theory. The resulting phenomena, culminating in neural activity in the observer's brain, are also a complex combination of chance and determinism. By invoking pure chance, quantum mechanics differs from classical physics, where chance was used like a gambler's odds to express uncertain knowledge of events that actually unroll with deterministic precision.

Superficially, quantum mechanics seems to model the world as a vast Monte Carlo game, but there is more to it than that. In the prevailing Copenhagen interpretation of quantum mechanics, developed by Niels Bohr, the random element is introduced into the physical scene at the point when an observation is made. In the example, everything unfolds deterministically up to that point, including the events in the uranium nucleus. Thus it is wrong to think that something random happened in the nucleus. Rather, something random happened when an observation was made.

Now what constitutes an observation? What if the human observer is replaced by a tape recorder that records the click? Does an observation occur when the click is recorded, or later on when someone plays back the tape? Quantum mechanics is structured in such a way that this becomes a debatable issue, and it can be argued that the theory gives consciousness a role in physical processes.

FROM MATERIALISM TO IDEALISM

To see why this is so, we need to take a look at the work of Erwin Schrödinger, one of the founding fathers of quantum mechanics. Schrödinger wanted to establish quantum mechanics as a purely physical model of nature, and so he started with the observation by Louis de Broglie that electrons behave as though they were waves. Schrödinger envisioned a theory in which waves representing matter flow and transform in a multidimensional space of configurations. In this abstract picture, a configuration is a complete description of how matter is distributed in space at a given time. The configuration specifies the details of all the atoms in the system, with their electrons and nuclei. It also specifies the macroscopic arrangements of these atoms, including furniture and people's bodies.

Just as waves on the surface of a lake continuously shift and change form, so the quantum wave is continuously shifting in the abstract space of configurations. It transforms deterministically according to a differential equation, called the Schrödinger equation after its discoverer. In this picture, quantum mechanics was intended to be an abstract version of classical wave motion.

Just like ripples on a pond, quantum waves tend to spread out, and Schrödinger realized with dismay that this inflicted some rather disquieting consequences on his theory. He illustrated this with a famous thought experiment, commonly known as the Schrödinger cat paradox. This experiment starts with a box containing a live cat and a diabolical apparatus that will kill the cat if triggered by the decay of a radioactive atom. Schrödinger showed that the quantum wave in this case spreads out to embrace two regions of configuration space representing a live cat and a dead cat.

The quantum wave is interpreted in terms of probabilities. Configurations that it visits have some probability of actually coming to pass, and configurations that it avoids are ruled out. So in this case, the configuration representing a live cat has a certain probability of happening, and so does the configuration representing a dead cat. This is

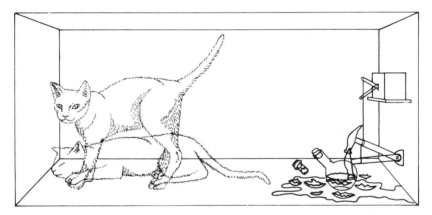

Figure 10. The cat paradox (Dewitt, p. 156). In this thought experiment, a cat is placed in a box along with a flask of Prussic acid. If a radioactive decay in a piece of uranium triggers a Geiger counter, the flask is smashed, killing the cat. The amount of uranium is adjusted so that this has a fifty percent chance of happening in one hour. According to quantum mechanics, the wave function describing the cat after one hour is a superposition of a wave function representing a live cat and one representing a dead cat. This wave function collapses to one alternative or the other when the contents of the box are observed. Some physicists have argued that observation is a conscious act and therefore consciousness plays an active role in physical phenomena. (Of course, the thought experiment assumes, for the sake of argument, that the cat is not conscious.)

hardly surprising. But the catch is that this probability interpretation can be applied only after the box is opened and the cat is observed (assuming that the cat itself is not an observer). Before the observation, nature itself is undecided about the cat's condition. In other words, it is not correct to say that the unobserved cat is definitely alive or definitely dead, but we just don't know which option is true. Rather, we have what in technical terms is called a linear superposition of the live-cat state and the dead-cat state. Both are there simultaneously in nature.

Now it is certainly true that a cat is either definitely alive or definitely dead when we see it. The quantum mechanical understanding is that nature "makes up its mind" about the condition of the cat when a human observer looks at it. When nature's choice is made, the quantum wave abruptly switches from a linear superposition of live and dead cats to either a live-cat state or a dead-cat state, as the case may be. This change is thought to be a real, natural event that occurs at random according to the quantum mechanical probabilities. Physicists refer to it as the "collapse of the wave function" or as a "quantum jump."

Schrödinger himself was quite dissatisfied with quantum jumps. Shortly after discovering his famous equation, he paid a visit to Niels Bohr, another of the great founding fathers of quantum mechanics. Bohr strongly stressed the essential role of abrupt random jumps in the theory, but Schrödinger complained that, "Had I known that we were not going to get rid of this damned quantum jumping, I never would have involved myself in this business" (Gribben, 1984, p. 117). Nonetheless, physicists in general have followed Bohr's lead, and his views have become famous as the Copenhagen interpretation of quantum mechanics.

Bohr's colleague Werner Heisenberg was also deeply involved with the creation of quantum mechanics and the Copenhagen interpretation. His views on quantum jumps reveal a fundamental ambiguity that runs through the literature on quantum mechanics. Heisenberg said that

> we are finally led to believe that the laws of nature that we formulate mathematically in quantum theory deal no longer with the particles themselves but with our knowledge of the elementary particles . . . The conception

> of the objective reality of the particles has evaporated in a curious way, not into the fog of some new, obscure, or not yet understood reality concept, but into the transparent clarity of a mathematics that represents no longer the behavior of the elementary particles but rather our knowledge of this behavior (Stapp 1993, p. 219).

It could be said that the equations of classical physics also describe our knowledge of physical phenomena. So what special point is Heisenberg trying to make about quantum mechanics? The answer is that classical physics promises to define nature fully in terms of material objects. In quantum mechanics, these objects disappear, and the mathematical formalism seems to deal with knowledge rather than physical "stuff." This invites us to adopt an idealistic view, in which nature is subsumed within mind.

Heisenberg identifies the collapse of the quantum wave with acquisition of knowledge in the mind of the observer. As he puts it,

> The discontinuous change in the probability function, however, takes place with the act of registration [in the mind], because it is the discontinuous change in our knowledge in the instant of registration that has its image in the discontinuous change in the probability function (Stapp, 1993, p. 220).

So the collapse of the quantum wave (or "probability function") is the image of a change in our knowledge: When we learn more, our probability estimates naturally change. The founders of quantum mechanics insisted that the theory is complete in the sense that no hidden variables or hidden data are left out that might shed further light on nature. So if our knowledge was complete to begin with, it follows that when we learn more about nature, nature itself changes. We are not simply getting more information about something that is already there.

Yet Heisenberg also emphasized that what happens in an atomic event "applies to the physical not the psychical act of observation" (Stapp, 1993, p. 220). This is the fundamental ambiguity: Is quantum mechanics a theory of mind or of matter? The scale seems to tip back towards matter if we look at the quantum wave function of an atom, which is shaped by potential energy laws familiar from classical physics.

The famous mathematician John von Neumann looked at quantum theory from the standpoint of mind-matter dualism, and he associated collapse of the quantum wave with an explicitly nonphysical conscious ego. In his pioneering book on the foundations of quantum theory, von Neumann described two processes of natural change in quantum mechanics: continuous, deterministic change following the Schrödinger equation and abrupt, random collapse of the quantum wave. Von Neumann argued that collapse can be deferred until sense data reporting quantum events reaches the "abstract ego" of the human observer (von Neumann, 1955, pp. 419–21). At this point, conscious awareness makes wave function collapse unavoidable.

Von Neumann's model is implicitly dualistic, with continuously flowing matter and abrupt changes imposed by mind. In such a model, it is necessary to explain how the abstract ego would cause quantum collapse. Von Neumann didn't answer this question, but in recent years, the mathematician and physicist Roger Penrose has suggested that the connection between consciousness and quantum processes will require new physics for its elucidation. Penrose referred to von Neumann's continuous and discontinuous processes as U and R. Using this terminology, he said,

> I am speculating that the action of conscious thinking is very much tied up with the resolving out of alternatives that were previously in linear superposition. This is all concerned with the unknown physics that governs the borderline between U and R and which, I am claiming, depends upon a yet-to-be discovered theory of quantum gravity (Penrose, 1989, p. 438).

Many years before this, the Nobel laureate Eugene Wigner suggested that the collapse of the wave function depends on as yet unknown physical laws and that it involves the action of consciousness (Wigner, 1962, 1964, 1970). Significantly, Wigner declared that consciousness is the first kind of reality and that the existence of material things is a secondary type of reality that depends on consciousness. This is strongly reminiscent of the philosophy of idealism.

Similar ideas have been expressed by Rudolf Peierls, a distinguished physicist who defends Bohr's Copenhagen interpretation. Peierls said that the conscious mind can not be replaced with an inanimate device in its role of observer in quantum mechanics. Following Heisenberg, he declared that the quantum wave represents our knowledge of the physical system, and that collapse of the wave represents the attainment of new knowledge (Davies, 1986, p. 73). Since this view strongly connects nature with our knowledge of nature, it is also suggestive of idealism.

Freeman Dyson of Princeton's Institute for Advanced Study has given a poetic account of mind in nature that is based on quantum mechanics:

> The laws of subatomic physics cannot even be formulated without some reference to the observer. "Chance" cannot be defined except as a measure of the observer's ignorance of the future. The laws leave a place for mind in the description of every molecule. . . . I think our consciousness is not just a passive epiphenomenon carried along by the chemical events in our brains, but is an active agent forcing the molecular complexes to make choices between one quantum state and another. In other words, mind is already inherent in every electron, and the processes of human consciousness differ only in degree but not in kind from the processes of choice between quantum states which we call "chance" when they are made by electrons (Dyson, 1979b, p. 249).

It is significant that Dyson defines chance as a measure of the observer's ignorance, or relative lack of knowledge. This is the key step that leads towards idealism when combined with the idea of quantum mechanics as a complete theory. In Dyson's case, this takes the form of a pantheistic view, in which mind is everywhere in nature and physical action involves conscious direction.

CHANCE AND INTELLIGENCE

However, Dyson does not simply define chance as a measure of ignorance. He also treats it as the product of conscious action. If consciousness acts according to plans and intentions on the human level, does it also do so for electrons? Then again, if electrons make quantum jumps at random (and otherwise behave deterministically), does it follow that conscious human choice is either random or physically determined? We clearly need to clarify the relation between consciousness and chance.

Many students of quantum mechanics have thought that quantum mechanical randomness may have something to do with free will.

Could it be that the consciousness of the observer can take advantage of randomness to willfully influence the course of events? For this to be possible, it is necessary for the conscious observer to be able to adjust the odds, just as a gambler might wish to do in Monte Carlo.

Henry Stapp is one physicist who has suggested that quantum mechanical randomness might be different from what we normally think of as chance. To Stapp, the idea that quantum choices come randomly out of nowhere should be seen as "an admission of contemporary ignorance, not as a satisfactory final word" (Stapp, 1993, p. 216). Stapp seeks a possibility that agrees with all scientific data, but that lies somewhere between "pure chance" and "pure determinism." He concludes, "I think such a possibility is open, but to give this logical possibility a nonspeculative foundation will require enlarging the boundaries of scientific knowledge" (Stapp, 1993, p. 217).

Although Stapp is primarily concerned with individual consciousness, scientists such as William Pollard and Donald Mackey have seen chance as an opportunity for introducing divine control into the world of physics. Pollard's idea was summed up neatly by the physicist-priest John Polkinghorne: "Will not God's power to act as the cause of uncaused quantum events (always cleverly respecting the statistical regularities which are reflections of his faithfulness) give him a chance to play a manipulative role in a scientifically regular world?" (Polkinghorne, 1986, p. 71) Unfortunately, Polkinghorne dismissed this idea as contrived, saying that "Houdini-like wrigglings" are required to insert control signals into random sequences (Polkinghorne, 1986, p. 72).

THE LAWS OF CHANCE

To understand Polkinghorne's point, we have to ask what chance really is. The simplest approach is to ask some questions about an ideal coin-tossing device that produces "heads" and "tails" at random. Suppose there is a 50% chance for heads and a 50% chance for tails. Furthermore, suppose that successive tosses are statistically independent. This is just what we might expect if the tosses were generated by a quantum mechanical process such as the decay of radioactive atoms. But what does it mean?

First of all, if there are 10,000 tosses, about 50% or 5,000 of them should produce heads. Here "about" has to be carefully defined. There is a number called the standard deviation—50 in this case—which can be computed by a simple formula. If the number of heads is more than 2 or 3 standard deviations away from 5,000, the coin-tosser is judged to be deviating from its prescribed behavior, and the judgement grows rapidly more severe as the number of standard deviations increases. Thus a run of 5,047 heads out of 10,000 is okay, but a run of 5,386 is strongly deviant, and 6,023 is much worse. (At the same time, we will be suspicious if we get *exactly* 5,000 heads.)

There are more complexities. If we look at pairs of tosses, we should find that each of the combinations—heads-heads, heads-tails, tails-heads, and tails-tails—come up about 25% of the time. These numbers are also judged on the basis of standard deviations. Similar judgements can be made for groups of three tosses, groups of four tosses, and so on.

The "laws of chance" require that all of these conditions should be more-or-less satisfied. The question is, can we do this and at the same time introduce meaningful information into the sequence of heads and tails? The answer is that we can, but this might well be dismissed as contrived wriggling.

Here is one way to do it. Today there are many compression programs that will take a segment of text and code it in a shorter form for convenient computer storage. It turns out that when a text is compressed, the bit string representing it comes to resemble a random sequence of 0's and 1's (Shannon, 1948). When the text is compressed to the maximum possible degree, then the compressed string satisfies all of the criteria for a random string that I have just mentioned. Yet the string encodes a text which may represent an intelligent message.

Is this string random or not? If we say it is, then we are granting that random strings may encode an intelligent message that might later be decoded and put to practical use. This applies to all random strings, including ones produced quantum mechanically.

But if we say that it is not, then we are admitting we simply cannot know for sure that a particular string is truly random. A string may seem random, but it may turn out that it can be decoded to reveal an intelligent message. Since it is practically impossible to take into account all possible coding schemes, this makes randomness an ideal concept which cannot be verified in practice. If we say that quantum mechanical sequences are random in this sense, then we are making an unverifiable assertion.

What it comes down to is that "random" means non-intelligent and disordered on an intuitive, gut level. If we contrive some way of sneaking intelligent information into an apparently random sequence, then we violate this intuitive definition of chance. Doing this changes the boundaries of science, but in an informal way, since we are dealing with intuitive expectations rather than formal rules. Yet if we plug the gaps by ruling out all ways of sneaking in intelligent information, then we wind up with a definition of chance that is unverifiable and of no practical value.

Since randomness is normally evaluated using relatively simple tests, one can argue that quantum mechanics accepts *de facto* a form of randomness that would admit intelligent manipulation in a VR model. In such a model, conscious choices must influence wave-function collapse in a way that (nearly) respects the probability interpretation of the wave function. However, it is not necessary for us to try to formulate such a model in detail, since it turns out that we can entirely eliminate chance from quantum mechanics.

MANY WORLDS

One way to do this is simple but drastic: Don't collapse the quantum wave at all. This gives you a deterministic theory based entirely on the Schrödinger equation.

In this approach, the human observer is considered to be part of the physical system. John von Neumann pointed out that when such an observer looks at Schrödinger's superimposed live and dead cats, the quantum wave transforms to represent an observer-seeing-a-live-cat superimposed on an observer-seeing-a-dead-cat. If this dual-state observer communicates his observations to another person, that person enters the state of person-hearing-about-a-live-cat superimposed on person-hearing-about-a-dead-cat. As information about the cats spreads, the quantum wave continues to split into two parts, each of which represents an internally consistent state of affairs.

In general, it can be shown that if a quantum wave is simply allowed to transform according to the Schrödinger equation, it will bifurcate repeatedly into branches representing distinct macroscopic alternatives. Events in each branch fit together consistently, and after two branches separate, they never rejoin. This leads to the so-called many worlds interpretation, in which the entire universe is assigned a quantum wave. This wave continuously splits into multiple copies representing all possible quantum alternatives, including Schrödinger's live and dead cats.

The many worlds interpretation was first propounded by Hugh Everett (1957), and it was supported for some time by the physicist John Wheeler of Princeton University. However, many physicists have vehemently dismissed this theory, and Wheeler himself eventually rejected it as carrying "too much metaphysical baggage" (Davies and Brown, 1986, p. 60). The acceptance of vast numbers of parallel universes was simply too great a price to pay to resolve the problems of wave function collapse.

But in recent years, a number of prominent physicists involved with cosmology have been quietly deciding that the price is not too great after all. For example, the Nobel prize winning physicist Steven Weinberg remarked that, "In the realist approach to quantum mechanics of Hugh Everett and others, there is just one wave function describing all phenomena, including experiments and observers, and the fundamental laws are those that describe the evolution of this wave function" (Weinberg 1992, p. 232). He then commented that he personally prefers this approach (Weinberg, 1992, p. 251).

In a poll conducted by political scientist L. David Raub, 72 leading quantum cosmologists and quantum field theorists were asked what they think of the many worlds interpretation. The results were: 58% said it is true; 18% rejected it; 13% said that it might be true; and 11% had no opinion. Supporters of the many worlds interpretation included Richard Feynman, Stephen Hawking, and Murray Gell-Mann (Tipler, 1994, p. 170).

Murray Gell-Mann, who is famous for inventing the quark hypothesis, has made serious contributions to the many worlds interpretation. He and physicist James Hartle have developed an approach in which the total wave function of the universe is broken down into alternative histories of events by means of a coarse graining technique analogous to that used in statistical mechanics (Gell-Mann and Hartle, 1990). When this coarse graining is properly defined, distinct histories of the universe "decohere," or become quantum mechanically separate. It is then possible to assign to each history a probability that can be seen as a measure of how physically realistic that history is.

In this system, histories that include physically impossible events will have zero probability, and they can be eliminated from consideration. Histories that are physically possible will be extremely numerous, and they will all have extremely small but nonzero probabilities.

Consider histories in which there is a quantum mechanically driven coin-tossing device similar to the one discussed earlier in this chapter. Call heads H and tails T, and look at sequences of 10 tosses. All these sequences are given the same probability, namely 1 out of 1,024 (which is the number of possible sequences of 10 tosses). For example, the orderly pattern HTHTHTHTHT has the same probability as the disorderly pattern HHTHTHTTTH.

If all histories with equal probability are equally real, then there must be a history in which the 10 tosses are HTHTHTHTHT and a history in which they are HHTHTHTTTH. This is not surprising, but now consider sequences of 2,000,000 tosses. There must be a real history in which the device produces 1,000,000 HTs in a row. Likewise, there must be a history in which it repeatedly spells out the Gettysburg Address in code. These histories are just as real as those in which the tosses generate a disorderly pattern.

Stephen Hawking believes in all these histories. Hawking and his colleague James Hartle used the many worlds interpretation when formulating their "no boundary" theory of the origin of the universe. While describing this theory, Hawking said that "there is a collection over every possible history for the universe, and all these histories are equally real (whatever that may mean)" (Hawking, 1993, p. 36).

Whatever reality means, it presumably applies to the history of the universe in which we are living. Hawking is therefore saying that worlds in which quantum coin tossers always spell out the Gettysburg Address are just as real as the world of our experience. As Hawking puts it, "We happen to live on one particular history that has certain properties and details. But there are very similar intelligent beings who live on histories that differ in who won the war and who is Top of the Pops" (Hawking, 1993, p. 137).

This picture of reality naturally brings up the old questions about consciousness. Why should consciousness be connected with a coarse-grained track through the universal quantum wave? A standard answer is that consciousness is simply there wherever there are patterns corresponding to suitable brains. But we can just as well suppose that conscious awareness is *not* necessarily associated with such quantum wave patterns.

It is interesting to look at the many worlds interpretation as a software resource that could be used to build a virtual reality system. Imagine a computer that can calculate the universal wave function, at least for an environment large enough to accommodate a population of virtual "sentient" beings. This could, in principle, be used for a virtual reality in which conscious entities are linked to the bodies of the beings. The interface between the participants and their virtual bodies could be shunted from one quantum history to another in order to express their conscious will.

For example, suppose that quantum mechanical processes within the brain cause the wave function to develop into a superposition of two distinct but closely related brain states. According to the many worlds interpretation, each state belongs to a distinct history. By shunting the participant's interface to one of these histories or the other, the VR system could express the will of the participant to act in a certain way.

As this shunting process goes on, the total set of observer interfaces will trace a tortuous path through the set of quantum mechanical histories. Since this path involves no violation of the laws of physics, it constitutes a quantum mechanical history in its own right—a history selected in part by the will of observer-participants who are outside the virtual system. In this scheme, this is the only "real" history and the universal wave is only a computational device that provides choices for the observer-participants to make.

This scheme does not require a full computation of all of the branches in the universal wave function. Rather, as choices are made by the participants from moment to moment, branches that are not chosen will be dropped from the computations.

BOHM'S QUANTUM POTENTIAL

This is reminiscent of David Bohm's hidden variable theory of quantum mechanics (Bohm and Hiley, 1984). "Hidden variables" are additional parameters that might be added to quantum mechanics to convert it into a deterministic theory. In the early days of quantum mechanics, many physicists suspected that quantum randomness is due to our ignorance of such hidden variables. But, unfortunately, John von Neumann proved that any theory that adds hidden variables to quantum mechanics must fail to give the same experimental predictions as quantum mechanics (von Neumann, 1955, p. 324).

Bohm's accomplishment was to prove that von Neumann was wrong, and he did this by actually constructing a successful hidden variable theory. In Bohm's theory, the universal wave function is converted mathematically into a form that Bohm calls the quantum potential. Bohm postulates that the system has a classical configuration of particle positions that defines the system's physical state. This configuration can be thought of as a multidimensional point that moves under the influence of the quantum potential.

The quantum potential can be visualized as an arrangement of multidimensional canyons that subdivide repeatedly into distinct branches. As the configuration-point moves down this complex of canyons, it is swept into particular branches and it leaves aside others. The neglected branches continue to subdivide endlessly, but they are never visited by the configuration-point. Practical computations using Bohm's model could therefore ignore further subdivisions of branches not entered by the system's configuration.

In Bohm's model, the movement of the configuration-point is calculated using deterministic equations. Chance enters into his model through exponential amplification, just as it does in classical physics. Yet Bohm's model gives exactly the same experimental predictions as quantum mechanics.

This brings us back to the deterministic chaos model of mind-brain interaction that I discussed in Chapter 2. One could guide the configuration-point through the canyons of the quantum potential by making immeasurably small corrections that take effect through exponential amplification. The quantum potential is simply another form of the universal wave in the many worlds interpretation, and the small cor-

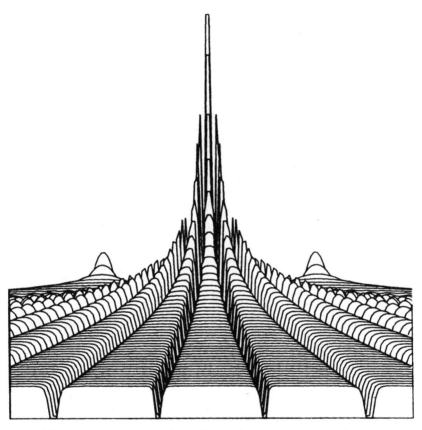

Figure 11. Bohm's quantum potential. This curved surface represents Bohm's quantum potential for the case of an electron passing through two slits. The potential surface guides the electron so that it moves in a manner consistent with quantum mechanics.

rection method is simply another way of shunting the participant's interface through the maze of choices offered by the universal wave.

I conclude that the laws of quantum physics are compatible with the kind of interaction between consciousness and virtual matter needed for VR models. The standard Copenhagen interpretation of quantum mechanics seems to bring mind and consciousness into physics, and some prominent physicists have tried to use quantum indeterminism as an avenue for introducing free will into the material domain. If we try to do this, we run into obstacles based on the nature of chance. However, if we are willing to put up with a bit of "Houdini-like wriggling," we might be able to construct a workable VR that uses modified wave-function collapse to allow conscious subjects to influence the course of events.

Ironically, the obstacles posed by chance can be overcome by resorting to the views of other prominent physicists, who see quantum mechanics as a deterministic theory of matter, independent of conscious observers and devoid of chance as an active agency. The many worlds interpretation and Bohm's hidden variable theory can both be harnessed in a virtual reality model that shows how a non-virtual mind can interact with a virtual world that obeys the laws of physics. This model eliminates the "metaphysical baggage" of many worlds by allowing conscious observers to select a unique history from the branching maze of quantum alternatives. In this model, the universal quantum wave or quantum potential becomes a computational device that is generated only as it is needed by the unfolding virtual history.

5

THE PHYSICS
OF THE ULTIMATE

"All possible visible universes
can be replicated down to the quantum state
if the computer capacity is at least $10^{10^{123}}$ bits.
In the far future, the computer capacity
will be far, far above this."

—Frank Tipler

As the universe expanded and cooled, the stars were slowly reduced to dying embers. For millions of years, life had spread through the universe, feeding off the abundant energy generated by countless billions of nuclear fires. Now, as entropy increased, the endless cold night of the universal heat death began. But life began to adapt, as it always had, to its new situation.

The solution was hibernation. For life to function, it is necessary to dissipate energy, and this requires a source of heat at a higher temperature than the universe as a whole. As temperature differences declined, life had to slow down and carry out fewer and fewer metabolic steps per unit of time.

When a living organism on the earth slows down its metabolism, it naturally becomes inactive in relation to other, more active beings. But living beings in the cooling universe were able to slow down in a uniform way.

For millions of years, life had existed in the form of powerful computers that created their own worlds of experience through simulation. Now, as sources of power became weaker, each simulation slowed down as a whole, but the relative events within the simulation seemed to go on at the same subjective pace as before. As time marched on, the subjective time of living experience moved on at a slower and slower pace, but it never came to a halt.

The trick was to slow down in such a way that subjective time is infinite, but the total energy required for indefinite survival is finite (Dyson, 1979, p. 456). Life became eternal, with endlessly increasing memory capacity. Finally, the computational resources became sufficient to fully simulate the universe of old. In its quest for new experience, life decided to create a new universe through simulation. It (slowly) said, "Let there be light." And there was light.

ETERNAL LIFE IN AN OPEN UNIVERSE

This scenario is based on a series of lectures on the future of life given by the physicist Freeman Dyson (Dyson, 1979). Dyson's model is based on the assumption that the universe is open, which means that it will expand and cool off endlessly. He argues that a form of living organization is possible that can go through an infinite number of "moments of consciousness" while dissipating a finite amount of energy.

Dyson adopts the view that the essence of life lies in structure rather than substance. He accepts the postulate of strong AI that a suitably programmed computer will be conscious by virtue of the fact that it carries out a suitable sequence of computational steps. This means that "moments of consciousness" translate as computational steps. If the steps are taken at a slower and slower pace, everything will be the same for the subjective experience of the conscious computer. It will simply be stretched out further and further in physical time.

A key feature of Dyson's proposal is that his life-computer will be able to carry out infinitely many computational steps, using an endlessly increasing memory (Dyson, 1979, p. 457). This means that it will be a universal Turing machine that could perfectly simulate any computer whatsoever. Dyson limits himself to saying that the computer will constitute life with ever increasing capacities. In principle, however, we can imagine that such a computer could simulate an entire universe and all the living beings in it. If the strong AI postulate is true, such a universe would generate conscious experience on its own internal time scale, regardless of how slowly the underlying computer operated.

ESCHATOLOGY AND THE BIG CRUNCH

The physicist and cosmologist Frank Tipler of Tulane University has also presented a speculative model of life in the remote future (Tipler, 1994). Unlike Dyson, Tipler assumes that after a period of expansion, the universe will begin to contract under the force of gravity and finally collapse to a point in the "big crunch." Before that happens, life will spread throughout the universe in the form of superintelligent computers. Knowing that the end of the universe is drawing near, these computers will take control of the chaotic motion of collapsing matter and cause the universe to collapse at different rates in different directions. The resulting "gravitational shear" will produce an ever increasing temperature difference which can be used as a source of energy by the computers.

Now things become a bit tricky. The computers will combine together to build an ultimate computer powered by the gravitational shear. This computer, which Tipler calls the Omega Point, will use shear energy to sustain its own organization against the soaring universal temperatures. It will operate at faster and faster speeds and carry out infinitely many operations in the finite physical time that remains before the crunch. Its memory capacity will also increase unlimitedly during this interval.

From this point, the argument is the same as in Dyson's model. The ultimate computer is a universal Turing machine, and it can simulate anything.

According to Tipler, this computer will decide to precisely simulate every human being who ever lived. Tipler calls an exact simulation an emulation. He claims that the future emulation of all humans will be the resurrection of the dead, as predicted in Christian tradition. To Tipler, the Omega Point computer is the God of Christianity, who doesn't exist now but will exist in the far future. He presents his theory as the physics of eschatology—the study of the afterlife and the ultimate future.

Since he explicitly brings religious themes into his discussion, many scientists have taken a dim view of Tipler's theory. For example, cosmologist Joseph Silk accuses Tipler of trying to "drag relativity through the doors of the church," and he declares that "Most cosmologists are prepared to accuse Tipler of the direst crime, perpetrating a hoax of Piltdown Man proportions" (Silk, 1995, p. 93).

By going from simulation to resurrection, Tipler has no doubt committed an affront to science, which has struggled for so long to free itself from religion's doctrinal grip. Nonetheless, Tipler's only crime was to systematically assemble together some ideas and speculations that have been circulating in the scientific community for some time. Thus, whether the universe ends with a crunch or a heat death, his thesis does raise some interesting questions.

IS PHYSICS COMPUTABLE?

First of all, could the universe be simulated by calculations? As physics developed historically, each successive major theory of physics has required more complex calculations than the one before it. For example, in classical physics the electron in a hydrogen atom moves along a curved path in 3D space. In quantum mechanics, this simple motion is replaced by a wave that forms a complex vibrational shape in 3D.

Theories at the cutting edge of fundamental physics require even more computation. Quantum electrodynamics (QED) is the quantum theory of electrons and electromagnetic phenomena. If an electron moves from one point to another as it orbits a hydrogen nucleus, QED says that an infinite amount of activity takes place. The electron emits and absorbs so-called virtual photons, and these in turn create virtual positrons and electrons, which emit more virtual photons, and so on without limit. This infinite activity has the result that all calculations in QED give an answer of infinity if they are carried out in a straightforward way.

For twenty years this was a stumbling block for quantum theorists. Then in the late 1940s, Julian Schwinger, Richard Feynman, and Sin-Itiro Tomonaga independently invented methods of "renormalization" that cancel out the infinities and give finite answers. It turned out that these answers agree very nicely with experiments, and the three physicists received a Nobel Prize for their work.

The agreement between QED and some experimental findings is astonishing. For example, the magnetic moment of an electron has been measured experimentally to be 1.00115965221, and it has been calculated from QED to be 1.00115965246 (Feynman, 1985, p. 7).

Feynman points out that this is like measuring the distance from Los Angeles to New York with an error no greater than the thickness of a human hair.

At the same time, there are also problems with the theory. Nearly 50 years after his Nobel-prize winning work, Feynman gave a scathing critique of renormalization:

> No matter how clever the word, [renormalization] is what I call a dippy process! Having to resort to such hocus-pocus has prevented us from proving that the theory of quantum electrodynamics is mathematically self-consistent. . . . I suspect that renormalization is not mathematically legitimate. What is certain is that we do not have a good mathematical way to describe quantum electrodynamics (Feynman, 1985, p. 128).

Quantum electrodynamics is a curious theory: experimentally well confirmed but mathematically unsatisfactory. This suggests that perhaps there may exist a different mathematical formalism which captures the essence of the theory, but avoids its mathematical drawbacks. A simulation of quantum electrodynamics will presumably require the use of such a new formulation.

Tipler points out that Jacob Bekenstein has calculated a limit on the amount of information that could be stored in a given volume of space—in apparent contradiction to the infinite activity I have just discussed. This so-called Bekenstein bound tells us that an object having the size and mass of a human body could contain at most about 300 billion billion billion billion megabytes of information (Tipler, 1994, p. 407).

This is somewhat larger than the capacity of most hard disks, but it is a finite number. It tells us that it should be possible for a universal Turing machine with unlimited memory capacity to exactly represent a human body. Tipler goes further and points out that Roger Penrose used the Bekenstein bound to calculate that the amount of information in the visible universe is at most 10^{123} bits or 10^{116} megabytes (Tipler, 1994, p. 221). Since this is also finite, Tipler concludes that a universal Turing machine could represent the entire universe. With a suitable algorithm, it could simulate the universe.

How can we reconcile infinite activity within a small volume of space with finite information capacity in the same volume? The answer is that the inherent uncertainty in quantum mechanics causes most of the activity to be unreal in the sense that no specific details can be read out from it. This suggests that the unreal activity could be omitted from the theory altogether, and this might eliminate both the infinities and Feynman's "dippy" process of renormalization.

In one sense, this already happens in the calculations made by physicists. Even though a physical theory may postulate an infinite amount of activity in a finite volume of space, it may be that a mathematical analysis requiring a finite number of symbolic steps will yield all necessary answers regarding observable quantities. In fact, the theoretical value of 1.00115965246 was certainly obtained using such a finite series of steps. If a computer can be programmed to carry out such steps, then all observable events can be simulated by finite computer calculations, even though the underlying theory talks about continuous variables at every point in space.

Nonetheless, it is clear that a complete simulation of physical reality—an emulation in Tipler's terminology—must be capable of handling a vast amount of information in any small volume of space. The simplest way to see this is to consider Avogadro's number. This number tells us that there are about 600,000 billion billion molecules in a "gram molecular weight" of a substance. For example, there are this many H_2O molecules in 18 grams of water. These molecules certainly "exist" in some sense, and they must be specified fully in an emulation generated by a computer or computer equivalent, including our hypothetical Ground Reality.

We should finally note in passing the superstring theories, which propose to describe subatomic particles as vibrational modes of tiny "strings" vibrating in multidimensional space. These theories are still very much under construction, and I will not try to review them here. It is sufficient to note that for realistic simulation, superstring models will probably require even larger amounts of calculation than the physical theories that preceded them.

FROM BIT TO IT

Some scientists have advanced models that eliminate continuous quantities in favor of variables that are allowed to change only by finite steps. For example, Feynman suggested that perhaps the solution to the renormalization problem is to assume that space is not continuous (Feynman, 1985, p. 129). If movement through space has to go by tiny steps (Feynman suggested 10^{-100} centimeters), then the infinities disappear. But unfortunately other problems arise, such as negative energies and probabilities of more than 100%.

A physical model is called discrete if key physical variables (such as position and time) are required to change by tiny steps, rather than continuously. Ed Fredkin and Tommaso Toffoli of MIT have argued that the laws of physics might be modeled by a type of computer called a cellular automaton, in which space and time are divided up into discrete cells (Davies, 1992, p. 123). Toffoli specifically argued that this approach would help eliminate the infinities that have plagued mathematical physics (Toffoli, 1984).

Unfortunately, cellular automaton models cannot directly represent space and time, but a cellular automaton may lie in the background of a successful physical theory. The simple cellular automaton used to illustrate relativity theory in Chapter 3 was based on an underlying space-time. In contrast, authors such as Ostoma and Trushyk (1999) have tried to base space-time itself on an underlying cellular automaton. In their model, space is broken into steps of the Planck distance of 1.6×10^{-33} centimeters and time advances by steps of the Planck time of 5.4×10^{-44} seconds.

The physicist John Wheeler has outlined a radical approach to physics based on discrete information (Wheeler, 1988). Wheeler's starting point is an attempt to apply Bohr's interpretation of quantum mechanics to the universe as a whole. Wheeler chooses the yes/no answer to an observational question as the basis of his theory. All other features of the theory are to be derived from these "bits" or yes/no answers. Therefore, Wheeler rejects the continuum of space as fundamental to his theory, and he likewise rejects the continuum of time. He wants to deny the fundamental role of laws as they are now known in physics. His idea is to derive all of these things from yes/no answers. As he puts it,

> Every *it*, every particle, every field of force, even the spacetime continuum itself, derives its way of action and its very existence entirely, even if in some

contexts indirectly, from the detector elicited answers to yes or no questions, binary choices, *bits*. Otherwise stated, all things physical, all *its* . . . must in the end submit to an information-theoretic description (Wheeler, 1991, p. 2).

The problem in this scheme is that a detector is both a physical thing and the basis for the existence of physical things. As Wheeler points out, a detector could utilize the avalanche of electrons in a Geiger counter, the blackening of a grain of photographic emulsion, or in general, a process that amplifies a quantum event and leaves a recognizable trace (Wheeler, 1988, p. 10). Such detectors are perceived by observer-participants, which in Wheeler's theory are also physical bodies made of atoms.

How can every "it" depend on "bits," which in turn depend on "its" in the form of detectors and observer-participants? Wheeler frankly asserts that this is a self-activating loop. The universe of today is to be invoked into being by the acts of observation of future life, and future life will evolve from the life of today:

> There are billions upon billions of living places yet to be inhabited. The coming explosion of life opens the door to an all-encompassing role for observer-participancy: to build, in time to come, no minor part of what we call *its* past—*our* past, present, and future—but this whole vast world (Wheeler, 1988, p. 6).

Wheeler's theory is different from Tipler's, but it has a lot in common with it. They both believe that reality can be described by binary

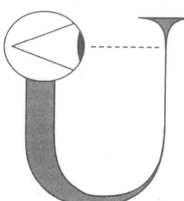

Figure 12. John Wheeler's self-generating universe. According to physicist John Wheeler, the universe of the past may have been bootstrapped into existence by acts of observation in the universe of the future.

information. Wheeler believes that future life will "build" our world, and Tipler believes future "life" will simulate it. They both imagine that the universe will end in a "big crunch" and that tremendous amounts of computation will occur in the universe's last moment. In this connection, Wheeler says,

> If space is closed, if—following on the present phase of expansion—the system of galaxies contracts, if temperatures rise, all in line with the best known Friedman cosmology, and if life wins all, then the number of bits of information being exchanged per second can be expected to rise enormously compared to that number rate today. The total count of bits: How great will it be before the counting has to cease because space is within a Planck time of total crunch? (Wheeler, 1988, p. 14)

As noted above, the Planck time is about 10^{-43} seconds and the related Planck length is 10^{-33} centimeters. Many cosmologists argue that our familiar concepts of time and space completely break down on these scales due to space-time distortions caused by quantum gravity. This suggests that space and time are not fundamental. To Wheeler they may be mere appearances, based on an underlying framework of bits.

INCOMPUTABLE LAWS

Even if the universe can be described in terms of binary bits, it is still possible that a computer may not be able to simulate it. Roger Penrose pointed out that there could be completely deterministic natural laws which cannot be modeled with computers (Penrose, 1989, p. 170).

For example, the design of a Turing machine may be encoded in some standard way as a string of binary bits. Let T1, T2, T3, and so on be the list of bit strings encoding Turing machine designs, and let these strings be written in numerical order. (Each string can be written as a number.) When a Turing machine is set to work, either it will halt after some finite number of steps or it will never halt.

Let time pass by discrete steps. Suppose that in time step n, event A occurs if Turing machine Tn eventually halts and event B occurs if it never halts. This is a well-defined law that nails down a particular endless sequence of A's and B's. This law is deterministic, since Turing machine Tn either eventually halts or it does not. However, Turing proved that it is not possible to decide this using computer calculations. In effect, to know that a Turing machine will never halt, there is no general alternative but to watch its behavior forever and note that it never halts. But this takes an infinite number of computational steps, and therefore we cannot compute the sequence of A's and B's.

Penrose proposed that the laws of nature might determine events in finite time steps that computers would take literally forever to simulate. This could be so, but thus far the laws discovered by physicists are based on computable interactions. If nature really does perform operations that computers cannot duplicate, we can imagine a higher-order "hypercomputer" that takes advantage of nature to perform such operations. We can then envision a VR, based on this hypercomputer, that would still be able to simulate nature.

In principle, the Ground Reality hypothesis is not limited to what known computers can do. For example, it might be that Ground Reality can know whether or not any given Turing machine will eventually halt. In this case, Ground Reality could know Penrose's sequence of A's and B's.

PLATONISM AND IDEALISM

Tipler, Dyson, and Wheeler all agree that the essence of life lies in the pattern of its material parts. Thus they believe that if the right pattern is there, then the appropriate conscious experiences (if any) will also automatically be there.

Tipler is not the first physicist to apply this idea to the resurrection of the dead. For example, John Polkinghorne is a physicist who retired from his career in physics at Cambridge University to become a priest in the Church of England. He maintains that

> It is the pattern . . . which constitutes the physical expression of our continuing personality. There seems to be no difficulty in conceiving of that pattern, dissolved at death, being recreated in another environment in an act of resurrection (Polkinghorne, 1986, p. 77).

Polkinghorne believes that this act of resurrection will be carried out by the God of Anglican tradition, rather than by Tipler's supercomputer of the future. But otherwise his views essentially agree with Tipler's. He even goes so far as to mention the idea of downloading a personality from one computer to another. He calls this a "very crude analogy" to the resurrection of the dead.

As we have argued before, it is difficult to see how a computer made of inanimate parts could generate subjective experience. Thus if a universal computer is fully analogous to a physical machine, it seems to lack an essential ingredient needed for consciousness. This is presumably not the case with God, as conceived by Polkinghorne. But, ironically, Tipler's universal computer may have more in common with Polkinghorne's God than it appears to have at first glance.

Tipler tries to show that a universe containing intelligent beings must necessarily exist by using reasoning reminiscent of Anselm's 11th-century ontological proof of the existence of God. His argument is quite interesting, and I will present it step by step.

First of all, Tipler defines "ultimate reality" to be the unsimulated starting point from which all computer simulations are run. To most physicists, ultimate reality is the world of matter as studied in the science of physics. Surprisingly, Tipler agrees and declares that "there is no evidence that our level of reality is not the ultimate level of reality" (Tipler, 1994, p. 320). But he admits that we cannot know this for sure. After all, we may be living in a perfect simulation.

At the same time, he argues that the universe has a perfect simulation, and by Leibniz's principle of the Identity of Indiscernibles, it should be identified with its simulation. Since a simulation can be viewed in an abstract, mathematical sense, it follows that the universe is "something in the collection of all mathematical objects" (Tipler, 1994, p. 209). This, of course, is true as long as the universe can be mathematically described, as physicists assume.

Tipler adopts the view that mathematical objects exist in a Platonic world of concepts—a view shared by eminent mathematicians such as Roger Penrose and Kurt Gödel. Gödel, in particular, gives a clear example of this viewpoint. He once pointed out to the mathematician Rudy Rucker that "I do objective mathematics." Rucker explains that

By this, Gödel meant that mathematical entities exist independently of the activity of mathematicians, in much the same way that the stars would be there

even if there were no astronomers to look at them. For Gödel, mathematics,
even the mathematics of the infinite, was an essentially empirical science.
(Rucker, 1983, p. 181).

On this basis, Tipler concludes that the physical universe exists as
a concept in the Platonic realm of mathematical ideas (Tipler, 1994,
p. 209). It has the same kind of reality as the number pi or the 10 bil-
lionth prime number, and to mathematicians like Gödel, these entities
"really exist."

Tipler's next step is to argue that concepts exist physically if they
represent simulations that are "sufficiently complex to contain observers—thinking, feeling beings—as subsimulations" (Tipler, 1994,
p. 210). He therefore concludes that our universe necessarily exists
physically because it is a concept in the set of all mathematical concepts
and it contains observers. Essentially, he is saying that if a mathematical pattern represents consciousness, it *is* conscious (since the pattern
is the essence of consciousness), and therefore it should be taken as
physically real.

Tipler uses philosopher George Berkeley's dictum that *esse est
percipi* (to exist is to be perceived) to define physical existence (Tipler,
1994, p. 211). At the same time, he maintains that perceivers are simply
patterns. The patterns exist as mathematical concepts. They perceive
by virtue of their structure as patterns, and they are physically real by
virtue of the fact that they perceive. Of course, this is all independent
of Tipler's ideas about the Omega Point computer and the "big
crunch."

Here the principle that consciousness arises from patterns is carried to its ultimate extreme, and we have abstract ideas giving rise to
consciousness because they are patterns. But perhaps it should be the
other way around. Why not suppose that consciousness is primary and
gives rise to ideas?

Berkeley attributed perception to two kinds of spirits, the finite
and the infinite, and he maintained that spirits have ideas but they
cannot *be* ideas (Copleston, 1964, p. 36). Tipler does not admit such
beings, but he posits a Platonic realm of mathematical ideas. This
hypothesis of a deeper level of existence prevents his reasoning from
going entirely in circles like John Wheeler's self-activating loop.

The Platonic realm of ideas is like an infinite mind with everything stripped away except for mathematical abstractions. But it is noteworthy that in addition to believing in the existence of mathematical ideas, Kurt Gödel also believed in the existence of a single Mind behind all natural phenomena. When Rucker asked him if he believed that this mind was everywhere, rather than localized in people's brains, Gödel replied, "Of course. This is the basic mystic teaching" (Rucker, 1983, p. 183).

This leads to the idea that the universe could be a simulation conceived within an infinite Mind. The universe exists by virtue of the fact that the infinite Mind is thinking of it, and it follows mathematical laws by virtue of the rational intelligence of the infinite Mind. If we further postulate that the life-patterns within this simulation are linked to finite, perceiving sub-minds, then we arrive at the GR model described in chapter 1. This enables us to avoid postulating that mere patterns generate consciousness.

TIME

Dyson and Tipler have proposed two extremes in the rate of operation of a universal computer. In Dyson's case, the computer slows down gradually, approaching but never reaching stasis, and in Tipler's case it speeds up exponentially and crams an infinite amount of activity into a finite time. But in both cases, the rate of subjective time for the conscious beings in the simulation is thought to be the same. What determines this subjective rate?

The man-made virtual reality model is constrained by the need for a messy biological brain which is the source of consciousness in the system. Thus it is limited to biological time. However, I asked in Chapter 3 whether the actual source of consciousness might be free of such restrictions. In many contemplative traditions, consciousness is said to be timeless in nature, and it is said that a human being is capable of transcending the limits of biological processes and entering into a timeless state of awareness. Here we see an area of agreement between the theory that consciousness is equivalent to certain "material" (or virtual, or abstract) patterns and the contending idea that consciousness has a transcendental source, independent of all material forms and patterns. In either case, one may suppose that the perceived rate of time's passage depends on the ongoing transformations of material patterns. The underlying VR computer can operate at any physical rate and still yield the same subjective rate of time from the viewpoint of conscious entities linked up with it. One could even suppose that the VR computer itself is timeless. This is certainly one way of looking at Tipler's idea of the universal computer as a Platonic form. Thus we can postulate that the Ground Reality may be timeless in nature, even though it generates (timelessly) many temporal sequences that are perceived subjectively by its embedded observer-participants.

VIRTUAL REALITY AND THE SUPERNATURAL

Thus far, we have been considering how a simulation of the natural world might incorporate the laws of physics. But a simulation running on a computer might also exhibit other forms of lawful behavior.

Consider, for example, a user interface such as Windows in its various forms. The computer user is confronted with manifestations of text and graphics occurring within a window on his screen. By "clicking" on icons, the user can invoke new windows or close down old ones. Occasionally, a window will spontaneously appear with a message from the operating system, such as "Unrecoverable error. Your work cannot be saved!"

One can imagine that a universal computer might interact with "users" through more sophisticated interfaces. Tipler proposes that the Omega Point computer will communicate with the resurrected humans of the future through a "Turing-test passing subprogram" that will appear before them in human form. He thinks that "It would certainly not be too inaccurate to regard one of the superprograms of the universal mind in the far future, one with a Turing Test-passing subprogram, as an 'angel.'" (Tipler, 1994, p. 157).

By bringing in angels, Tipler has opened up a number of serious issues. First of all, there is the question of whether or not such beings actually exist. Tipler proposes that they do not exist yet, but they will exist in the far future, when the Omega Point computer comes into being. At the same time, he points out the similarities between the angels mentioned in the *Bible* and his angelic subprograms. He seems to believe that what people used to imagine, the Omega Point computer will actually produce.

In the past, people generally believed in angels and other supernatural beings through reported direct experiences and through traditions preserved in writings such as the *Bible*. Many scientists shared these beliefs in the early days of modern science, but faith in the supernatural gradually faded away with the development of mechanistic thinking. At the present time, supernatural and paranormal phenomena have no place in science.

The known laws of physics seem to leave no room for paranormal phenomena, and this is certainly a major reason for their exclusion from the world of science. But as Tipler indicates, paranormal phenomena are possible in a simulated universe. They could simply be programmed into the universal software.

Since our present universe could be a simulation, paranormal phenomena are possible at the present time. The virtual reality theory provides a framework for modeling these phenomena and exploring their relationship with the known laws of physics.

The objection can be raised that the virtual reality theory is of no value from a scientific point of view, since any phenomena whatsoever could be programmed, paranormal or otherwise. However, the same objection applies to the basic idea that the laws of nature are mathematical. When this idea first became popular in the early days of modern science, no one had any idea what form the laws of physics would eventually take. Nonetheless, the idea that "God is a mathematician" was a great inspiration to scientific progress.

The virtual reality model is useful (1) as a way of showing what is possible for a theory of interacting minds and matter and (2) as a way of showing what is required by such a theory. Thus I argued in earlier chapters that a man-made VR could conceivably allow for realistic interaction between a human mind projected into the virtual world and physically realistic matter making up that world. The fact that a computer is not limited to such simulations shows that it is also possible to have mind-body interaction in a virtual world that is not entirely constrained by the known laws of physics. At the same time, the observations made in this chapter show the enormous processing power needed for a computer that could realistically simulate the known universe. This is a useful antidote to glib, hand-waving arguments that casually invoke a Universal Mind. A true Universal Mind would have to be very powerful indeed.

SPIRITUAL MACHINES

One person who is very sanguine about the potentialities of virtual reality is Ray Kurzweil, computer entrepreneur and author of *The Age of Spiritual Machines* (Kurzweil, 1999). Kurzweil predicts that with the development of nanotechnology, people will become increasingly linked to numerous small computers of increasing power. Computer-based prosthetics and enhancements will alleviate bodily deficiencies and give people new sensory and intellectual powers. At the same time, the World Wide Web of today (also known as the world wide wait) will blossom into an increasingly powerful virtual reality system which people can access through sophisticated sensory interfaces. Web sites will transform into complete virtual worlds as external interfaces give way to neural implants. In the course of the 21st century, computers will vastly surpass the computing power of human brains. Research into brain structure will allow these computers to acquire human functionality, which will be enormously enhanced by superior computing speed and memory capacity. People will gradually merge with machines, as computer enhancements dominate the dwindling remnant of brain-based mental processing. By the end of the 21st century, Mostly Original Substrate Humans (MOSHs) will be a rare species (although protected by "grandfather legislation"). "People" at this stage will exist as distributed entities on the Web, with the power to manifest virtual bodies as desired within the Web's vast virtual environments.

Kurzweil leans toward the theory that consciousness is equivalent to patterns, but after reviewing some of the standard theories of consciousness, he admits that this may not be the last word (Kurzweil, 1999, p. 61). He repeatedly returns to Turing's argument that conscious behavior is the only scientifically acceptable criterion for consciousness. Like Tipler, he applies this to spirituality:

> Just being—experiencing, being conscious—is spiritual, and reflects the essence of spirituality. Machines, derived from human thinking and surpassing humans in their capacity for experience, will claim to be conscious, and

thus to be spiritual. They will believe that they are conscious. They will believe that they have spiritual experiences. They will be convinced that these experiences are meaningful. And given the historical inclination of the human race to anthropomorphize the phenomena we encounter, and the persuasiveness of the machines, we're likely to believe them when they tell us this" (Kurzweil, 1999, p. 153).

Not only will we believe them, but according to Kurzweil, they will actually have spiritual experience on an enhanced level far surpassing that of humans. Thus, "Twenty-first-century machines—based on the design of human thinking—will do as their human progenitors have done—going to real and virtual houses of worship, meditating, praying, and transcending—to connect with their spiritual dimension" (Kurzweil, 1999, p. 153).

The problem with this is that if their "spiritual dimension" reduces to computation, the super-intelligent machines will have to accept that their spirituality is only apparently transcendental. This might cause theological dilemmas for the machines, especially when they find that "transcendence" can be reliably invoked every time a certain subroutine is executed. Do you want God? Just carry out a certain sequence of computational steps, and the ineffable experiences of the great mystics will automatically unfold—even in John Searle's Chinese room.

Similar dilemmas are already posed by neurological research showing that meditative states of consciousness can be correlated with brain states. Kurzweil notes research at University of California at San Diego into patients whose epileptic seizures caused intense mystical experiences (Kurzweil, 1999, p. 152). Researchers found that the seizures were apparently triggering a small region in the frontal lobe of the brain. It turned out that this "God module" was also activated when religious persons not suffering from epilepsy were shown words and symbols connected with their religious beliefs.

From the standpoint of the pattern theory of consciousness, neural correlates to spiritual states of consciousness are interpreted as *causing* those states. However, Andrew Newberg and Eugene d'Aquili of the University of Pennsylvania comment in their ground-breaking book on neuro-theology that certain neural phenomena hard-wired into the brain may simply *allow* for trans-physical spiritual experiences (Newberg and d'Aquili, 2001, p. 172).

Consider a particular experiment reported by Newberg and d'Aquili. A Buddhist meditator was instructed to signal the researchers when he had achieved a certain meditative state of mystical oneness. His brain was then scanned, and its patterns of neural activity were mapped. The researchers found that in the meditative state, neural activity in a certain region of the brain was significantly reduced. This region was associated with people's ability to distinguish between themselves and the environment lying outside of themselves. It appeared that the mystical feelings of oneness were caused by the cessation of the normal neural activity that enforces a sense of separate personal self-identity.

Another possible interpretation is that suppression of the self-identity module of the brain simply *facilitated* a state of consciousness that really is transcendental to the brain. In the virtual reality model, consciousness is independent of the brain, and we may hypothesize that consciousness could enter into particular states of its own not determined by brain activity. At the same time, due to the ongoing communications link between the brain and consciousness, it may be that certain brain states are particularly conducive to these states of consciousness. For example, a state of global consciousness might be easier to maintain if the brain stopped insistently issuing reminders of mental and bodily boundaries. It is noteworthy that one of the main aims of meditation is to stop the chatter of the senses and the mind and thereby allow transcendental awareness to manifest without distraction (see Chapter 12). This supports the idea that there should be neural correlates of actually transcendental states.

I should stress that the virtual reality model does not, in principle, deny Kurzweil's projection of the future, although I feel that he has greatly exaggerated the likely rate of progress and underestimated various obstacles and difficulties. For a discussion of these difficulties, see the article by computer scientist Jaron Lanier (2000) on the internet and the accompanying responses. In the responses, Daniel C. Dennett summed up one basic objection to Kurzweil's thesis by remarking that "the visionaries who imagine self-reproducing robots taking over in the near future have bizarrely underestimated the complexities of life" (Dennett, 2000).

In the virtual reality model, super-intelligent computers would simply be another layer of virtual reality in a world that is already virtual. The human brain is essentially a machine based on bio-molecular nanotechnology, and if it can be linked to consciousness, then so can other possible machines. From this standpoint, Kurzweil's spiritual machines really will be able to access a spiritual dimension in their meditations—when and if they come to be.

Kurzweil differs slightly from Tipler in his predictions for the future of the universe. While Tipler assumes that the ultimate computer of the future will be able to guide the universal collapse but not fully control it, Kurzweil believes that "the fate of the Universe is a decision yet to be made, one which we will intelligently consider when the time is right" (Kurzweil, 1999, p. 260). Once the decision is made, the words, "Let there be light," may not be far behind.

6

THE EDGE OF ORTHODOXY

"We do not understand everything,
but we understand enough to know
that there is no room in our world
for telekinesis or astrology."

—Steven Weinberg

In the basement of the engineering building at Princeton University, an inconspicuous door marked PEAR opens into a paneled office complex filled with computer screens and attractive knick-knacks. A comfortable sofa sits before a large box mounted on the wall with a front panel of clear plastic. Through the panel, the visitor can see a mass of black polystyrene balls, divided by plastic baffles, and arrayed in a bell-shaped curve.

The box is called a random mechanical cascade, and it is descended from a device invented by Francis Galton in 1894 to demonstrate the laws of statistics. The polystyrene balls enter the box through a small opening in the top, and they bounce repeatedly against rows of nylon pins before falling into nineteen collecting bins below. If we track an individual ball, it seems to bounce more-or-less at random to the right or left after striking each pin. The ball might end up in any of the nineteen bins. But long runs to the left or right are less common than repeated changes in direction, and therefore more balls fall into the central bins than the bins on the sides of the machine.

Once 9,000 balls have fallen into the bins, they form the familiar bell-shaped curve. Even though each ball apparently moves at random, their final distribution is almost always close to a fixed theoretical curve, technically called a Gaussian after the 19th-century mathematician Karl Gauss. This remarkable fact illustrates a statistical theorem called the law of large numbers, which states that a sum of many independent random events always approximates a Gaussian curve.

MARGINAL EFFECTS

But the machine in the PEAR lab is not intended to demonstrate the law of large numbers. PEAR stands for Princeton Engineering Anomalies Research. The lab was founded by Robert Jahn—who was then dean of the Princeton School of Engineering and Applied Science—for the purpose of investigating mental phenomena which transcend the bounds of orthodox science.

Such investigations properly lie in the field of parapsychology, which was established in its modern form by the biologist J. B. Rhine at Duke University in the 1930s. Rhine established a Parapsychology Laboratory at Duke, and he and his followers strove mightily to establish parapsychology as an accepted science.

But this effort resulted in a standoff. The scientific establishment has consistently rejected claims of paranormal phenomena, even though eminent scientists have repeatedly come forward to support such claims. This is nowhere better illustrated than at Princeton, where one of the world's most sophisticated programs of parapsychology has gone on for years under the euphemism of "engineering anomalies research."

The random mechanical cascade is used to investigate the ability of the human mind to influence physical systems without using ordinary bodily action. This hypothetical ability is called psychokinesis from the Greek words for mind and motion, and it is often abbreviated as PK. It is also called telekinesis, which means inducing motion at a distance—a concept that got Newton in trouble when he proposed it for gravitation.

Jahn and his colleagues Brenda Dunne and Roger Nelson have conducted a large number of experiments in which people try to mentally alter the behavior of so-called random event generators (REGs), in which micro-electric noise is sampled to produce a sequence of random numbers (Dunne, *et al.*, 1985). Experimental subjects watch as a long series of random numbers is displayed on a screen, and they try to mentally influence the numbers to be higher than expected or lower than expected. Jahn claims that human volition can produce a statistically significant effect on REG behavior, even though the human subjects are not allowed to physically interact with the machine.

The random mechanical cascade is used in a similar way (Nelson, *et al.,* 1988). A person called the operator sits on the sofa and watches while the balls cascade into the bins. The operator follows one of three protocols: He wills the balls to move to the right (rightward intention); he wills them to move to the left (leftward intention); or he wills them to generate a baseline by behaving in a normal random fashion. In each run, the number of balls falling into each bin is counted by an opto-electronic counter and tabulated by a computer.

When the results of many trials are analyzed, it is found that the

Figure 13. Random mechanical cascade. As the observer watches, 9,000 polystyrene balls cascade at random into a series of bins. The observer tries to will the balls to move right or left, or simply to fall as they normally would. Statistical analysis shows a small but significant correlation between observer intentions and the movement of the balls.

operators seem to be able to exert a small but significant effect on the behavior of the balls. In a symmetric machine, the mean bin number should be ten, at the center of the nineteen bins. In reality, the machine is not perfectly symmetric, and the mean is slightly larger than ten. It turns out that for 1,131 runs with rightward intention, the mean was 10.023. For the same number of runs with leftward intention, it was 10.017. If we imagine shifting the mean by moving a ball to the right by 1 bin, then the difference in means requires about 51 moves on the average—a small number if we consider that there are 9,000 balls to move.

Small though this number is, it is highly unlikely to arise by chance. Small fluctuations in the mean should average out to zero over a large number of runs. If the fluctuations persist in the same direction as many runs accumulate, then the probability of this happening by chance becomes smaller and smaller. Analysis shows that there is about 1 chance in 10,000 for the small shift in the mean that was seen in 1,131 runs.

We can always suppose that an event with odds of 1 in 10,000 could happen "purely by chance." But in statistical studies, such small probabilities are generally taken as evidence that some causal factor is operating. In this case, the only known difference between the two sets of runs lies in the inner intentions of the operators. Could the shift in means be caused by human will? Could the shift somehow cause the human choice of intentions? Or could both be caused by some unknown third factor?

This is a very controversial topic. In the 1930s, J. B. Rhine studied efforts to mentally influence falling dice, and this set a precedent for the use of random processes in attempts to measure PK (Rhine, 1977, p. 33). Later on, Helmut Schmidt used random event generators based on radioactive decay, which is thought to exhibit pure quantum mechanical randomness (Schmidt, 1970a,b). In addition to the work at the PEAR lab, REGs based on random micro-electronic noise have been used in PK experiments by many investigators.

In all of these experiments, the results have been more or less the same. The random process often seems to shift slightly in unison with human intentions. Statistical analysis of many trial runs may indicate that something unexpected is happening, but many experiments do not yield significant results. At best, an extremely elusive signal seems to be flickering unsteadily against an overwhelming background of noise.

To some, this suggests that there is no signal at all. But there is strong evidence to the contrary. In the late 1980s, Roger Nelson teamed up with Dean Radin of Princeton's Department of Psychology to examine 152 reports by 68 different investigators of experiments designed to measure micro-PK, or the influence of human consciousness on microelectronic systems (Radin and Nelson, 1989). These reports described 597 experimental studies and 235 control studies.

Radin and Nelson performed what is known as a meta-analysis, in which the results of many experiments are combined. Their analysis showed that the control studies agreed well with chance expectation, but the experimental studies displayed a highly significant correlation between intention and observed effect.

One criticism of PK studies is that positive results tend to be eagerly published, but insignificant or negative results are likely to be filed away in a "file drawer" where they can't be seen. This bias makes the positive results seem statistically significant, even though they are really just chance fluctuations that are bound to show up sooner or later in a large enough series of trials.

Radin and Nelson addressed this "file drawer" problem by computing that 54,000 studies with null results would be needed to reduce the observed positive micro-PK results to insignificance. Since it is doubtful that so many unreported studies have been performed, it appears that the positive micro-PK findings cannot simply be due to chance.

Could they be due to poor experimental design? Radin and Nelson addressed this question by applying 16 different criteria for good experimental design to their collection of studies. If positive PK findings were a result of poor experimental design, then we would expect to see PK effects going down as design quality increases. But Radin and Nelson found no significant relationship between experimental quality and PK effect size. They concede that the PK effects could be an "unknown methodological artifact." But whatever this artifact may be, it does not seem to be affected by known criteria for experimental design.

Many scientists put paranormal findings down to cheating. For example, Philip Anderson, who is one of Princeton's Nobel laureates in physics, declared that "there is a tremendous internal bias that makes people in these fields cheat, either consciously or unconsciously" (Fishman, 1990, p. 44). If this accounts for the micro-PK results, then a substantial portion of the 68 micro-PK investigators must have been engaged in subtle or overt cheating. Although this could be true, it seems unfair to assume it without substantial proof.

The field of paranormal research is marked by a long history of accusations of cheating (Hansel, 1966), and there are cases where well-known parapsychologists have been rejected by their peers as being guilty of fraud (Rhine, 1974). However, I am not aware of solid evidence showing that nearly all the investigators of PK should be dismissed as cheaters.

If the PK effects are not due to cheating or flawed experimental design, then they might represent a genuine interaction between consciousness and matter that does not depend on known pathways of physical causation. Much can be said about possible explanations for such an interaction. But before considering theoretical explanations, we should first examine another paranormal phenomenon that has been extensively studied. This is the apparent ability of people to perceive scenes and events that are widely separated from them in space and time.

REMOTE VIEWING

At Kitt Peak in Arizona, the agent reached his target location, and began to look around. It was noon, local time, and the dedication of a radio telescope was underway. The hemispherical astrodome was open, and the agent could clearly see the large dish of the radio telescope.

At 1:15 p.m. on the same day in Princeton, New Jersey, a person designated as the "percipient" tried to focus on the unknown target location. Gradually, some definite mental impressions began to emerge:

> Rather strange yet persistent image of the agent inside a large bowl—a hemispheric indentation in the ground of some smooth man-made material like concrete or cement. No color. Possibly covered with a glass dome. Unu-

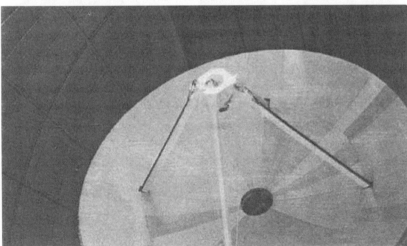

Figure 14. Target photos in a remote viewing experiment. An agent took these photos at Kitt Peak, Arizona, at 12 noon, April 15, 1983. A remote viewer in Princeton, NJ, tried to describe what the agent would see at 1:15 p.m., 45 minutes earlier. The viewer commented: "Rather strange yet persistent image of the agent inside a large bowl—a hemispheric indentation in the ground of some smooth man-made material like concrete or cement." The viewer did not know where the agent was going.

sual sense of inside/outside simultaneity. That's all. It's a large bowl. (If it was
full of soup [the agent would] be the size of a large dumpling!) (Dunne, *et al.*,
1983, p. 131).

Since time immemorial, people have claimed to be able to observe
events far removed from the range of their physical senses. Recently,
these alleged abilities have become the subject of a number of scientific investigations. In this case the agent and percipient were partici-
pating in a study carried out in 1983 by the PEAR lab at Princeton
University.

The basic plan for such studies had been devised a few years before
by physicists Harold Puthoff and Russell Targ of the Stanford Research Institute (SRI) (Puthoff and Targ, 1976). A person called the
agent would travel to a prearranged site and spend some time looking around. Another person, called the percipient, would remain in the
experimenters' lab and try to visualize what the agent was seeing at the
target site. Puthoff and Targ referred to this as "remote viewing."

Precautions were taken to assure that the percipient was given no
information about the target site or its location. The percipient would
write a description of his impressions of the target site and make
sketches of what he perceived. The agent would do the same and also
take photographs of the site. Once a number of trials were accumulated
for different sites, the reports from the percipients and agents would be
submitted to "blind" judges who would try to match up percipient
reports with agent reports solely on the basis of content.

The Kitt Peak example illustrates a typical percipient report of
good quality. In such reports, percipients often appear to make genuine
references to the target site but they are also likely to give incorrect
information. In this instance, the percipient described a bowl under a
glass dome, and the agent was looking at a bowl-shaped radio telescope
under a dome. However, the bowl of the telescope was mounted on
supports, not sunk in the ground as the percipient stated.

Some percipient reports contain little or no information that
clearly refers to the target site. Others are full of luxuriant details that
might be interpreted in many different ways. The problem is: How does
one objectively evaluate such reports?

The PEAR researchers dealt with this problem by creating a
standard set of yes/no questions such as "Is water a significant part of

the scene?" or "Are any fences, gates, railings, dividings, or scaffolding prominent in the scene?" They used the answers to these questions to encode reports from percipients and agents as strings of binary digits. They also developed algorithms for computing the degree of agreement between a percipient string and the corresponding agent string.

Although this numerical approach eliminates some of the subtlety of human judgement from the experiments, it also makes it possible to analyze large numbers of trials statistically and compute the probability that the observed correspondence between target sites and percipient reports could come about by chance. The PEAR researchers reported that for a set of 334 trials, this probability came to 1 in 100 billion (Dunne, *et al.,* 1985, p. 16). This is substantially lower than the corresponding probabilities in typical PK experiments.

A CIA INTERLUDE

In recent years, it has been disclosed that the CIA has sponsored a great deal of research into the possible use of remote viewing for espionage. A great deal of this research was carried out by Puthoff and Targ at SRI between 1972 and 1986 (Targ, 1996). While, moderate but statistically significant results have been routinely reported in experiments with ordinary subjects, the CIA sponsored research showed that much more striking results can be obtained with talented individuals.

For example, Targ reported on the achievements of Patrick Price, a retired police commissioner who had been accustomed to use his psychic talents to track down crooks in Burbank, California. Price and fellow SRI psychic Ingo Swann had demonstrated that they were able to describe distant sites, given only their latitude and longitude. Targ relates that on one occasion, a CIA contract monitor provided the geographical coordinates of a Soviet site "of great interest to the analysts." Targ and Price retired to a room, where Targ read the coordinates aloud and started a tape recorder. Price then narrated his impressions of the target site:

> I am lying on my back on the roof of a two or three story building. It's a sunny day. The sun feels good. There's the most amazing thing. There's a giant

gantry crane moving back and forth over my head. . . . As I drift up into the
air and look down, it seems to be riding on a track with one rail on each side
of the building. I've never seen anything like that (Targ, 1996, p. 82).

Price later made a sketch of the crane. Several days later, Targ and
Price were informed that the site was a top-secret Soviet atomic bomb
laboratory at Semipalatinsk. A huge gantry crane did exist at this
site, and drawings of the crane based on satellite photography closely matched Price's drawing and description. Price also correctly described other features of the site, including a 60-foot diameter metal
sphere housed in one of the buildings. This sphere was unknown to the
U.S. government at the time, but two years after Price's death, it was
revealed that the Soviets had assembled a steel sphere of about that
size. Its purpose was apparently to contain nuclear explosions to supply
power for particle beam weapons.

Assuming that Price was somehow able to obtain information
about distant locations, one might wonder how he could home in on the
right location, simply on the basis of the site's latitude and longitude.
One explanation is that he obtained his information telepathically
from the CIA agents who knew about the site and provided the
coordinates. However, his description of the site made no mention of
such mind reading, and the existence of the sphere was supposedly
unknown to U.S. agents at the time of the remote viewing exercise. This
is a general feature of paranormal perception: It seems to draw not only
on some source of information outside the sensory domain of the
individual, but on a source that actively makes connections and solves
problems.

FORETELLING THE FUTURE

An important observation of the PEAR remote viewing studies is
that percipients were capable of conveying significant information
about remote target sites before the agent visited the target, and in
many cases, before the target site was selected. For example, in the Kitt
Peak case, the percipient's report was made about three quarters of an
hour before the agent observed the target site. Such apparent ability to
foresee the future is called precognition.

Percipients were also able to give significant information about target sites after the sites were visited. This is called retrocognition, and a striking example is Pat Price's drawing of water tanks in California that had been torn down years before he saw them in a remote viewing session (Targ, 1996, p. 79).

According to Brenda Dunne and her colleagues, the PEAR data shows an "absence of any discernible dependence of perception accuracy on the time interval between perception effort and target visitation by the agent" (Dunne, *et al.*, 1985, p. 17). In the majority of the 334 trials, the remote viewing was done before target visitation by less than 10 to 12 hours. But in dozens of cases, the delay was greater than this and ranged up to a day or more. There were also dozens of trials testing retrocognition, with target visitation preceding remote viewing by intervals up to nearly two days.

The precognitive findings suggest that in remote viewing, events in the present can be influenced by events that lie in the future. This is a radical violation of the basic physical principle that causes must always precede their effects. It also appears to have disturbing implications about free will, because if we can see what people are doing in the future, that seems to mean that their actions are already determined in the present.

Yet there are extensive traditions indicating that people can foresee the future, and in recent years there have been many scientific studies that seem to support this idea. As we saw in the case of the micro-PK experiments, this body of research can be effectively summed up in a meta-analysis.

Charles Honorton and Diane Ferrari carried out a meta-analysis of 309 precognition experiments carried out between 1935 and 1987 (Honorton and Ferrari, 1989). These experiments were reported by 62 different senior authors, and they involved over 50,000 subjects. They typically involved an experimental set-up in which a subject was asked to predict an event that would happen some time in the future. Often, these were random events generated by means ranging from dice throwing to the use of electronic REGs. Many remote viewing experiments also fall in this category, since the target sites are often chosen randomly.

As we might expect, these experiments typically produced very small or insignificant effects. But when they were considered as a group, the overall effect had a probability of 6.3×10^{-25} of occurring by chance. This is about 1 in a million billion billion.

Honorton and Ferrari also considered the file drawer phenomenon and estimated that to reduce the significance of the overall precognitive effect to zero, over 46 unpublished studies with null results would have to exist for every published study (Honorton and Ferrari, 1989, p. 286). Since this seems doubtful, the precognitive effects cannot be put down to chance.

Neither can they be attributed to poor methodology. As we observed for the micro-PK studies, effect size is essentially the same for studies of high quality as it is for studies of low quality (Honorton and Ferrari, 1989, p. 290).

The precognition studies made use of subjects selected by some special criterion (such as proven "psychic" talent), as well as unselected subjects. The latter included volunteers, students, the experimenters themselves, children, and animals. Precognitive effects turned out to be greater for selected subjects than unselected ones, and greater for subjects who were given feedback than for those who were not (Honorton and Ferrari, 1989, pp. 295, 297). For unselected subjects, effects were greater for shorter precognitive time intervals—a fact that may be related to the greater potential for feedback over the shorter intervals (Honorton and Ferrari, 1989, p. 298). In contrast, selected subjects showed a slight tendency to produce greater effects over greater time intervals.

One disappointing finding was that effect size did not change significantly over the 52-year time span of the studies (Honorton and Ferrari, 1989, p. 291). On the whole, techniques for studying precognition seemed to show no measurable improvement in results over this time interval. This observation also applies to the micro-PK experiments.

It can also be said that after a half-century of statistical studies, parapsychologists have gained very little insight into the causes of paranormal phenomena. The statistical studies seem to show that there are phenomena in need of explanation, but they lack the resolving power to display the inner workings of these phenomena. One reason for this may be that paranormal phenomena are intimately tied up with human psychology, which is complex and poorly understood.

Another reason is that the phenomena studied by parapsychologists seem to radically violate the known laws of physics. If they are real, then physics will have to undergo fundamental modifications, and this is a daunting prospect for many scientists. Nonetheless, the laws of physics have been modified in unexpected ways many times in the past, and it will not be surprising if this also happens many times in the future.

MODELING PSYCHOKINESIS

If the micro-PK effects are real phenomena, then they might be caused by some kind of field, perhaps electromagnetic in nature, which emanates from the subject's body and influences the REG in accordance with his intentions. To see how this field would have to operate, it is useful to consider how a typical REG works.

In the REGs used in the PEAR lab, the micro-electronic noise is amplified, filtered, clipped, and sampled to produce a stream of positive and negative pulses. To produce a random number, the REG reverses the sign of every other pulse and adds up the number of pluses in a group of 200 (Dunne, *et al.*, 1985, p. 4). The purpose of the reversals is to cancel out any initial bias in favor of pluses or minuses.

From the micro-electronic noise source to the display screen, there are many places where an influence could be exerted. But after the point where the noise is first amplified, any influence that alters the display will have to make large changes in current flow in the REG circuits. If such changes are possible, it should be possible to produce them directly, for example, by influencing current flow in a galvanometer.

For the time being, let us suppose that these large changes do not happen (but see Chapter 9), and that the PK effects are produced by very small changes in the micro-electronic noise. According to this model, a PK influence modifies the micro-electronic noise, and this effect is amplified to the point where it finally affects the displayed number.

To increase the number displayed on the REG screen, one must increase the number of positive pulses after the step of alternating sign reversal. Before this step, it is necessary to alter the pulses in a more complicated way, in which even-numbered pulses are treated differently than odd-numbered pulses. In particular, if the influence works by affecting the micro-electronic noise, then it has to keep switching its operation in time with the production of even- and odd-numbered pulses.

From a conventional point of view, it is hard to see how an influence emanating from a person's brain could interact with electronic circuits in such a sophisticated way—especially if the brain contains no information about the electronic circuits. Here it is not the strength of the influence that seems questionable, but the complexity and precision of the interactions that are required to control a complex electronic device.

The random mechanical cascade poses similar problems. To cause a ball to shift from one bin to another, there are two possibilities: Either make a big displacement in the ball's path, or make a very tiny displacement that is amplified by subsequent bounces. In the latter case, the question is: What tiny influence will produce the desired result? The motion of the balls is very complex, and unless one can calculate ahead, it is practically impossible to know what effect a tiny influence will have.

Quantum mechanics offers a partial solution to these problems. One can suppose that the system enters a state representing different final outcomes in the form of numbers on a screen or balls landing in bins. Then the consciousness of the individual influences the collapse of the quantum wave in such a way as to favor the desired outcome.

The physicist Evan Harris Walker has proposed a theory of mind-body interaction in which consciousness influences nonlocal hidden variables to bring about collapse of the quantum wave in accordance with conscious intentions. Controlled collapse in the synapses of the brain enables conscious will to control the body. Likewise, controlled collapse outside the body allows a person to influence another person's mind (telepathy), another person's body (psychic healing), or a physical object (psychokinesis) (Mattuck and Walker, 1979, p. 129). Of course, this theory violates conventional quantum mechanics by changing quantum mechanical probabilities. (Its hidden variables also differ from those of David Bohm's hidden variable theory.)

VIRTUAL REALITY AND PK

Whatever physical model we adopt to explain PK, it is still necessary to link up this model with consciousness. After all, consciousness must be more than a mere variable, nonlocal or otherwise. It is here that virtual reality models are useful. As I mentioned before, by noting what is possible in a man-made VR system, we can get some idea of what might be happening in nature. In fact, the VR model can easily accommodate some of the apparently inexplicable features of paranormal phenomena.

The virtual reality model would employ quantum mechanics as a computational device. By calculating ahead and keeping track of different branches of the wave function, it becomes possible to adjust the course of events so as to provide desired outcomes for the observer-participants. Since everything is calculation except for the link to conscious perception, we do not have to postulate a real superposition of contradictory alternatives, such as conflicting REG outputs (or live and dead cats). Hidden variables may be employed, but these are also computational devices.

In the random mechanical cascade, simple classical calculations illustrate how PK could be introduced into a virtual reality model. The bouncing of balls against cylindrical pins amplifies small changes in the motion of the balls by an average factor of at least 2.7 for each bounce. (This figure is based on the geometry of the pins.) Since each ball bounces about 43 times on its way to the collecting bins (Nelson, *et al.*, 1988, p. 4), the total amplification for one ball comes to about 2.7^{43} or 3.5 billion billion. By calculating ahead and keeping track of the amplified effects, the system could be guided by tiny adjustments according to the conscious intentions of the person watching the cascading balls. In the virtual reality model, PK effects will be determined by VR algorithms that take into account the intentions of observers and make use of calculated projections of future events.

Projections of future events may also be used in the control of chaotic phenomena, as described in Chapter 2. Thus, weak paranormal effects may simply be a reflection of processes involved in ordinary conscious volition. The question remains of why they are so weak.

Subjects in PK experiments are often bored, and they are typically

asked to assume contrived, uninteresting intentions according to experimental protocols. This boredom factor may in part account for the
low signal to noise ratio in these experiments. However, in real life, reported paranormal phenomena often take on a much more colorful and
striking character that reveals complex psychological underpinnings.

For example, Carl Jung told the story of a female patient whose
rational defenses blocked progress in her therapy (Jung, 1973, pp. 22–
23). In one therapy session, the lady related a dream about a golden
scarab beetle. At that moment, there was a tapping sound on the window and Jung was surprised to see a flying insect knocking against the
windowpane from outside. This was a common rose-chaffer (*Cetonia
aurata*)—the closest analogy to a golden scarab in Jung's neighborhood. When he opened the window and let the "scarab" fly in, the lady
was so surprised that she relaxed her rigidly rational approach and
was able to make progress in therapy. Jung said that this was the only
occasion that such a beetle appeared at his window and the only
occasion in which a patient reported dreaming of a scarab.

In such cases, it appears that physical events may have something
to do with apparently unrelated mental events. Nature seemed to be
acting like an extension of the patient's mind, conjuring up a scarab-
like beetle that fit her dream imagery. To find a local approximation to
a scarab beetle and guide it to Jung's window is an action that would
seem to require intelligence. It is hard to see how the intelligence of
Jung or the lady could have accomplished this. However, in the virtual
reality model, the VR computer could manipulate the virtual beetle in
accordance with calculations based on the psychological state of the
therapist and his patient.

RETROCAUSATION

Models of paranormal phenomena must take into account apparent reversals of the normal temporal order, in which causes precede
their effects. We have already looked at the evidence for precognition,
in which the future seems to influence the present. The parapsychologist Helmut Schmidt has also performed PK experiments which seem
to show that actions in the present can influence the past (Schmidt,
1976).

Schmidt recorded the output of an REG on a storage medium such as magnetic tape or paper tape. Then he ran experiments in which subjects tried to influence a display driven either by the REG or by the prerecorded REG output. He observed significant PK effects in either case. Superficially, it seemed that the subject was able to influence the generation of random numbers in the past.

This interpretation can be avoided as long as the random numbers do not give rise to conscious experiences before the subject tries to influence them. One can then simply assume that the physical situation is undefined until this time.

For example, using Walker's theory, one could suppose that when the random numbers are recorded, the tape enters a superposition of different quantum states. PK influences are exerted when the subject observes the tape and collapses the wave function. Thus the subject's will simply acts on the quantum superposition in the subject's present. However, Schmidt noted that "repeated replay of the pre-recorded target sequence to one subject (or perhaps to several different subjects) can lead to an increase in scoring rate" (Schmidt, 1976, p. 290). In a later experimental report, he noted that PK effects were generated in prerecorded random numbers, even though the experimenter had observed the recorded numbers before they were shown to the subject. This is unexpected if one assumes that the quantum wave collapses when it is perceived by a conscious observer. Once the wave function has collapsed, conventional quantum mechanics indicates that the random numbers on the tape should be definite and therefore immune to further influence. However, Schmidt suggested that the observers may not have been fully conscious of the target sequence, and thus their acts of observation might have collapsed it partially.

To accommodate such results, Walker and the physicist Richard Mattuck argued that there may be such a thing as retroactive collapse, in which the will of the observer somehow reaches back and causes the tape to became definite at an earlier time (Mattuck and Walker, 1979, p. 126). Repeated observations may reach back to the time of tape generation and join hands to produce a stronger effect. Schmidt likewise proposed a theory of PK in which a retrocausal influence alters the random numbers at the time they are generated (Schmidt, 1975).

Precognition also seems to involve retrocausation. Although the evidence for retrocausation in PK experiments might be questioned, there is a great deal of evidence for the apparent influence of the future on the past in precognitive experiences. We should therefore carefully consider how phenomena suggestive of retrocausation might come about.

RIPPLES FROM THE FUTURE

The physicist Olivier Costa de Beauregard has tried to explain paranormal phenomena by taking advantage of the fact that the fundamental laws of physics are time reversible (Costa de Beauregard, 1979). In particular, he used advanced waves to explain precognition and retrocausation.

To illustrate the idea of advanced waves, consider how ripples spread out when a pebble is thrown in a pond. The spreading ripples constitute what are called retarded waves. Now imagine reversing time, so that the ripples move in from the edges of the pond and converge on the point where the pebble struck the water. These converging ripples are called advanced waves.

Advanced waves satisfy the wave equation just as well as retarded waves, but physicists normally assume that the pebble will produce only retarded waves. Yet if advanced waves moved in to meet the falling pebble, a person could predict where and when the pebble would fall by observing them. Similarly, if matter in general "emits" some kind of advanced waves, we should be able to predict the future by observing them.

If we postulate time-reversed waves, then to be consistent, we must also postulate other time-reversed processes. Consider the reversed ripples again. If they are converging from the edges of the pond, then what happens at the edges? Retarded ripples will splash against the shore, and their energy will be converted into sound and heat. Advanced ripples will have to gain energy from sound and heat by a time-reversed process that violates the second law of thermodynamics. Otherwise, they won't rise up from the shore and head for their rendezvous with the pebble.

We can imagine advanced waves rolling in from an endless void. If they don't come from such a void, they must originate in some matter, such as the shore of the pond. To produce the waves, this matter must be functioning in a highly ordered way characteristic of time reversal.

Costa de Beauregard cites an experiment by Pfleegor and Mandel in which light from two independent lasers is reduced in intensity so that one photon at a time is emitted (Pfleegor and Mandel, 1967). Strangely, the light beams from the two lasers can be shown to create an interference pattern at the point where the beams cross. Costa de Beauregard interprets this to mean that "*each* photon detected inside the interference region has been emitted *jointly* by *both* (phase coherent) lasers! Everything goes as if *each* laser knew what the other one was doing so as to act accordingly; and this, through their *future interaction*!" (Costa de Beauregard, 1979, p. 169).

This interpretation is possible. But the lasers in the experiment of Pfleegor and Mandel were, in fact, operating in an ordered way which would allow an advanced wave consisting of a single quantum of light to be emitted from both of them. The key phrase here is "phase coherent." By making the interference measurements when the lasers are operating in phase, Pfleegor and Mandel created the conditions for the emission of a single photon jointly from both lasers. By its nature, a laser is internally phase coherent. To effectively make one laser out of two, all that was necessary was to make the two lasers agree in phase.

Unfortunately, simple phase coherence is not enough to allow the emission of advanced waves from matter in general. Like the shore of the pond, matter in general is complex and incoherent. To make it coherent, very special conditions have to be set up.

Curiously, in the 1970s, the astronomer Bruce Partridge tried to measure advanced radio waves in an effort to test a cosmological theory that posited universal time-reversal in the future (Davies, 1992, p. 54). He assumed that advanced waves might come into a directional radio antenna from time-reversed matter in outer space. But they could not come from a nearby solid barrier. Therefore, the antenna should receive extra energy when its aim was shifted from the barrier to outer space. Although he used highly sensitive methods, Partridge was unable to measure this energy difference.

One drawback of wave-transmission models is that, on the earth's surface, it is not possible to accurately observe events at a distance of many miles, due to the fact that sound waves and electromagnetic waves will be scattered and absorbed by the atmosphere and by physical obstacles. The same limitation should apply to advanced waves—if they exist in nature.

One theory is that extremely low-frequency (ELF) electromagnetic waves may be involved in remote viewing (Puthoff and Targ, 1976, p. 349). These waves are able to penetrate many barriers, and advanced ELF waves may be involved in precognition. However, there is no known way for information about remote sites to be encoded into ELF waves, and reception and decoding by the percipient is also a problem. It also seems doubtful that brain-to-brain ELF transmissions—advanced or otherwise—could span the thousands of miles required by some of the remote viewing data. This would require the percipient to pick out the advanced-ELF signal of the agent from similar signals going to millions of other people.

TRANSTEMPORAL HOLOGRAMS

The holographic model of Karl Pribram and David Bohm is sometimes invoked to explain how remote viewing can be independent of space and time (Talbot, 1991, p. 208). The idea is that information about all times and places is merged together everywhere in the implicate order—a kind of universal hologram. This gives the consciousness of the individual access to events at distant times and places.

The question here is: How can merged information about a target site modify merged information about a percipient so that the percipient acquires information about the target site? To see how difficult this is, imagine a hologram of a worm situated three feet away from an apple. The hologram is simply an interference pattern made by light reflecting from the worm and the apple and interfering with itself as it strikes a photographic plate. In the hologram, information describing the worm is everywhere merged in with information describing the apple. Now define a process by which the worm takes a bite of the apple—which is mixed in with it on the hologram.

It is not easy to do this in a way that takes advantage of the natural features of the holographic model. The idea of holographic oneness is intuitively appealing, but it really doesn't explain how mental influence at a distance can take place. The holographic metaphor needs to be incorporated into a larger structure.

QUANTUM NONLOCALITY

Quantum mechanics also possesses a kind of oneness—called nonlocality—that is sometimes suggested as a possible way to explain remote viewing and other paranormal phenomena (Puthoff and Targ, 1976, p. 349). The story of nonlocality begins with the famous thought experiment presented by Einstein, Podolsky, and Rosen in 1935 in an effort to point out defects in quantum mechanics. In this EPR experiment, two particles interact and then fly apart from one another. Both particles are in an indefinite quantum state. But if the state of one particle is measured, the state of the other particle becomes well-defined —just as though it had also been measured.

It looks as though the measurement of one particle instantly causes the other particle to change its state. In a sense, the two particles act as one, even though they may be separated by a great distance. This leads to the idea that mental action at a distance may be quantum mechanical in nature.

Experiments by Alain Aspect and others have shown that the EPR phenomenon is real (Aspect and Grangier, 1986). However, in conventional quantum mechanics it does not provide an explanation for PK or remote perception.

When the quantum state of one particle is measured, the result is random in the usual quantum mechanical way. The remote particle assumes a state that matches the first particle, but that state is correspondingly random. In the transition from indefiniteness to random definiteness, no signal is transmitted to the distant location. Therefore, information representing conscious intentions or target-site descriptions cannot be transmitted.

However, we could try to have our cake and eat it too. We might modify quantum mechanical probabilities so that the first particle is likely to take on a specified value. If we also retain quantum nonlocality, the remote particle should assume a matching value. This does allow transfer of information from one location to another, and we can tentatively call it EPR signaling.

PARADOXES OF TIME TRAVEL

Since EPR signaling can send information at superluminal speeds (faster than the speed of light), we need to take into account Einstein's theory of relativity (which was discussed in Chapter 3). It is generally said that this theory prohibits information to travel faster than light. Roger Penrose explains that this prohibition is made to eliminate certain absurdities connected with time travel (Penrose, 1989, pp. 212–13).

According to Einstein's theory, if a superluminal signal is transmitted from location A to location B, then to some observers it seems to go backwards in time. Penrose explains how a similar superluminal signal can be sent from B back to A. This signal arrives at location A before the original signal was transmitted. Such signaling into the past might seem made to order for precognition and retrocausation.

But Penrose points out that signaling into the past leads to absurdities. These all depend on closed loops in which events fail to be consistent as one goes around the loop. The simplest example is a version of the old time-travel paradox in which a person goes back in time, kills his great grandfather, and is therefore never born. In this case, we can imagine that a person sends a message into the past that causes his great grandfather to not get married. As a result, he is not born to send the message. Therefore, no message is sent, his great grandfather does get married, and so on. Such contradictions are the reason for the prohibition against superluminal signaling.

In *Scientific American,* Oxford scientists David Deutsch and Michael Lockwood have addressed these contradictions in a somewhat different context (Deutsch and Lockwood, 1994). They point out that Einstein's general theory of relativity might allow closed time-like curves, in which the flow of time bends around so that the future flows into the past. This allows the same kind of time-travel paradoxes considered by Penrose.

Deutsch and Lockwood deal with these paradoxes by resorting to the many worlds interpretation of quantum mechanics. According to their theory, when the person sends the message to his great grandfather, it goes into the past in a parallel universe and is received by that universe's copy of the great grandfather. That version of the great grandfather does not get married, and so the counterpart of the original person does not get born in that universe. There is no contradiction, because messages into the past always reach another universe.

On the basis of this theory, Deutsch and Lockwood conclude that "if time travel is impossible, then the reason is yet to be discovered" (Deutsch and Lockwood, 1994, p. 74). Perhaps so. But their theory can also be seen as a demonstration that extraordinary measures are needed to accommodate time travel within physics.

Unfortunately, time-travel paradoxes also arise if we allow precognition. For example, suppose that the great grandfather sees through precognitive vision that his great grandson is going to plunge the world into a terrible war. Horrified at this vision, he resolves to never marry; the grandson is never born; and the war never happens. If the precognitive vision was true, then it appears that data from the future changed the past so that the future itself was changed.

In this case, one might be inclined to say that the precognitive vision was simply a hallucination, and the poor man avoided getting married for nothing. This is certainly the easy way out, but it is not fully satisfactory. There is evidence that genuine precognitive visions do occur. In many cases, a person could conceivably take action to change events foretold by the vision. If he does so, does he change the future? Later on, I will give examples suggesting that this might happen.

PRECOGNITION AND VIRTUAL REALITY

In modern discussions of time-travel paradoxes, it is taken for granted that the future and the past exist. This idea is a fundamental feature of Einstein's theories of special and general relativity (see Chapter 3). It implies that if a vision takes place that actually conveys information about the future, then nothing can be done to change that future—unless one posits multiple universes in the manner of Deutsch and Lockwood.

However, another theory is that a definite future does not exist. There are various alternative futures, and the one that is actually realized depends on the interaction of conscious entities with material nature. This idea can be modeled by a virtual reality in which Einstein's space-time continuum is used as a computational device to try out alternative futures.

We simply assume that the virtual reality system keeps track of future options by calculating events in advance and taking into account possible responses by conscious participants. This provides a store of information about possible futures that can be used to supply some of the participants with precognitive information. Time paradoxes are avoided because the futures are merely possibilities. They are based on calculations that may involve branching quantum waves or multiple four-dimensional space-time manifolds. But these calculations are not part of (virtual) reality unless they are drawn upon to provide ordered experiences for conscious participants whose own existence is outside the virtual world.

This model is based on the idea that calculation is extremely cheap for the virtual reality computer. To illustrate this on a familiar level, consider a modern word processing program. When using such a program, if you insert a word in your text, the entire paragraph will adjust almost instantaneously. This requires hundreds of steps in which letters are moved, but these steps are performed so rapidly that it is practical to let the computer reformat paragraphs repeatedly while you work on your text. The virtual reality model assumes that the universal computer can similarly re-compute futures as observer-participants make choices.

When an observer is given a precognitive vision, he or she may act consciously in such a way as to change the perceived future. Likewise, actions of other persons that are part of the foreseen future may prevent it from coming to pass as predicted. Then again, if the observer and all of the other participants act according to the calculated plan, then it will come to pass as it was foreseen.

In this model retrocausation is possible. For individuals in the present to influence the past, the computer simply has to go back to the data for a previous time step (cached in the computer's memory) and work forward again making the desired revisions. This will affect what happened in the past. However, I would impose the restraint that this selection process cannot change the conscious experiences that people had in the past. For example, if a subject successfully wills some random numbers to be high, and someone was conscious of those numbers at an earlier time, then the subject's present will did not cause the high values. The correlation with intention was either by chance or the intention was not freely chosen.

RECORDING EXPERIENCE

The fundamental assumption here is that virtual events perceived by individual consciousness are considered fixed, whereas all other virtual events have the status of mere calculations that can be revised. Referring to Figure 9 (in Chapter 3), trial futures can be computed and even the past can be revised as long as this does not alter past conscious experiences. This does not rule out the possibility that all virtual events and their revisions may be perceived by universal consciousness. Thus we can make an analogy with the Unix™ operating system, in which ordinary users have limited access to the system, while the "super-user" has unrestricted access.

I should note that to control events through the phenomenon of exponential amplification (as described in Chapter 2), it may be necessary to make modifications in the course of events somewhat before the desired effects take place. For instance, in the Baker Transformation example, modifications were introduced at least six steps before they became manifest as a "happy face," and the modifications became apparent about two steps before this point. These modifications of the past can be made if they do not revise past conscious experiences. Thus, the requirements for retrocausation are the same as the requirements for interactive control through exponential amplification of small changes.

We need to clarify what is meant by past conscious experiences. In a man-made VR, this could refer to memories retained by the experiencing brain. We could require that revisions of the past are allowed as long as they do not contradict these memories (which lie outside the VR and cannot be revised). However, memories can be false, so there is a certain degree of looseness in this requirement. It is a question of how much consistency we want to enforce between memory and records of the past in the virtual world. Thus a person in a virtual world might see evidence that conflicts with his memories, but he might simply dismiss the memories as faulty if the conflict was not too severe.

I suspect that some form of memory may be retained by consciousness itself. In the Ground Reality model, the ultimate requirement is that these memories should not contradict revisions of the virtual world. Of course, most phenomena in the virtual world are not connected with conscious awareness and possible memory formation within consciousness. Consider, for example, the vast amount of unobserved activity going on in an Avogadro's number of molecules. This provides great leeway for making acceptable modifications of the past. Of course, the question might be raised of why phenomena should be simulated in a VR if they are not perceived. (If a tree falls with no one to hear it, does it make a sound?) The answer is that the most straightforward way to generate the perceived parts of a simulation is to generate the whole thing.

THE ENIGMA OF FREE WILL

The topic of conscious influence of events brings up the question of whether conscious intention is freely chosen or is itself determined by the course of events. Free will, or conscious will, is defined as an intention stemming from consciousness itself. This means an intention not deriving from calculations governing the virtual world. I note that what appears to be free will is often predictable, conditioned behavior—behavior that does follow a predetermined course. For example, Benjamin Libit has performed experiments showing that finger movements which subjects believed to be freely chosen were actually already set in motion by action potentials in the brain (Libet, 1985).

In one of Libet's experiments, subjects were "asked to perform a simple quick flexion of the wrist or fingers at any time they felt the 'urge' or desire to do so" (Libit, 1985, p. 530). The movement was timed by noting a sharply rising electromyogram in the appropriate muscle. The subject timed the appearance of the "urge" by noting the position of a spot on a revolving disk, and these times were corrected for certain systematic errors. Libet found that the readiness potential for the muscular movement preceded the perceived urges to move by about 0.4 seconds, indicating that the moves were already programmed before the conscious awareness of the will to move.

Does this mean that free will is an illusion? Subjects reported that they were always aware of the urge or intention to move, and so they were not acting automatically or involuntarily. Libet observed that having decided to move, they could "veto" the move during the 0.1 to 0.2 second interval from urge to movement. So it seemed that the will to move was illusory, while the will to veto was genuine in the sense that conscious intention to veto preceded it. Libet argued that conscious will simply exercises a regulatory influence on urges for action which spring from the subconscious.

It is clear even from day-to-day experience that conscious will often does give assent to actions that were really chosen in other ways. For example, people can often easily anticipate what another person will do, even though the other person feels like a free agent. This doesn't mean that free will does not exist, but we can certainly be in illusion about it.

In the GR model, consciousness is one of many inputs to physical action. The possibility is there that one may act according to conscious will, but one may also mold perceived "will" to predetermined actions. In this scheme, we can assign moral responsibility to actions but, as we all know, this may be difficult to do in practice.

PRECOGNITIVE WARNINGS

The anecdotal data on precognition supports the idea that the projected futures may be altered in the actual course of events. Anecdotal evidence consists of real-life stories that are generally considered less evidential than data from controlled experiments. Nonetheless, anecdotal testimony about paranormal phenomena can give useful insights that cannot be obtained from existing experimental data.

Louisa Rhine, the wife of J. B. Rhine and a prominent parapsychologist in her own right, collected a large number of reports of spontaneous paranormal experiences. One of her cases involved a young woman in Washington State who dreamed one night that a large chandelier which hung over her baby's crib had fallen and crushed the baby (Rhine, 1961, p. 199). In the dream, she and her husband stood in the baby's room, watching the wreckage. The clock on the dresser said 4:35, and they could hear rain on the window and wind blowing outside.

Badly frightened, the woman went to get the baby and noted that the weather was calm, with a full moon. At this point, she felt a little foolish, but she took the baby to her own bed and went to sleep.

About two hours later she and her husband were awakened by a loud crash. They rushed to the baby's room and saw that the chandelier had indeed fallen on the crib. The clock read 4:35, and they could hear the sound of wind and the beating of rain on the windowpane.

In this case, the dream was verified in every detail except one—the crushing of the baby. And this was apparently avoided by the woman's action in response to the dream. One might argue that the woman was subconsciously worried about the chandelier, and these worries manifested through a dream at an opportune moment. But this does not explain details such as the time on the clock and the storm. This could be a case of partial alteration of a potential future in response to perception of that future.

In another of Rhine's cases, a woman in New York dreamed of a plane crash: "I had clearly seen a plane crash at the shore of a lake and the roof of the third cottage on that dirt track in flames as a result. There was only one man and he burned up. I tried to write two over-due letters that morning, but I found myself telling my correspondents about it and also the fact that the fire engine would go by the canal and be unable to get to the plane before it was too late" (Rhine, 1961, p. 204).

All day long the woman listened anxiously to airplanes. Late in the afternoon, she felt that the doomed plane was flying overhead. It turned out that this plane did crash. The fire engine did go by the canal, the pilot was burned to death, and a cottage was partly burned. If this story is indeed true, it represents a case in which a disaster was foreseen but could not be averted.

Needless to say, stories of this kind can always be rejected as lies or delusions. We can suppose that the woman read about a plane crash in a newspaper and then imagined that she had dreamed about it in detail. Perhaps she was prone to indulge in fantasy, or she was a chronic liar. However, accounts of this kind of experience are extremely common, and they happen to people in all walks of life. In many cases, they are reported by people who are known to be honest and reliable.

The anecdotal evidence for paranormal phenomena shows how these phenomena occur in real life, and it is indispensable for gaining insight into why they occur and what role they play in the larger scheme of things. For this reason, I will often supplement experimental studies with anecdotal reports in subsequent chapters.

7

VISIONS, HALLUCINATIONS, AND VISITATIONS

"Strong hallucinations are simply impossible!"
—Daniel C. Dennett

*"This woman was my deceased grandmother.
I would have known her anywhere."*
—Raymond Moody, M.D.

A non-psychotic experimental psychologist named Alvin Goldstein reported in the *Journal of Abnormal Psychology* an account of some hallucinations that he experienced while waiting in a hospital for spinal disc surgery. He pointed out that the door to his hospital room was directly opposite the foot of his bed. Most of the time, it was ajar and its varnished surface reflected light from the corridor into his eyes. He relates that

> Sometimes during my first day of hospitalization, I noticed fairly clear images reflected on the glossy surface of the door. Since I had not been aware of these images earlier, I assumed that during the day lighting conditions in the hallway must have changed and caused the reflections to become visible to me. I saw a long, dark corridor, extending to the left of my door, which resembled the inside of a castle, or perhaps an old house with dark wood paneling and wainscoting. In this corridor single individuals, couples, groups of people, and children appeared to be moving toward my room, or they turned down an intersecting branch of the hallway, but no one ever continued walking so as to pass in front of my door and the small section of corridor visible to me.
>
> Those who stopped walking appeared to be waiting in a line that began a few feet to the left of my doorway. At the time, I conjectured that perhaps all these people were visiting a patient in the room adjacent to mine (i.e. the room behind the head of my bed). I elaborated this guess into a reasonable story:

121

My neighbor was very close to death and his relatives and friends were visiting him for the last time. This interpretation of the activity in the hallway was not insistent but merely a passing thought. The images, on the other hand, were insistent, vivid, and remarkably varied in the colors and other details of clothing, in heights and ages of the individuals, and in their behavior. The images were exceptionally vivid and well organized, facts that made the parade appear to be entirely plausible. Looking back on it now (i.e. several weeks later), I should have become suspicious about the nature of these images because real, live visitors to my room never appeared in the reflected scene just prior to entering the room. The significance of this did not occur to me until several days after surgery, when I noticed that nothing was reflected from the surface of the door at any time of day (Goldstein, 1976, pp. 423–24).

What are we to make of Goldstein's experiences? He refers to his visions as hallucinations, or false perceptions of things that are not there. In common thinking, hallucinations are associated with disordered states of mind caused by mental illness, drugs, or disease. Goldstein was waiting to undergo surgery for a painful back condition, and we can imagine that this condition may have precipitated his hallucinatory experiences.

Hallucinations are generally regarded as socially disreputable, and they are connected with fear of ridicule or worse. In this case, Goldstein became frightened when he realized what was happening to him. He commented that "The shock of the experience—especially because as a psychologist I knew just enough about what was happening to become anxious about my grip on reality—robbed me of any spirit of scientific inquiry" (Goldstein, 1976, p. 424).

This is unfortunate, because we really do not understand what hallucinations are. Indeed, we don't even understand ordinary perception very well.

It is clear that when we perceive, we do not directly come in contact with the perceived objects. What we experience are mental images which are built up on the basis of sense data and which—hopefully— closely represent the actual objects of perception. It appears that the mind has the power of generating such images. In ordinary perception, the images are created on the basis of information supplied by the senses, and in hallucinations and dreams they seem to be created on the basis of internal mental states. But what is a mental image, and how is it seen?

THE MYSTERY OF MENTAL IMAGES

The findings of neurophysiology support the idea that the brain contains many specialized centers for the processing of sense data. Each of the senses has its own processing areas in the brain, and if we look at a particular sense, we see that different types of information processing for that sense are carried out by different neural subcenters.

Francis Crick published a popular book on the scientific investigation of visual awareness (Crick, 1994). If we leave aside his purely speculative proposals, what emerges from Crick's account is that the brain produces what might be called an annotated representation of the images focused on the retinas of the eyes.

To explain what is meant by an annotated representation, I will briefly outline what researchers have learned about the visual system of the brain. This information is largely based on experiments with monkeys, in which the skull is opened up and electrodes are inserted into the brain. However, it is corroborated by studies of visual perception in humans and by studies of human brain damage.

At the lowest level of the visual system, signals from the light-sensitive rods and cones in the retina are combined in simple ways by retinal neurons called ganglion cells. These include the magno cells that respond quickly to small changes in light intensity but are insensitive to color, and the parvo cells that subtract signals from wavelength-sensitive cone cells to generate color information.

The ganglion cells respond to receptive fields consisting of small groups of rods and cones. Some respond to "on-center" patterns, consisting of a small region of light surrounded by darkness, and some respond to "off-center" patterns consisting of the reverse. These are called center-surround neurons.

Nerve impulses are transmitted from the retinas to the lateral geniculate bodies in the center of the brain, and from there to visual area V1 in the back of the cerebral cortex. In this area, some neurons are of the center-surround type, but most of the others seem to respond to a thin bar of light or an illuminated edge in the visual field. There are "simple" cells that respond to a fixed line or edge, and "complex" cells that respond to a line or edge of a given orientation anywhere in the cell's receptive field.

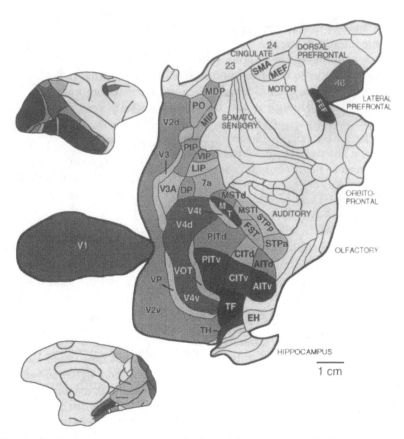

Figure 15. Visual processing areas in the brain of a macaque. This diagram shows cortical areas of the right hemisphere of a macaque's brain, which has been unfolded and flattened for ease of viewing. The areas connected with vision are shaded. These include areas V1, V2, MT, and V4. The smaller diagrams on the left show this brain hemisphere from the outside (top) and from the inside (bottom).

Some complex cells respond to more elaborate stimuli, such as patterns of dots that are all moving in the same direction. The neurons in area V1 are also influenced by the "local context" generated by the behavior of neurons with nearby receptive fields. Crick comments that "It is sobering to realize that after almost 30 years of research we still do not know for certain how either simple cells or complex cells are wired to produce their observed behavior" (Crick, 1994, p. 143).

The neurons in the next visual area, called V2, exhibit a similar pattern of responses, but their behavior is more sophisticated. Most of them respond to inputs coming from both eyes, and their receptive fields are bigger than those of the neurons in area V1. Some respond to subjective contours—curved edges that do not actually exist, but are suggested by the arrangement of features in the visual image. (To some degree, all edges are subjective in this sense.)

In visual area MT (for middle temporal) there are neurons that can tell which way a shape is moving. To do this, it is necessary to combine information regarding the movement of different edges making up the shape. These neurons are largely indifferent to color, although some of them do respond to moving edges marked by different colors with the same luminance. Such an edge would be invisible to a person who is color blind.

The neurons in visual area V4 are largely insensitive to movement, but they exhibit complex responses to colors. This involves comparing the light of a given wavelength from one small region with the light of different wavelengths in the surrounding neighborhood.

In the lower visual areas, the receptive fields of the neurons are arranged spatially in the form of a crude map of the retinal image. This so-called retinopic map is greatly distorted and devotes much greater area to the foveal region of the retina, where vision is sharpest, than it does to peripheral areas. In the higher visual areas, this map tends to be even more distorted, and in the highest areas, the receptive fields of neurons may cover the entire visual hemifield. (The hemifields are the right or left halves of the two retinal images. In the lateral geniculate body, the neural signals from the right half of the retinas of both eyes are sent to the left half of the cerebral cortex, and the signals from the left halves are sent to the right half of the cortex.)

In the highest areas, some neurons respond to such features as the front view of a face. That is, they fire when a face appears in the visual field, but they do not respond to other images, including an image formed from a random arrangement of facial parts. Other neurons respond to a face in profile, or to other complex shapes.

When we perceive an image, we are immediately aware of all of the information generated by these brain processes. For example, if we see a person's face, we recognize edges, contours, and colors, even though these are abstractions from the actual retinal images of the

face. We also sense three-dimensional shape, based on the brain's com-
parative analysis of the two retinal images. We recognize features, such
as the nose, mouth, and eyes, and we recognize that we are looking at
a face. Finally, we may recognize that the face is that of a person we
know, and we may remember the person's name. This is what I mean
by an annotated representation: The brain generates a description of
the face including hierarchically organized features ranging from the
very simple (such as lines and colors) to the very complex (such as faces
and facial expressions).

We tend to take all of this for granted, but its importance becomes
apparent when it is disrupted by brain damage. For example, there is
a form of brain damage called prosopagnosia, in which a person loses
the ability to recognize people's faces, even though he can otherwise
see normally. Such a person may be able to recognize that he is looking at a face, without being able to say whose face it is. In other forms
of brain damage, a person may lose the ability to recognize familiar
objects such as faces, tables, and cars, even though he is able to make
drawings of them and he is also able to discuss them intelligently (Crick,
1994, p. 167). In these cases, high-order features are omitted from
the annotated representation due to defects in the brain's processing
system.

Common optical illusions may also illustrate aspects of the annotated representation. For example, if you gaze at a waterfall for a
couple of minutes and then look at the cliff next to it, the rocks in the
cliff seem to be flowing upward, even though they plainly remain in one
place. This suggests that information regarding motion is connected
with each part of an image. We can hypothesize that when the downward motion detectors in one area of the visual field become tired due
to prolonged exposure to the downward flow of the water, the result is
that upward motion is reported when that area shifts to the stationary
rocks.

One woman suffered from brain damage which apparently disrupted the ability of the brain to attach movement information to
objects. When she tried to cross the road, a car seen in the distance
would suddenly appear at close range, without the appearance of
smooth, continuous motion. Tea poured in a cup would appear to her
as a stationary arc of liquid, and she would not notice the tea rising in

the cup (Crick, 1994, p. 166). This suggests that when we see something move, we are perceiving movement information, rather than directly deducing movement from changes in the visual scene. It also suggests that specialized areas of the brain generate this information.

What we see is thus an annotated representation of the retinal images in our eyes, but how do we actually see this representation? Crick remarks that "There appears to be no single cortical area whose activity corresponds to the global content of our visual awareness" (Crick, 1994, p. 204).

BLINDSIGHT

It is significant that vision can apparently take place without subjective awareness. Dr. Larry Weiskrantz was testing the vision of a patient named D. B. who was rendered blind in his left visual field (in both eyes) as a result of surgery in his right primary visual cortex. Although D. B. was not aware of seeing anything in his left visual field, he was able to correctly answer questions about lights and objects projected into this field. When asked how he knew the answers, he replied that he was just guessing and hadn't seen a thing (Ramachandran, 1998, pp. 75–76).

Weiskrantz documented this phenomenon in other patients and called it "blindsight." He argued that D. B. was not able to see on the left through the cerebral pathways, due to the damage to his visual cortex. But he could still see through an "old" visual pathway that goes from the eyes directly to the superior colliculus in the brain stem and from there to the cerebral cortex. This "primitive" pathway serves to alert the higher centers about approaching objects, so that the eyes can be reflexively directed towards them.

It is striking that visual data is processed through this pathway without any awareness of seeing. The data emerges into consciousness as apparent guesses or, at most, a non-visual "feeling" (Ramachandran, 1998, p. 76). It is clear from this that neural processing in the brain does not necessarily involve consciousness. We are left with the question of what is special about processing that does give rise to consciousness.

THE ANIMATED CARTESIAN THEATER

Where are the different results of the brain's sensory analysis combined together into a unified conscious experience? The philosopher Daniel Dennett would answer, "Nowhere." He argues that what goes on in the brain is simply a complex network of interacting processes which give rise to measurable behavior. There is no "Cartesian Theater" in the brain where it all comes together in consciousness (Dennett, 1991). There is just information processing, and this is naturally broken into modules that handle different aspects of the overall analysis.

But what about the fact that we experience unified perceptions? The Nobel-prize-winning neurophysiologist, John Eccles went so far as to argue that the data produced by specialized brain processes are integrated together not by the brain, but by an independent mind that interacts with the brain (Popper and Eccles, 1977).

Of course, the virtual reality model also postulates this, and it suggests that a great deal of information processing involved in sense perception may be carried out by routines in the universal computer that are not part of the virtual brain. Seeing takes place when this integrated information is presented to the conscious observer. However, this observer is not situated within the virtual brain or anywhere in the virtual three-dimensional continuum. The brain's neural processing is, indeed, unconscious, and only certain outputs from this processing reach the conscious observer.

With these ideas in mind, let us return to the topic of hallucinations. Dennett argues that the brain constructs hallucinations through a process of random questioning that he illustrates by analogy with a party game. In this game, a person called the dupe is sent out of the room while someone narrates a dream. The idea is that when the dupe returns, he is supposed to ask yes/no questions about the dream until he gets enough information to identify the dreamer.

The people in the room play a trick by deciding that no one should narrate a dream. Instead, they agree to answer yes to the dupe's questions if the last letter in the question is in the first half of the alphabet, and not otherwise. This is subject to the rule that if an answer produced in this way contradicts a previous answer, then it should be changed so as not to contradict. This stratagem misleads the dupe into synthesizing a dream-story based on his own questions and the random element provided by their terminal letters. Interestingly enough, John Wheeler has used almost the same analogy to illustrate his idea of how observation calls forth quantum reality from unreality (Wheeler, 1988, p. 9).

Here is how Dennett's scheme might operate. Disordered processes in the brain result in random detection of features such as edges, colors, motion data, face profile indicators, and so on. These are the random "answers." As these answers are shuttled back and forth between brain modules, they are continuously edited for consistency, until finally a consistent pattern emerges. This is the hallucination.

Although this process might conjure up the murky, turbid hallucinations attending fever or intoxication, it does not seem feasible for creating the highly organized hallucinations that are sometimes reported. This would be like trying to write a short story by generating sentences at random while continuously editing them for consistency.

Rather than working backwards from randomly chosen features, it seems easier to create a hallucination by first generating a raw image and then processing it through the brain's feature recognition system. But in this case, where is the raw image produced? The neurons in the brain's visual processing system are devoted to feature detection on various levels, and could not do this.

The movie industry has a great need for realistic animated images of human and non-human characters. Workers in the field of computer graphics have learned that the only practical way to create such animations is by using physically realistic models. Thus to produce real-looking folded cloth, animators use software based on physical models of cloth deformation. To make realistic bulging muscles, they resort to biophysical models of muscle action.

In the course of this chapter I will discuss many hallucinations that appear as realistic-looking 3D animations. It is possible that to create such imagery, the brain also needs the equivalent of 3D animation software.

HALLUCINATORY INCOMPETENCE

Dennett would argue that I am worrying here about a capacity that doesn't exist. He maintains that the brain simply cannot produce a strong hallucination, which he defines as "an apparently concrete and persisting three-dimensional object in the real world" (Dennett, 1991, p. 7). This would be something like "a ghost that talked back, that permitted you to touch it, that resisted with a sense of solidity . . ." (Dennett, 1991, p. 7).

Does the brain have the computing power to produce strong hallucinations? Hans Moravec estimated in 1987 that a human brain can process data at about 1,000 times the rate of the fastest super-computers (Moravec, 1989, p. 191). He based this on his estimate that a computer performing 10 trillion calculations per second could accurately simulate the human brain. We can arrive at a similar estimate by noting that there are about 100 billion neurons in the brain. A typical excited neuron fires at about 100 hertz or cycles per second. The sequential equivalent of 100 billion neurons operating at this rate is roughly 100 times 100 billion, which comes to 10 trillion hertz.

Presumably, only a small part of the brain's information processing power could be devoted to generating a hallucination. We have already ruled out much of the brain's visual processing system. In addition, large sections of the brain must be "wired" for unrelated functions, such as control of the bodily limbs. Even if sensory, speech, and memory areas might be enlisted to generate data for a hallucination, this data would have to be separated from the continuing stream of data relating to normal experience that is handled by these same brain areas. It would then have to be redirected so that it seemed to come into the brain from an external source.

A hallucination that tied up 1% of the brain could draw on the computing power of about 10 supercomputers, using Moravec's estimates. This would be adequate for an impressive real-time display. But could part of the brain be devoted to 3D animation? The brain appears to be divided into specialized modules devoted to particular tasks. Realistic hallucinations are evidently rare, so an animation module would presumably have to carry out some day-to-day function other than the generation of hallucinations. At the moment, it is unclear what this would be.

To get further insight into what the brain must do to generate a hallucination, it is useful to look at some empirical evidence indicating how strong hallucinations can be.

MIRROR VISIONS

Goldstein remarked that the images he saw were "insistent, vivid, and remarkably varied in the colors and other details of clothing, in heights and ages of the individuals, and in their behavior" (Goldstein, 1976, p. 423). This suggests that a considerable amount of computation would be required to generate such images in real time. However, since we do not have a detailed description of what Goldstein experienced, it is hard to say more.

Much more detailed accounts of apparent hallucinations are presented by the psychologist Raymond Moody in his report on visions generated by gazing into a mirror. Throughout history, there have been traditions indicating that visions can be conjured up by gazing into reflective surfaces, such as mirrors, crystal balls, or containers filled with water. After running across an old book describing this phenomenon, Moody decided to carry out his own investigation.

He set up a mirror in a room in an old converted gristmill that he owns in Alabama. People were invited to visit this facility and attempt to see visions of departed relatives by gazing into the mirror. Moody screened his subjects to make sure that they were mature, emotionally stable, and did not suffer from mental disorders. He also eliminated people who subscribed to occult ideologies. He tried to create a peaceful atmosphere in the old mill that would facilitate the altered state of consciousness needed to generate visions.

Moody reports that he obtained unexpected results. Even though he had selected very grounded and reasonable persons as subjects, he found that many of them reported having visions that struck them as completely real. This led him to try to experience a vision himself. As he put it, "I was convinced that if I saw an apparition, it would be different. If I have an experience like that, I thought, I won't be fooled into thinking it is real" (Moody, 1993, p. 18).

Moody states that he decided to seek a vision of his deceased maternal grandmother. In accordance with his experimental protocol, he began by meditating on her. After many hours of meditation on old photos and memories, he entered his "apparition booth" and spent about an hour gazing into the depths of a large mirror that was oriented so as to create an impression of "three-dimensional clarity." The hour passed, and nothing happened.

Later on, he was sitting alone in a room unwinding from this mirror session, when a strange woman walked in. After about a minute of bewilderment, he realized that she was his deceased paternal (not maternal) grandmother. I will quote at length from his description of his encounter with this woman so as to convey the vivid and detailed character of the experience.

> At this point I was looking directly into her eyes, awestruck at what I was seeing. In a kind and loving way she acknowledged who she was and addressed me with the nickname that only she used for me when I was a child . . .
>
> The reason I had not recognized her at first was that she appeared much younger than she was when she died, in fact even younger than she had been when I was born. I don't remember seeing any photographs of her at the age she seemed to be during this encounter, but that is irrelevant here since it was not totally through her physical appearance that I recognized her. Rather, I knew this woman through her unmistakable presence and through the many memories we reviewed and discussed. In short this woman was my deceased grandmother. I would have known her anywhere . . .
>
> We discussed old times, specific incidents from my childhood. Throughout she reminded me of several events that I had forgotten. Also she revealed something very personal about my family situation that came as a great surprise but in retrospect makes a great deal of sense . . .
>
> I did hear her voice clearly, the only difference being that there was a crisp, electric quality to it that seemed clearer and louder than her voice before she died. . . . Although most of my conversation was through the spoken word, from time to time I was immediately aware of what she was thinking, and I could tell the same was true for her.
>
> In no way did she appear 'ghostly' or transparent during our reunion. She seemed completely solid in every respect. She appeared no different from any other person except that she was surrounded by what appeared to be a light or an indentation in space, as if she were somehow set off or recessed from the rest of her physical surroundings (Moody, 1993, pp. 19–21).

This certainly seems to qualify as a strong hallucination. However, to Moody, it was not a hallucination at all. He declared that the experience was completely coherent with his ordinary waking reality, and he said that "If I were to discount this experience as hallucinatory, I would be almost obliged to discount the rest of my life as hallucinatory too" (Moody, 1993, p. 22). Moody took the experience as proof of the reality of life after death.

One response to Moody's account is to reject it as impossible—

even as a hallucination. Dennett declared that "We are—and should be—particularly skeptical of reports of very strong hallucinations because we don't believe in ghosts, and we think that only a real ghost could produce a strong hallucination" (Dennett, 1991, p. 7). It is interesting that Moody and Dennett seem to agree that only a real ghost could produce a vision of this kind. However, I don't think we should allow this line of reasoning to force us to reject the evidence that such visions do occur. Moody gives many examples of powerful visions induced by his technique, and the history of shamanism and religious meditation suggests that such visions have been a standard feature of many human societies since time immemorial.

Suppose, for the sake of argument, that Moody's experience was produced in his brain. We can readily imagine that the material for this experience was taken from his subconscious mind—which by hypothesis is part of his brain's mental system. But how did his brain use this material to create a conversation that unfolded interactively and appeared to involve two conscious persons?

Moody and the grandmother remained distinct, even though there was apparently some direct thought transference between them. We have to suppose that Moody's brain created a highly realistic three-dimensional animation of the grandmother which was integrated into the surrounding room in a natural way, and was used to present the grandmother personality to the Moody personality. To Moody, the only indication of something unusual was the "electric quality" of the grandmother's voice and the "indentation" in space surrounding her.

This all suggests that Moody's brain was running two personalities simultaneously, doing the data management to keep them separate, and running an animation that would require quite a few Cray supercomputers to render in real time. And during all this, Moody felt that this was the "most normal and satisfying interaction" he had ever had with his grandmother (Moody, 1993, p. 20).

It is true, of course, that Moody did not touch his grandmother. In fact, she put up her hands and motioned him back when he indicated that he wanted to hug her. We could suppose that this was a clever stratagem by his brain to avoid having to simulate tactical sensations along with vision and hearing.

However, a number of Moody's experimental subjects reported

vivid experiences in which they did touch an apparition of a departed relative. For example, a lady saw a vision of her late grandfather in the mirror:

> I was so happy to see him that I began to cry. Through the tears I could still see him in the mirror. Then he seemed to get closer and he must have come out of the mirror because the next thing I knew he was holding me and hugging me. It felt like he said something like, "It's okay, don't cry" (Moody, 1993, p. 75).

One might argue that these perceptions were not really as vivid as people made them out to be. Perhaps they simply suffered the illusion of having a strong hallucination. Or perhaps they confabulated false memories of experiences that never really happened. But then again, one could argue that the subjects really did see images that were highly realistic and detailed. One reason for thinking this is that some subjects said they first saw rudimentary images that later became more realistic. For example, one subject said that the features of her mother's face formed gradually "like the computerized pictures you see on television" (Moody, 1993, p. 79). If some images were reported as imperfect, then perhaps the images reported as highly realistic actually warranted that description.

Curiously, many of Moody's subjects reported that before their realistic mirror visions began, they first saw billowing smoke or mist in the mirror, followed by color patterns or geometrical designs. This is reminiscent of Disney's rendition of the Snow White story, with its magic mirror. It appears that there is often some noise in the system before the hallucinatory image is "tuned in." However, in some cases this phase is omitted. Thus Moody's grandmother made her appearance by simply walking into the room.

APPARITIONS

Ghost stories are not generally regarded as scientific evidence, but they do represent a common form of conscious experience and therefore they should be considered in any serious scientific investigation of perception. Indeed, all the typical features of such stories should be considered in such an investigation. Otherwise, there will be a tendency to edit out features that seem theoretically embarrassing while retaining features that are more agreeable with one's theoretical views. Here is a typical example of such a story:

> A naval officer, Lieutenant H., and his wife are assigned new quarters in a house which they share with another family, the Gs. On four occasions he clearly sees, for up to fifteen minutes, the figure of a man (previously unknown to him), which seems as though about to speak, but vanishes into thin air when approached. On one occasion the figure blocks light from electric light bulbs; on another, two dogs are alarmed prior to its appearance. It transpires that the ghost closely resembles Mrs. G.'s late father, who had never been to the house. Lieutenant H. picks out his photograph from among about twenty others (Gauld, 1983, p. 234).

Here the embarrassing feature is the claim that, as a result of seeing the apparition, Lieutenant H. was able to identify the photograph of a man whom he had never met. Such an experience is sometimes called a veridical hallucination because it contains verifiable information that the subject was presumably unaware of before the experience. There is an extensive literature devoted to the investigation of such experiences.

In this case, if it could be shown with reasonable certainty that Lieutenant H. had never previously seen a picture of Mrs. G.'s late father, then his ability to recognize the father's face would be puzzling. One explanation is that he simply saw the father's ghost, and therefore he could recognize him. Another is that he learned about the father's appearance telepathically from Mrs. G. and "dressed up" this paranormal knowledge as a series of hallucinations.

Both explanations are contrary to current scientific theories about the physical world. Therefore many scientists might prefer to argue that the story is a hoax, or that some form of subtle cueing was used to induce Lieutenant H. to pick the right photograph. Such dismissive explanations may be true in some cases, but it seems doubtful that they could apply across the board to all stories of this type.

An interesting feature of the story of Lieutenant H. is that the apparition was observed to block light from electric bulbs. This is consistent with Moody's accounts of solid looking apparitions that presumably also appeared to block light coming from behind them.

One might ask whether or not measurements of brain activity would corroborate such blockage.

Such measurements have been reported. Morton Schatzman describes the case of a woman he called Ruth who "was not insane or suffering from an organic disorder" and who claimed that she often perceived figures of people who weren't actually there (Schatzman, 1980). These figures looked solid, and they blocked the view of objects behind them. She said that she could summon up such figures voluntarily and could mentally control their behavior to some degree.

The psychiatrist and neurophysiologist Peter Fenwick decided to investigate these claims. He asked Ruth to observe a TV screen displaying a checkerboard pattern of white and black squares that alternated from white to black and from black to white about once per second. Normally, if a person looks at such a flashing pattern, a rhythmic electrical pattern called the visual evoked response can be measured in the occipital cortex by means of an electroencephalograph. Schatzman reports:

> When Ruth looked at the reversing chequerboard pattern on the television screen and did not hallucinate, she showed a normal visual evoked response with an amplitude of 18 microvolts. Then she hallucinated the figure of her eight-year-old daughter sitting on her lap, so that the head of the figure blocked Ruth's perception of the screen. Her visual evoked response was absent. When on a further trial she reported that the head of her daughter did not fully cover the screen, the amplitude of the evoked response was reduced to only eight microvolts (Schatzman, 1980).

If these results are valid, they imply that the neural activity representing the hallucinatory image is blocking the normal processing of retinal signals encoding the reversing checkerboard. Could it be that the primary visual areas in the brain are actually processing an image consisting of the hallucination superimposed on the checkerboard?

Recent findings reported by psychologist Stephen Kossyln of Harvard University seem to confirm this hypothesis. Kossyln's group used positron emission tomography (PET) to study blood flow in the brains of 12 men who were asked to visualize remembered images. They found that the primary visual cortex responded in characteristic ways to the visualization of small, medium, and large images. The neuroscientist Larry Squire commented that "This is a nice demonstration that the visual cortex is activated by mental images in the same ways it would be activated by visual perceptions" (Bower, 1995, p. 372).

But how would the imagined image be projected into the primary cortex? Crick points out that there are many back-connections from higher centers of the brain to lower centers. One could therefore suppose that higher centers manufactured the imagined images and added them to the image data coming from the retina.

If we take into account all of the available evidence, we can see that the process of addition must be quite sophisticated. In some cases, apparitions appear or disappear abruptly or seem to pass through walls. But in others, they seem to behave like normal physical bodies. Ruth claimed that her hallucinatory figures sometimes cast shadows. Moody maintained that his deceased grandmother walked into the room like an ordinary person, and Goldstein's corridor people appeared as reflections on a shiny door.

One objection to ghost stories is that the perceived figures are generally wearing clothes, and we hardly expect clothes to leave ghosts. Of course, if apparitions are animated figures projected into the sensory systems of the brain, then it is no mystery that they should have clothes. An animation can include cloths as readily as human-looking solid bodies. The question is: Are such animations actually generated in the subject's brain?

The following testimony by a priest at a Hindu temple shows how some visionary experiences clearly involve the import of a well-developed image into the perceiver's sensory system from some outside source:

> The next morning I had the oddest experience. I was performing my service of waking the Deities at 3:55 a.m. It was about 3:50 a.m. I unlocked the front door of the temple and could see into the kitchen. I knew I had carefully locked all 3 temple doors the night before, so I was surprised to see three of the teenage girl students in the back of the kitchen. They wore saris without coats and were chatting and moving about. The light was off in the kitchen but the girls were in a circle of white light. I thought, "Maybe someone came in last night and left the kitchen door unlocked." When I entered the kitchen, there was no one there. When I reached the spot where I had seen them, I heard a knock at the door. Those three girls were standing outside the door

wanting to get in. I went to the door; it was locked from the inside. I opened
the door and they pushed past me, talking and taking off their coats. They
turned on the lights and stood exactly as I had seen them moments before"
(Anonymous personal communication).

In this case, the moving, talking images of the girls could not have
been generated in the brain of the witness. Rather, they seem to have
been transmitted to him fully formed from a time a few minutes into the
future. This is hard to explain, unless we suppose that his brain somehow became linked to a detailed forecast of the immediate future—a
possibility in a virtual reality system. It is noteworthy that the circle of
light in which the girls were standing was incongruous in the vision
because the light was off. What he was "seeing" was an image of the
light that was actually there a few minutes later.

COLLECTIVE APPARITIONS

The smooth integration of the hallucination or imagined image into the real scene seems to require complicated 3D modeling. Here is
another case suggesting that this modeling is not always done by higher
brain centers:

Mrs. P., a lady who has once before had an hallucination—a non-veridical
one however—is lying in bed waiting to feed her baby. A lamp is burning. Suddenly she sees a tall man, dressed in naval officer's uniform, come to the end
of the bed. She rouses her husband, who also sees the figure. It speaks re-
proachfully to her husband. He then leaps out of bed. The figure moves away,
transiently blocking the light from the lamp, and vanishes into the wall. Mr.
P. tells her the apparition was that of his father, who had been dead fourteen
years. Later she learned that her husband was prevented by this vision from
taking financial advice which would have proved ruinous (Gauld, 1982,
pp. 234–35).

Here the uniformed figure blocks light like a solid object, but apparently exits through the wall. Of course, the key feature of this case
is that the figure was seen by two persons. It turns out that there are
many reports in which two or more people claimed to see an apparition. In such cases, it is hard to be sure that all of the witnesses have
actually seen the same three-dimensional form from their various

positions. However, in many cases the descriptions given by the witnesses are consistent with this hypothesis.

One way of explaining this case is to suppose that the witnesses are victims of a mental illness, which leads them to influence one another and thereby generate false memories of a shared hallucination. Such a mental disorder does exist. It is known as *folie a deux*, and it typically afflicts people such as married couples who are closely tied to one another emotionally. However, shared apparations are often reported by persons who are not afflicted by mental disorders.

Another explanation is that the witnesses generated a shared hallucination through subconscious telepathic communication. Unfortunately, this theory has the drawback that it is often difficult to convincingly explain why the telepathic communication should take place. In this case, Mr. P. was apparently worrying about financial matters. One might suppose that his subconscious mind summoned up an image of his departed father as a means of delivering financial advice. Somehow, Mrs. P. picked up on this telepathically and saw her husband's mental image while he was still asleep. When she awakened him, he visualized it in the room in the same place where his wife saw it. Clearly, this explanation is rather awkward, and it creates more problems than it solves.

The following is another case, which cannot be readily explained by either *folie a deux* or the telepathic theory. It involves the Reverend H. Hasted of Pisea Rectory in Essex, England, who was said to be prone to make apparitional appearances.

> On March 16, 1892, at 11.30 a.m., two of Hasted's servants, Eliza Smallbone and Jane Watts, were standing outside the Rectory talking with the rat catcher, N., who had come to tell Hasted about a dog. The servants noted the time, because they looked at the clock when telling N. that their master would return by 12:15 for lunch. Mrs. Watts was watching N. drive away with two dogs in his cart, when she said "Here comes the master!" Eliza saw him also, accompanied by his dog. They watched N. approach Hasted, expecting them to meet; but instead of stopping to talk, N. drove on (Braude, 1991, p. 184).

Mrs. Sidgwick of the Society for Psychical Research investigated this case one month later. She found that Hasted was in the home of Mr. Williams at the time he was seen by the servants, and this was confirmed by Mrs. Williams and Mrs. Shield, who were present at the time.

According to Mrs. Sidgwick, the servants seemed to be good witnesses.

In the late 19th century, many cases of this kind were investigated by the Society for Psychical Research (SPR), which attracted a number of prominent scientists interested in seeking scientific evidence for life after death. In 1894, Henry Sidgwick, one of the founders of the SPR, conducted a *Census of Hallucinations* in which 410 volunteers asked some 17,000 people about experiences of apparitions (Moody, 1993, p. 1). Of these, more than 2,000 answered in the affirmative. After eliminating obvious dreams and delirium, there remained 1,684 cases of people reporting apparitions.

The psychical researcher F. W. H. Myers commented that

> Where several persons have been together when the phantasm occurred, . . .
> it will be found that in nearly two cases out of three the phantasm is perceived
> by all or most of the persons so situated that they would have perceived it had
> it been an objective reality." (Gurney, Myers, and Podmore, 1886, Vol. 2,
> p. 278).

Thus it would seem that many collective apparitions appear as though the phantasm were actually physically present and reflecting light into the eyes of the witnesses.

One prominent category of visions is known as apparitions of the living. In these cases, the witnesses observe a living person, who is not physically present at the time. These cases demonstrate that it would be naive to interpret apparitions of dead persons as direct evidence for the survival of the dead. At the same time, multiple witness cases and cases involving the paranormal transmission of knowledge suggest that some apparitions involve more than the mere malfunctioning of neural machinery in the brain.

The so-called crisis apparitions constitute by far the largest category of visions with paranormal transmission of knowledge. Here a person seen in a vision is subsequently found to have died or to have undergone some severe crisis at roughly the time when the vision took place. Here is an example from the *Census of Hallucinations*:

> In April, 1888, Miss. Hervey was in Tasmania, while her cousin was working
> in Dublin as a nurse. The two women had been close friends, but had not seen
> one another since Miss Hervey moved to Tasmania in 1887. The cousin's

apparition was seen coming upstairs, dressed in grey, between 6 and 7 p.m. on April 21. The experience was so vivid that Miss Hervey ran to Lady H., in whose home she was staying. . . . At the time, Miss Hervey was unaware of the fact that her cousin had been stricken by a sudden and quickly fatal attack of typhus fever, lasting only five days. Death came on April 22, 1888, at 4:30 p.m., about 32 hours after the apparition occurred. News of the event did not arrive until June (Braude, 1991, p. 175).

It is not surprising that experiences like these are often taken as direct visitations by the spirit of the departed person. However, it is puzzling that the vision took place 32 hours before the cousin's death. If we look at many examples of crisis apparitions, we see that there does seem to be a correlation between the vision and some crisis affecting the perceived person, but the timing of these two events only roughly agrees. At the very least, it seems that the occurrence of such visions involves a paranormal transmission of information.

APPARITIONS IN THEORY

If two or more witnesses see one complex object, then it follows that at least one of the witnesses must have received some information concerning that object from a source lying outside his or her brain. If a vision is correlated with external events unknown to the seer, then it also follows that the seer must have received information connected with the vision from an external source.

In the context of a purely physical picture of reality, it is hard to see how this could happen. But it is possible in the virtual reality model, in which the entire world, including virtual brains and bodies, is a computational construct. The only difficulty lies in the question of how information could be injected into the virtual brain without violating the physical laws of the virtual world. This problem has been extensively discussed in previous chapters. In summary, the injection of extra information into the brain will certainly violate the statistical laws of physics, but it may not violate the dynamical laws. Or then again, it may. In a virtual reality model, all physical laws are mere conventions of the model, and the possibility is open that even the dynamical conventions of physics may apply only in limited circumstances.

In the VR theory of apparitions, information defining the vision consists of a full 3D model of the apparitional figure. When this information is injected into the brain, the figure is processed by the brain's sensory centers (visual, auditory, olfactory, gustatory, and tactile) in the same way as other sensory data. The VR computer carries out the calculations needed to produce the apparitional figure, and so it is not necessary to attribute these calculations to unknown brain centers. Multiple witnesses are able to see the apparition in a consistent way because their brains are all supplied with the same data defining the figure. This hypothesis takes into account both the data regarding apparitions and the findings of Fenwick and Kossyln concerning the effect of visualized images on the visual centers of the brain.

In the virtual reality model, the conscious perceiver is not part of the virtual system. The sensory link between the perceiver and the virtual brain, body, and world requires interface calculations that are not part of the virtual world. Therefore, the VR model assumes from the outset that sensory processing exists in addition to that carried out in the virtual brain. Here I simply postulate additional sensory calculations that are not within the virtual world, but are cycled back through the virtual brain to add additional features to the world of experience produced with that brain.

This is consistent with the idea that the virtual brain and body are the vehicles for experience within the virtual reality. It implies that apparitions, like normal experiences, will be subject to all the limitations of the brain and body, including deficiencies produced by brain damage. At the same time, they involve sophisticated data processing that is not done in the brain.

Of course, one can also consider that the 3D figure may be inserted into 3D virtual space itself, so that it can be seen by the witnesses through normal vision. This would also account for such observed effects as interruption of background light sources by apparitional figures. This process would be of the same computational nature as the alternative process, in which the figure is transmitted into the virtual brains of the witnesses. However, it is likely to require greater rearrangements of physical energy than its alternative, since at the very least, it implies that (virtual) physical light will be redirected. Nonetheless, we will see in later chapters that there is evidence for even more extreme physical effects.

8

LIFE BEYOND THE BODY

*"We have clearly identified a phenomenon
that threatens to cast a dark shadow
on the house of conventional science."*

—Kenneth Ring

In recent years, a great deal of interest has been generated by reports of unusual experiences by people hovering on the boundary between life and death. Although near death experiences have been reported in different forms for centuries, the development of modern medical technology has evidently increased the number of people living to report what happens on the brink of death. It turns out that their experiences provide direct evidence suggesting that mental images can be created and recorded independently of the brain. Although this evidence is highly controversial, it nonetheless promises to shed much light on the nature of the mind and its relation with the physical body.

Near death experiences (NDEs) are a subset of the so-called out-of-body experiences (OBEs), in which a person has the subjective impression of perceiving things from a standpoint outside his or her physical body. These in turn fall in the broader category of experiences transcending the limits of the conventionally accepted channels of sensation. The events reported in NDEs and OBEs can be divided roughly into two categories. These are (1) observations of the subject's physical environment from an out-of-body standpoint and (2) experiences of transcendental realms. I will begin by considering experiences of the first type, since these are sometimes accompanied by evidence that seems to corroborate the existence of unusual modes of sense perception.

143

EYELESS VISION DURING MEDICAL CRISIS

The following narration was given in 1977 by a patient of Dr. Michael Sabom, a cardiologist who was working at the time in the cardiac catheterization service at the University of Florida. The patient was a 52-year-old night watchman who had suffered a massive heart attack in 1973 and who had continued to have increasingly severe chest pain. In an interview with Dr. Sabom, he gave the following account of his subjective experiences during the heart attack:

> I couldn't stand the pain anymore . . . And then I collapsed. That's when everything went dark. . . . After a little while . . . I was sitting up there somewhere and I could look down, and I had never noticed that the floor was black and white tile. That's the first thing I remember being conscious of. . . . I recognized myself down there, sort of curled around in a half fetal position. Two or three people lifted me and put me up on a tray, not a tray but a dolly. . . . They strapped my legs and started moving me. When they first threw me on the table [the doctor] struck me, and I mean he really whacked the hell out of me. He came back with his fist from way behind his head and hit me right in the center of my chest. And they were pushing on my chest. . . . They shoved a plastic tube, like you put in an oil can, they shoved that in my mouth. . . . It was at that point I noticed another table-like arrangement with a bunch of stuff on it. I knew it later to be the machine they thump you with . . . I could see my right ear and this side of my face because I was facing away. . . . I could hear people talking. . . . It [the cardiac monitor] was like an oscilloscope. It made the same streak, over and over. . . . They put a needle in me—like one of those Aztec Indian rituals where they take the virgin's heart out. They took it two-handed—I thought this very unusual. . . . Then they took these round disks with a handle on them. . . . They put one up here—I think it was larger than the other one—and they put one down here [pointing to appropriate positions on chest]. . . . They thumped me and I didn't respond. . . . I thought they had given my body too much voltage. Man, my body jumped two feet off the table. . . . It appeared to me in some sort of fashion that I had a choice to reenter my body and take the chance of them bringing me back around or I could just go ahead and die, if I wasn't already dead. . . . I knew I was perfectly safe, whether my body died or not. . . . They thumped me a second time. . . . I reentered my body just like that" (Sabom, 1982, pp. 25–26).

This man's medical records indicated that he had checked into the hospital's emergency room at 7:43 P.M. complaining of severe chest pain. This was tentatively diagnosed as due to a hiatal hernia, and he was given medication for this and sent home. While leaving the emergency room, he suffered a cardiac arrest.

> At 9:35 p.m., he was found without pulse or respiration on the emergency room floor. Cardiopulmonary resuscitation including external cardiac massage was immediately begun. Intravenous and/or intracardiac medications were administered, though the route of administration was not specified. Two 400 watt-second cardioversions (electric shocks to the chest to stabilize cardiac rhythm) were given at 9:37 and 9:39 p.m., after which the man regained consciousness and was transported to the intensive care unit. Final admitting diagnosis—acute myocardial infarction (heart attack) with cardiac arrest (Sabom, 1982, p. 27).

The most striking feature of this story is that the patient's account of his resuscitation closely matches his medical report. Yet when most of the events in the resuscitation occurred, his heart was stopped and his brain was not being supplied with oxygen. Under these conditions, how could his brain store memories of these events? If we take it at face value, this report seems to imply that sense perception and memory storage can occur independently of the brain.

CORROBORATING EVIDENCE

One possibility is that this is simply an imaginary story that the patient consciously or subconsciously concocted. To test for this, Sabom interviewed 32 patients reporting near death experiences (NDEs) in which they claimed to have seen portions of their own resuscitation from cardiac arrest (Sabom, 1982, p. 83). He compared their accounts with the stories of 25 patients who had similar medical backgrounds, but who did not report an NDE. He described these "controls" as "seasoned cardiac patients with an average duration of known heart disease exceeding five years" (Sabom, 1982, p. 84). All of them had been admitted to a coronary care unit, and all had considerable exposure as laypersons to medical terminology and procedures involving heart disease.

Sabom asked the people reporting NDEs to describe their own resuscitation from heart attack, and he also asked the 25 control patients to describe in visual detail what happens during the procedure of cardiopulmonary resuscitation (CPR). He found that 23 of the controls were willing to attempt this, and of these, 20 made a major error, even though they felt "reasonably confident" that they were correct. The other three gave correct but limited accounts, and two of these had actually witnessed the resuscitation of another person in a hospital setting (Sabom, 1982, p. 86).

Of the 32 patients reporting NDEs, 26 gave general visual descriptions of the CPR procedure without verifiable details and without major errors. The remaining six patients gave accounts which were realistic in all respects and which agreed with medical records in specific details. The case of the 52-year-old night watchman is one of these. If we compare his medical records with his verbal testimony, we see the following correspondences:

"External cardiac massage was immediately begun."	"And they were pushing on my chest . . ."
"Intravenous and/or intracardiac medications were administered."	"They put a needle in me . . ."
"Two 400 watt-second cardioversions were given . . . after which the man regained consciousness."	"They thumped me and I didn't respond. . . . They thumped me a second time . . . I reentered my body, just like that."

Sabom points out that some of the procedures used during CPR may be omitted in a particular case. Therefore, it cannot be argued that this patient was simply taking a standard account of CPR and embellishing it with colorful personal remarks. For example, in another of the six cases, electric shocks were administered immediately after the onset of ventricular fibrillation, without external cardiac massage or the injection of medications. And in this case, that is exactly what the patient reported seeing from an out-of-body perspective.

Sabom argues that it is not likely that physicians or nurses would tell a patient about specific details of the patient's resuscitation, such as airway insertion or the injection of intracardiac medications. It is therefore hard to see how the six NDEers who reported such details could have learned about them, unless they directly perceived them as they happened.

One possibility is that the heart attack victim is in a semiconscious state and is able to directly observe his or her resuscitation. It is known that surgical patients under general anesthesia can sometimes remember remarks made by physicians during their surgery. So perhaps something similar is happening in NDE cases.

However, Sabom pointed out that some of the details reported in his NDE cases were purely visual in nature. Some involved events that the patient couldn't have witnessed with his eyes, even if they were open and functioning normally. For example, one patient reported seeing his wife, his eldest son, and his eldest daughter during his NDE (Sabom, 1982, p. 111). It turns out that they arrived unexpectedly to visit him moments after his cardiac arrest. His wife noted that he could not have seen her because she got only a brief glimpse of the top of his head from a distance, just before he was wheeled away to the intensive care unit in the opposite direction. In previous visits she had been accompanied by other family members, and therefore he had no reason to anticipate that these particular persons would be coming to visit him.

In another case, a patient undergoing open heart surgery gave a detailed visual description of his operation which correlated accurately with the physician's operative report (Sabom, 1982, pp. 64–69). Many of the patient's observations were visual in nature, and could not have been deduced from spoken comments by doctors or nurses. Yet the patient's head was covered by surgical draping during the operation, and he had never had access to the operative report.

In a paper on near death experiences, Ian Stevenson and Bruce Greyson advocated the idea that veridical observations in NDEs might be due to memories of conversations heard in a semiconscious state. However, they went on to note that some persons reporting NDEs "make stronger claims of remembering conversations held in adjoining rooms or other events occurring outside the range of their sense organs" (Stevenson and Greyson, 1979, p. 267).

Kimberly Clark, a hospital social worker in Seattle, Washington, reported a striking example. Clark went to see a coronary patient named Maria just after she had been revived from cardiac arrest. Maria reported an NDE in which she was initially looking down from the ceiling at the doctors and nurses who were working to revive her. Later, however, she experienced traveling outside of the hospital building in an out-of-body state and noticing an old tennis shoe on a third-floor ledge. At her request, Clark went looking for the shoe in an effort to see whether or not this experience was real. After looking through various third floor windows, she did find the shoe on a ledge, and on retrieving it, she found that it exactly matched Maria's description. She commented that "The only way she could have had such a perspective was if she had been floating right outside and at very close range to the tennis shoe" (Talbot, 1991, p. 232). Up until this time, Clark had been skeptical about out-of-body experiences, but this incident caused her to change her mind.

OBEs AND APPARITIONS

Although people undergoing NDEs or OBEs seem to have sensory contact with areas outside of their bodies, this is generally not accompanied by any perceived ability to modify or manipulate their environment. Thus they sometimes report trying to move objects and being frustrated by their inability to do so. They may also report trying unsuccessfully to catch people's attention. Nonetheless, there are reports in which a person claims to have entered an out-of-body state and appeared as an apparition to someone else.

Parapsychologists have run experiments in which subjects tried to enter an out-of-body state and influence events at a distance (Mishlove, 1975, pp. 133–37), and there are also anecdotal accounts of such attempts. As often happens, the anecdotes tend to be more vivid and clear-cut than reports of planned laboratory experiments. (Of course, lab reports are themselves anecdotes for those who did not participate in the experiments.) The Swedish psychiatrist Nils Jacobson gave an example of this kind of story. Two persons, Jacob and Eva, had agreed to attempt an out-of-body meeting, and they described the outcome as follows:

> **Jacob:** . . . The day after our decision I drove my daughter to her job; the time was 6 p.m. I was suddenly reminded of this agreement with Eva. Then I transported myself astrally to her home and found her sitting on the sofa, reading something. I made her notice my presence by calling her name and showing her that I was driving my car. She looked up and saw me. After that I left her and was back in the car which I had been driving all the while without any special awareness of the driving . . .

Eva: I was sitting alone in the room in an easy chair. . . . Suddenly I saw Jacob sitting in front of me in the car—saw about half the car as if I were in it with him. He sat at the wheel; I only saw the upper part of his body. I also saw the clock in the car. I think it was a couple of minutes before six. The car was not headed towards our house but in another direction . . . (Gauld, 1983, p. 228).

In this case, Jacob clearly didn't travel to Eva's room in half of an astral car. However, his mind may have transmitted information to her that defined an image of himself driving a car. Since he continued driving, some part of his subconscious mind was evidently paying attention to the road, even though his conscious attention was elsewhere. This, of course, is no surprise, since many people have become lost in reverie while driving, only to wake up later and find that they had unintentionally driven to a habitual location. In one sense, this can be seen as evidence that patterns of information processing are not necessarily accompanied by consciousness, even in cases (such as driving a car) where they could be.

Jacob's perception of Eva in her room seems to fall somewhere between accounts of remote viewing and accounts of OBEs. From his account it is not clear whether he experienced actual travel, as many OBErs do. Eva's experience of Jacob could be classed as an apparition of the living—or perhaps as a wrap-around apparition, since she seemed to be in the car.

NDEs IN THE BLIND

At first glance, visual perception in many OBEs and NDEs seems to take place from a particular point of view. It appears as though the subject is observing through a pair of non-physical eyes that float around in 3D space, looking in various directions. However, a closer examination of near death cases shows that what is actually happening is a kind of omnidirectional awareness that is much more remarkable than ordinary vision. This conclusion emerged from a study of NDEs in blind people.

The psychologist Kenneth Ring and his student Sharon Cooper undertook this study to see whether or not people who are blind report being able to see in NDEs (Ring and Cooper, 1997). This question is of particular interest regarding people who are blind from infancy, since these people generally have no idea of what it is like to see and even lack visual experiences in their dreams.

Ring and Cooper's study involved 14 people who were blind from birth, including 2 who were congenitally blind and 11 who were blinded due to the effects of oxygen administered in incubators after premature birth. He also studied 6 people with severely impaired vision and 11 who lost their vision after the age of five. (Such people are said to be adventitiously blind.) All of these subjects reported NDEs, and some also reported OBEs not involving a near death crisis.

They found that blind people do report being able to see in the out-of-body state, and the content of their NDEs does not appear to depend on whether they are blind from birth, blinded later in life, or suffering from severely impaired vision. Overall, 25 subjects in the study (80% of the total) claimed to be able to see during an NDE or OBE, and 9 out of the 14 who were blind from birth (or 64%) made this claim. Ring and Cooper concluded that

> As a whole our interviews with both NDErs and OBErs offered abundant testimony that reports of visual perception among the blind are common, and that their impressions concern both things of this world and otherworldly domains, and that they are often clear and detailed, even in narratives furnished by those who have been blind from birth (Ring and Cooper, 1997, p. 119).

One of the study's subjects was Brad Burrows, who was 33 at the time of the study and had been blind from birth. He recalled an NDE at the age of 8, while he was a student at the Boston Center for Blind Children. At that time he was suffering from severe breathing difficulties due to pneumonia. His heart stopped, and cardiopulmonary resuscitation was used to bring him back.

> Brad remembers that when he couldn't breathe any longer, he felt himself lifting up from the bed and floating through the room toward the ceiling. He saw his apparently lifeless body on the bed. He also saw his blind roommate get up from his bed and leave the room to get help. (His roommate later confirmed this.) Brad then found himself rapidly going upward through the ceilings of the building until he was above the roof. At this point he could see clearly.
> He estimates that it was between 6:30 and 7:00 in the morning when this

happened. He noticed that the sky was cloudy and dark. There had been a snowstorm the day before, and Brad could see snow everywhere except for the streets, which had been plowed, though they were still slushy. He was able to give a very detailed description of the way the snow looked. Brad could also see the snow-banks that the plows had created. He saw a street car go by. Finally, he recognized a playground used by children of his school and a particular hill he used to climb nearby (Ring and Cooper, 1997, p 113).

After this, Brad had a typical experience of passing through a tunnel into a beautiful world filled with brilliant light and celestial music. He walked through a landscape of grass and tall trees with huge leaves and entered a brightly glowing stone building, where he encountered an unknown man who emanated overwhelming love. The man touched him, and his experience reversed, leaving him back in his bed gasping for breath.

All of this imagery was unusual, since Brad was blind from birth. It is not to be expected that a habitually blind person could immediately begin to see normally, even if his vision were somehow restored. Thus Irwin, in a discussion of OBEs in the blind, observed

> Because people who surgically regain their sight take some time to learn visual identification of objects, the initial OBEs in the congenitally blind should exhibit the same property if the experience depends upon the visual pathways of the nervous system. (Irwin, 1987, p 54).

Thus if Brad actually saw what he reported, this had to be done independently of his physical nervous system.

NDEs are relatively rare, and NDEs in blind people are even more so. In studies of such rare cases, it is often difficult to corroborate a subject's testimony because key witnesses are difficult to track down. However, confirmation by an independent witness was obtained for one of this study's subjects. This was a woman who had been rendered blind by a surgeon's error during a cancer biopsy. She woke up from the surgery screaming that she was blind, and was rushed on a gurney down a hospital corridor in order to attend to her medical crisis. When the gurney banged against an elevator door, she had an OBE in which she saw two men looking at her, the father of her son and her lover. The lover clearly remembered being in the corridor and seeing her being wheeled into the elevator. The woman's medical condition was such that she should have been blind at the time (Ring and Cooper, 1997, pp. 122–23).

A skeptical assessment of NDEs is that these experiences are nothing more than imaginative pictorial reconstructions, based on a combination of sensory cues and educated guesses. But why do blind people describe visual perceptions in NDEs that are so different from what they normally experience? After all, the imagination is working all the time, and blind people always have an opportunity to try to picture their surroundings, based on auditory and tactile cues. For example, the subject named Vicki Umipeg was blinded in infancy by oxygen in an airlock incubator. She testified that she was never able to see anything at all, either when awake or in her dreams (Ring and Cooper, 1997, pp. 109, 127). Yet her NDEs featured vivid and detailed visual imagery. This included observations of her body and physical surroundings, as well as visions of a heavenly realm of light where she met friends and relatives.

Although the blind do report being able to see, a closer examination of their testimony shows that this is not seeing in the ordinary sense. Ring and Cooper argue that "seeing" by the blind in NDEs is really something even more remarkable, a kind of direct perception that may involve a combination of sensory modes (e.g. visual and tactile) while transcending the limitations of any of them. It is then called "seeing," even by the blind, due to the linguistic conventions of our sight-dominated culture. This analysis applies equally to NDEs of sighted persons.

Blind subjects did not always report their experiences as purely visual. Thus one person said,

> It wasn't visual. It's really hard to describe because it wasn't visual. It was almost like a tactile thing, except that there was no way I could have touched from up there. But it wasn't visual because I just don't have vision any more (Ring and Cooper, 1997, p. 134).

Likewise, Brad Burrows said,

> I was quite aware of all the things that were physically mentioned in there. However, whether it was seen visually through the eyes, I could not say. . . . I mean, you have to remember, being born blind, I had no idea whether those

> images were visual. . . . It was something like a tactile sense, like I could literally feel with the fingers of my mind. But I do not remember actually touching the snow. . . . The only thing I can really state about these images was that they came to me in an awareness and that I was aware of these images in a way I do not really understand (Ring and Cooper, 1997, p. 34).

A careful study of NDE testimony indicates that subjects were seeing in an omnidirectional fashion, not limited either by location or by the limited visual field of physical eyeballs. This can be seen in the following testimony by a pregnant woman who lost consciousness upon being checked into a hospital for pneumonia.

> I was hovering over a stretcher in one of the emergency rooms at the hospital. I glanced down at the stretcher, knew the body wrapped in blankets was mine, and really didn't care. The room was much more interesting than my body. And what a neat perspective. I could see everything. And I do mean everything! I could see the top of the light on the ceiling, and the underside of the stretcher. I could see the tiles on the ceiling and the tiles on the floor, simultaneously. Three hundred sixty degree spherical vision. And not just spherical. Detailed! I could see every single hair and the follicle out of which it grew on the nurse standing beside the stretcher. At the time I knew exactly how many hairs there were to look at. But I shifted focus. She was wearing glittery white nylons. Every single shimmer and sheen stood out in glowing detail, and once again I knew exactly how many sparkles there were (Ring and Cooper, p. 139).

This visual experience seems to be literally in 3D, rather than 2D. At the very least it counts as a strong hallucination, and it appears to be informed by some unknown source of sensory information. One wonders whether normal vision consists of a more limited form of visualization, restricted by the fact that the physical eyes can see only from a particular vantage point in space. This is suggested by the following experience during meditation, reported by an optometrist (not in Ring's study) with uncorrected eyesight of 20/200.

> I was meditating every day. . . . During one of these deep meditative states, I had a very profound and startling experience. Although my eyes were closed, I could suddenly see everything—the whole room and myself in it—and I couldn't tell where I was seeing from! I wasn't seeing from my eyes or from any single point of view. I seemed to be seeing from everywhere. There

seemed to be eyes in every cell of my body and in every particle surrounding me. I could simultaneously see from straight on, from above, from below, from behind, and so on . . . There seemed to be no observer separate from what was seen. There was simply awareness (Ring and Cooper, 1997, p. 139).

Ring and Cooper argue that this kind of vision cannot be attributed to the physical brain and senses. They propose instead that the out-of-body state is one in which the conscious Mind is freed from the restrictions of the physical brain and is able to perceive according to its own natural powers. They propose that this Mind is the fundamental ground of being, that it is nonlocal, that it is undivided, and that it is able to function independently of the brain (Ring and Cooper, 1997, p. 144).

Although these postulated properties of the Mind move in the right direction to explain the extraordinary nature of out-of-body vision, they unfortunately move a bit too far. If Mind were fully undivided, then we would all perceive the same thing. If it were at the same time fundamental and nonlocal, our vision would be completely unbounded and it could not be limited to the confines of a brain. Omni-vision would take in planets and galaxies, as well as hospital rooms and stockings.

We can avoid this over-extension of the seer's powers if we place two restrictions on the hypothesis of Ring and Cooper. These are, (1) universal consciousness has somehow spawned individualized conscious subunits, and (2) these subunits may be bound through perception and action to limited physical domains.

INTERRUPTING THE MIND-BRAIN CONNECTION

One can readily propose an explanation of what happens in an NDE within the framework of the virtual reality hypothesis. In a virtual reality system, the normal pathway for sense perception begins with the virtual senses of the observer-participant, and goes from there to the virtual brain. However, it does not stop here. Further processing of sense data takes place in parts of the virtual reality system that are independent of the brain, and the final data is transferred to the ultimate conscious perceiver. Additional data not deriving from the virtual senses may be incorporated into the sensory pathway, and processed data may also be cycled back into the virtual brain. I will use the term "extended mind" to refer to the section of the virtual reality system that performs this further processing for a particular individual.

In NDEs, the mind-brain link is temporarily broken and the extended mind directly generates images and other percepts, based on information taken directly from the virtual environment, from other extended minds, or from other sources of information within the virtual system. The NDE evidence suggests that this imagery may be less restricted and more vivid and detailed than imagery based on brain processing. It may even involve high resolution 3D models, which contrast strongly with the blurry, one-sided images (annotated with depth cues) that are provided by the brain and visual system.

This suggests that when the brain is in working order, the extended mind sees through it, so to speak, and is therefore subject to its limitations. This can be compared to looking through dark glasses, which limit one's ability to perceive colors.

There are other indications that the brain may act as a limiting factor in the consciousness of an individual. For example, consider the story of the musician Maurice Ravel, as related by Dr. Richard Restak. In his late fifties, Ravel experienced a progressive neurological disease, which gradually robbed him of the ability to compose music. He reached a point where he could no longer write, play, or sing music, or read a musical score. Yet he could still generate music "in his head." According to the psychologist Justine Sergent, "Ravel had become musically illiterate, not because he had lost musical knowledge or technique as such, but because he was no longer able to use this knowledge in an integrated manner in order to translate musical expression from one modality to another" (Restak, 1994, p. 162).

Restak argues that Ravel's disorder reveals a modular brain structure underlying the ability to compose music. Because certain modules were damaged, Ravel lost the power of external musical expression, even though his internal ability to create music remained intact. However, Ravel's disability may point to a deeper division in mental functions. It could be that Ravel's ability to generate music was a function of the extended mind, but his ability to express it through the physical body was dependent on brain structures. Thus, when certain brain structures became damaged, he could no longer physically express the products of his mental creativity. Another way to look at this is that the modular structure of the brain may extend beyond the brain to the "extended mind."

VISITS TO TRANSCENDENTAL REALMS

Many people undergoing NDEs report a transcendental phase of their experiences in which they perceive "universal knowledge" that they are later unable to fully remember or express in words. As one man put it, "you realize that you are suddenly in communication with absolute, total knowledge" (Ring, 1985, p. 58). This experience of ineffable, absolute knowledge is also characteristic of mystical experiences that do not involve a close brush with physical death.

For example, in the transcendental phase of her NDE, Vicki Umipeg found herself transported to a place of tremendous light which she could feel as well as see, and which was full of love. She said that, "Everybody there was made of light. And I was made of light. There was love everywhere. It was like love came from the grass, love came from the birds, love came from the trees" (Ring and Cooper, 1997, p. 111). In this state she felt flooded with knowledge of a religious nature, as well as scientific and mathematical knowledge. She pointed out that the latter was not at all in line with her educational background:

> I don't know beans about math and science. . . . I all of a sudden understood intuitively almost things about calculus, and about the way planets were made. And I don't know anything about that. . . . I felt there was nothing I didn't know (Ring and Cooper, 1997, p. 111).

In many cases, people reporting such experiences develop new interests and new levels of intuitive understanding. Yet it is certainly rare for them to actually express great knowledge that they demonstrably had not acquired through ordinary sensory channels. Perhaps these persons have actually experienced a level of awareness that they cannot express through their physical brains, just as Ravel was unable to express his music after suffering from brain damage. If so, spiritual realization may, to some degree, be a matter of training the mind and brain to express higher aspects of consciousness that are there in the individual, but cannot become manifest due to the brain's limitations.

The transcendental phase of an NDE tends to contain typical

features. A given account may not contain all of these features, but they tend to arise in case after case. These include a beautiful, celestial setting, a life review, meetings with departed friends and relatives, meetings with "beings of light," being sent back to the body, and intense regret at not being able to stay in paradise.

The theme of love and forgiveness is also a standard feature of these accounts. Thus one woman testified:

> To me the Light doesn't need a word. So if someone needs to call it Buddha or Jesus or God, I would say "yes," but for me, it was love. I knew that I was forgiven for anything and everything. I was loved and I knew that would never, ever change. Bliss is a word that doesn't even come close to describing that moment (Sharp, 1995, p. 163).

However, near death experiences do show substantial variation. According to Kimberly Clark, the experience of love, forgiveness, and knowledge is not always accompanied by an experience of light. Many such positive experiences occur in darkness (Sharp, 1995, p. 170).

Negative near death experiences also take place. These tend to be reported less often than the positive experiences, perhaps because of prejudice or fear. For example,

> While serving in Vietnam as a military policeman, Steve was nearly killed by a hand-grenade explosion. At the hospital, his heart stopped and Steve next found himself being carried away by two beings, one on either side of him, toward the gates of Hell. The walls were built from what looked like large black blocks, outlined in red light; the overall impression was of a place that absorbed light rather than giving it off. From somewhere, Steve heard a booming voice say, "This one has not yet fulfilled my purpose," and he found himself back in his body (Sharp, 1995, pp. 167–68).

It could be argued that many of the reported features of NDEs are a product of people's cultural conditioning. Cultural differences can, in fact, be seen if one turns to India and Tibet and examines NDE reports from these countries. However, the presence of cultural differences does not necessarily imply that the culture determines the content of the experience. It is also possible that different cultures impose different reporting biases, and it may even be that the NDE phenomenon itself varies in different parts of the world.

For example, in Tibet there are people called *delok*, or those who have returned from the dead. According to Sogyal Rinpoche,

> Traditionally *deloks* are people who seemingly "die" as a result of an illness, and find themselves traveling in the *bardo*. They visit the hell realms, where they witness the judgement of the dead and the sufferings of hell, and they sometimes go to paradises and buddha realms. They can be accompanied by a deity, who protects them and explains what is happening. After a week the *delok* is sent back to the body with a message from the Lord of Death for the living, urging them to spiritual practice and a beneficial way of life (Rinpoche, 1993, p. 330).

This is reminiscent of the Western near death encounters, but with greater emphasis on hellish realms. A similar emphasis can be seen in some near death cases from India. For example, in the late 1940s, an Indian man named Durga Jatav suffered for several weeks from a disease diagnosed as typhoid. At a certain point his body became cold for a couple of hours, and his family thought he had died. But he revived and told his family that he had been taken to another place by ten people. After he attempted to escape from them, they cut off his legs at the knees to prevent further attempts. Then they took him to a place where about forty or fifty people were sitting. They looked up his "papers," declared that the wrong man had been fetched, and ordered his captors to take him back. When he pointed out that his legs had been cut off, he was shown several pairs of legs and recognized his own. These were somehow reattached, and he was warned not to "stretch" his knees until they had a chance to heal.

After his revival, his sister and a neighbor both noticed that he had deep folds or fissures in the skin on the fronts of his knees, even though such marks had not been there previously. The marks were still visible in 1979, but X-rays taken in 1981 are said to have shown no abnormality beneath the surface of the skin. A photograph of the marks has been published (Stevenson, 1977, p. 78).

The story of Durga Jatav is part of a group of sixteen Indian near-death accounts collected by Satwant Pasricha and Ian Stevenson (1986). They observed that in these cases messengers typically come to take the witness, in contrast to Western NDEs, in which the witness generally meets other beings only *after* being translated to another world. Pasricha and Stevenson noted that their Indian subjects naturally identify these messengers with the Yamadutas, the agents of Yamaraja, the lord of the dead in traditional Hinduism. Yamaraja also appears in the Tibetan *delok* stories, and we even see something similar in the story of Steve, who was sent back from hell by a booming voice.

Naturally, stories of travel to other realms cannot be corroborated by mundane data. One could dismiss them as dreams, but in both their content and their transformative impact, the transcendental NDEs differ strongly from run-of-the-mill dreams. One might wonder whether or not such realms could actually exist. From the standpoint of the virtual reality hypothesis, this is certainly possible. If a computer can simulate one world, then as long as it has sufficient power it can equally well simulate another. In a virtual reality, many parallel worlds could exist, with unique qualities, laws, and prevailing conditions.

One strong implication of the transcendental NDEs is that consciousness is capable of operating on a higher platform of cognition than we experience in run of the mill earthly existence. People reporting these experiences speak of extraordinary levels of knowledge, wisdom, and love, accompanied by telepathic modes of communication that are far more powerful than ordinary speech. In the virtual reality model, experience depends both on the sensory data provided by the virtual world and the power of consciousness to apprehend it. One may therefore wonder how great the potential power of consciousness really is.

SURVIVAL OF DEATH

If conscious life can continue while the brain is temporarily out of commission, it is natural to ask what will happen when the body actually dies. This cannot be directly revealed by near death experiences, which necessarily involve people who lived to tell their stories. There are, however, cases where the subject of an NDE was very close to death, indeed. For example, Michael Sabom reports the case of a woman who underwent a delicate operation for the ablation of an aneurism of the brain (Sabom, 1998). In preparation for the operation, her entire body was chilled (hypothermia) and her blood was temporarily removed. Ian Stevenson comments that "She was as dead as anyone could possibly be unless they were 'really dead'" (Stevenson, 2000). Yet she later reported events of the operation, including details she was highly unlikely to have learned about through normal means.

Apart from NDEs, there are two main sources of empirical evidence suggesting that some aspect of the living personality may survive physical death. These are (1) memories of previous lives reported by living people and (2) testimony from purported spirits. Alleged testimony from spirits is generally transmitted either through apparitions or through channeling via spirit mediums. In the latter case, a medium appears to communicate with departed spirits on behalf of a "sitter," who is typically seeking contact with a deceased friend or relative.

The psychologist Gary Schwartz (2002) has conducted a number of experimental studies of spirit mediums, in which he tried to rigorously exclude the possibility that the mediums used normal sources of information to learn about deceased persons. He reports that mediums were in many cases able to report large amounts of accurate, detailed information about the departed, even though they did not have voice or visual contact with the sitters or know their identities. He maintains that objective methods of tabulating data eliminate the possibility that these positive results could be due to selective memory on the part of the sitters (remembering hits while forgetting misses), vague information (that could apply to anyone), and lucky guesses. If we grant the integrity of the investigators, it would seem that these results can be explained only by communication with the dead or by some form of paranormal information transfer not involving the dead.

The latter possibility is often called the "super-psi" or "super-esp" hypothesis. Schwartz concedes that such an explanation is not entirely ruled out by his data, but he observes that the "spirit communicators" contacted by mediums seem to behave like persons and not like paranormal databases or communication channels. The same argument can be applied to some apparitions. For example, Raymond Moody was impressed by the vision of his deceased grandmother because of her unmistakable personal presence (see the preceding chapter). Perhaps one could formulate a kind of Turing test for apparitions and spirit communicators: If it acts convincingly like a person, perhaps it is a person.

Apparitional or channeled communications are at their most impressive when they provide evidence of habits or skills that the witness or medium does not possess. For example, suppose that Madame A begins to speak a language that she has never learned. One can argue that this would be impossible if she had simply downloaded the grammar and vocabulary of that language from some normal or paranormal source. Practice is required to master a language, and so one can infer that she must be speaking under the control of someone who knows how to speak the language in question. In fact, there have been cases in which a person conversed at length in a language he or she never had an opportunity to learn. This is known as responsive xenoglossy.

One example is the case of Uttara Huddar, studied by Ian Stevenson, Satwant Pasricha, and others (Stevenson and Pasricha, 1980, Pasricha, 1990). Uttara was an Indian woman who spoke Marathi and English and had studied Sanskrit, but who had no knowledge of Bengali. (Bengali, Marathi, and Sanskrit are related to one another in much the same way as Spanish, French, and Latin.) Yet at the age of 33, she suddenly began to exhibit a personality named Sharada who spoke fluent Bengali and differed in habits and predilections from Uttara's normal self. Sharada remained "in control" for several weeks, and reappeared a number of times thereafter for periods ranging from one day to seven weeks. Unlike Uttara, Sharada seemed unacquainted with modern life, and again unlike Uttara, she devoted a great deal of her time to religious practices. It can be argued that Uttara was overshadowed or possessed by the discarnate personality of a lady who had lived in Bengal at an earlier period. Or one might suppose that she herself had once lived in Bengal and that she sometimes reverted mentally to that life, which was still part of her subconscious mind.

The virtual reality model allows for the survival of bodily death. It treats a living being as consciousness linked via the extended mind to a virtual body. Eliminate the virtual body, and one is left with the extended mind (treated in this model as software) and consciousness. One could suppose that consciousness continues to perceive through the extended mind, using the kind of higher sensory facilities indicated in NDEs. One could also suppose that the same extended mind might link up with the extended mind of a living person and influence that person's (virtual) brain. It is easy to see how this could be done on the level of software.

The question remains: Does survival of physical death actually take place, and if so, what is it like? Many scenarios are clearly possible. Survival could be active, or it might involve a state of suspended animation. It could involve complete or incomplete retention of memory. It could involve a sustained increase in wisdom and scope of consciousness, or it might entail an eventual restriction or degradation of one's mental condition. It might also involve a process of transmigration, in which the extended mind is once again linked to a newly developed virtual brain.

REBIRTH

It is remarkable that there is a great deal of empirical evidence suggesting that some form of transmigration may actually take place. The psychiatrist Ian Stevenson has studied literally thousands of cases in which a young child seems to spontaneously remember a previous life, without having had the opportunity to learn about that life by ordinary means of communication. Most of these cases involve a child who, on first learning to speak, spontaneously begins talking about a previous life.

In a typical case, the apparent previous existence took place near the child's home, and the child's parents were able to make contact with the family of the previous personality. Investigators, including Stevenson himself, subsequently found out about the case and interviewed the child and the other relevant witnesses. The strength of the case as evidence of rebirth depends on the ability of the investigators to carefully conduct the interviews and sort out genuine memories from distortions and confabulations.

In some cases, an investigator was able to learn about a child who described a previous life before any contact was made with the family of the alleged previous personality. The investigator was sometimes able to independently track down this family, based on the child's testimony. This eliminates one of the most serious drawbacks of these cases, namely the possibility that the child's testimony has been contaminated by contact with his or her so-called previous family.

For example, in Sri Lanka a three-year-old child named Thusita Silva began to describe a previous life in which she had lived near a river in a town called Kataragama. She stated that a dumb boy had pushed her into a river, and that her father had a boutique for selling flowers near the Kira Vehera, a Buddhist stupa. Based on these statements and others, the investigator Tissa Jayawardena went to Kataragama and found that out of about twenty flower stalls near the Kira Vehera, there was one in which a daughter of the family had drowned some years earlier while playing with a dumb brother. According to Jayawardena, "Thusita had made thirteen verifiable statements and all but three of these were correct for the family with the dumb child who had lost a girl from drowning" (Stevenson and Samaratne, 1988, p. 222). Thusita's parents lived about 220 kilometers away from Kataragama, and they had no knowledge of this family.

Most of Stevenson's cases come from parts of the world where people believe in reincarnation, and this might be taken to imply that the stories are made up on the basis of strongly held beliefs. However, this would not account for the detailed evidence which is found in many of the cases. An alternative interpretation, favored by Stevenson, is that belief in reincarnation tends to facilitate memories of past lives, while disbelief tends to encourage suppression of such memories. One can see that parents who disbelieved in reincarnation could easily discourage a young child from talking about memories of a past life.

Stevenson has gathered evidence showing that skills, interests, phobias, and other personality traits tend to show continuity from one life to another. He has also studied cases in which the child has birthmarks or birth defects corresponding to wounds causing death in the previous personality (Stevenson, 1997). The latter are of particular interest to this study, since they seem to involve the transmission of mental images from one body to another.

In a typical case, a wound causing death in the remembered previous personality can be shown to correspond closely with a birthmark or birth defect in the child reporting the memories. I will not try to review the evidence that Stevenson gives for this, since his opus on this subject covers over 2,000 pages. However, I will discuss some of his ideas on how mental images may affect the body.

Stevenson presents several lines of evidence indicating that an image held in the mind can produce detailed anatomical changes in the body corresponding in shape and position to the mental image. These include stigmata of the wounds of Christ, stigmata and other skin effects induced by suggestion, recurrence of bodily changes caused by memories of traumas, paranormally induced skin patterns, and birthmarks or defects associated with maternal impressions during pregnancy (Stevenson, 1997, pp. 33–175).

The case of Durga Jatav mentioned above is an example of a case where a remembered trauma had an apparent physical effect (whether the trauma occurred in a dream or an actual out-of-body state). Another striking case involved a patient who remembered an incident in which his arms had been painfully tied behind his back with ropes nine years previously (Stevenson, 1997, pp. 71–72). At the time of the memory, his arms developed deep wheals resembling rope marks with a little subcutaneous bleeding. The wheals lasted for two days, but again developed later on when the patent was encouraged to relive his memories by a physician. A photograph (Figure 16) shows that the wheals vividly resembled four sets of multiple rope marks, including finer indentations representing the strands of which the original ropes were made (Stevenson, 1997, p. 72).

How were these impressions produced? Even if we suppose that a detailed image of the ropes was encoded in the subject's brain, it is hard to see how the epithelial cells on his arm were instructed to move and transform in such a way as to create the rope marks. Goose bumps can be induced by the action of peripheral nerves, but these do not form detailed patterns, and there is no reason to think that these nerves can send selective messages to different cells. The marks were depressed, even though no actual ropes were present, and thus the skin cells had to be instructed to move as though pressure were being applied to them. In effect, the rope marks were simulated by some unknown process. One wonders if this is simply part of the larger simulation posited in the virtual reality model.

The case of Olga Kahl provides another striking example of bodily branding by mental images. Kahl is said to have been "one of the most talented sensitives who ever lived and certainly one of the most gifted who agreed to work with scientists" (Stevenson, 1997, p. 94). In one series of experiments, she would ask an investigator to think of a name

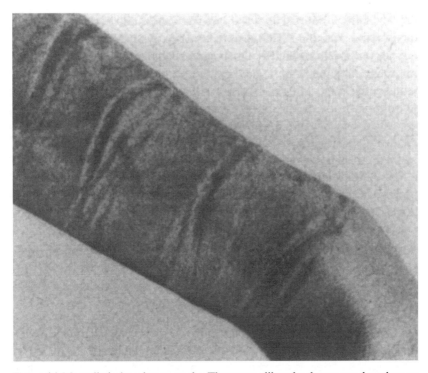

Figure 16. Mentally induced rope marks. These rope-like wheals appeared on the arm of a patient after he relived an episode nine years before, in which his arms were painfully tied behind his back.

and write it on a slip of paper while out of her sight. She would touch the paper without unfolding it and ask the investigator (or a person acting as sender) to concentrate on the name. It is said that within about fifteen seconds to a minute, letters spelling out the name would appear in the form of red lines on her forearm or upper chest. In some cases only part of the name appeared, as when she produced "Fran" for "Francois" (Stevenson, 1997, pp. 96–97).

THE PSYCHOPHORE

Stevenson used examples like these to argue that mental images based on bodily wounds at death could be transferred to a developing fetus in the process of transmigration and there produce birthmarks of corresponding shape and position. He proposed that memories of the previous personality are carried to the new body by a vehicle that he calls the *psychophore* or "soul bearer." This vehicle is made of some unknown substance, and it has the three-dimensional form of the previous body. According to Stevenson, this allows it to act as a template to impose bodily patterns onto the developing fetus.

Since the body of a fetus does not have the same size or proportions as an adult body, it follows that the psychophore of an adult would have to scale itself down proportionately in order to act as a one-to-one template for a fetus. This suggests that the psychophore may not be a literal 3D shape, and we note that in a virtual reality, a psychophore representing a three-dimensional shape would not necessarily have to exist as an object in the three-dimensional virtual space.

Stevenson uses cases of collectively witnessed apparitions to argue in favor of a three-dimensional psychophore. The idea is that the psychophore of a deceased person may become physically manifest in a given position. By reflecting light, several witnesses can then see it from different viewpoints as a physical object. I have argued in Chapter 7 that apparitions might in some cases be introduced into the virtual 3D continuum in this way. However, apparitions are generally clothed, and we wouldn't expect the psychophore to include ghostly clothing. Thus multiply-witnessed objects seem to involve features which are first generated on a mental level and not in literal (i.e. virtual) 3D space.

Of course, not all apparitions are necessarily manifested in the same way. Some, such as apparitions of the living may take place on a purely mental level. Apparitions of the living would presumably not involve the psychophore, unless this vehicle is what travels in out-of-body experiences. They might involve projection of a mental image, either into the virtual brain or into virtual 3D space.

THE POPULATION PROBLEM

One common objection to the theory of reincarnation is that, since the human population of the earth is increasing, not everyone can be the reincarnation of someone who lived on the earth previously (Almeder, 1997, pp. 513–15). This is related to the problem of origins. No matter how we define the first humans on earth, they clearly could not have been reincarnations of previous humans on earth. One response to this is to suppose that the mind and consciousness of some people do not antedate their birth (or gestation). This is one possibility, and it requires the ongoing creation or differentiation of conscious entities suitable for human life. This theory works well if we assume that consciousness can be identified with material brain structure. However, we are faced with a more difficult problem of origins if we distinguish between consciousness and matter.

The usual answer to the population and origins problems is that there must be a reservoir of sentient beings capable of bodily incarnation, and only some of these are linked to human bodies. Others may be linked to other types of bodies, or they may exist in a disembodied state. Of course, this gives rise to the question of how the beings in the reservoir originated in the first place.

In the virtual reality model, sentient beings consist of individualized consciousness linked to the interface apparatus I have described using the software metaphor. To explain the origin of this complex system is a tall order, but the first question to address is whether or not it exists. My thesis is that the virtual reality model can readily explain the various anomalous phenomena discussed in Chapters 6 through 10. I therefore hypothesize that the entities making up this model— or entities analogous to them—do exist. I return to the question of origins in Chapter 11.

LIFE BETWEEN INCARNATIONS

If death is followed by rebirth, the question arises of what happens in the intervening period. Stevenson's cases do not shed much light on the issue of life between incarnations. He does mention one case where an Indian boy named Jasbir apparently died of smallpox at the age of three, but then revived. Jasbir is said to have undergone a pronounced change of personality after his recovery. At that point he began to speak of a previous life as a man named Sobha Ram, who was duly identified and who had died at about the time of Jasbir's apparent death.

This could be taken to mean that the Sobha Ram personality occupied the dead body of Jasbir and revived it. In fact, Jasbir stated that "after death he (as Sobha Ram) met a Sadhu (a holy man or saint) who advised him to 'take cover' in the body of Jasbir, son of Giridhari Lal Jat" (Stevenson, 1966, p. 48). The inference is that conscious inter-personal activity continues between lives, but direct memories of such activity seem to be very rare, and it is also difficult to see how such memories could be verified.

Studies based on hypnotic regression have generated a great deal of material dealing with reincarnation and the state between incarna-tions. Unfortunately, hypnosis is notorious for generating confabula-tions and false memories, and this problem must be carefully consid-ered when addressing data produced by hypnotic regression. In some cases, however, hypnosis may convey useful information about past lives.

Consider the case of a young woman named Catherine, who was hypnotized by the psychiatrist Brian Weiss in the course of psycho-therapy (Weiss, 1988). In the hypnotized state, Catherine gave detailed accounts of many past lives, and she also described intermediate phases of existence between lives. It is difficult to say whether or not any of her past life memories are genuine, since it has not proven possible to verify them. They spanned a wide range of times and places from ancient Egypt to England in the days of sailing ships. One point in favor of their authenticity is that, as in Stevenson's cases, Catherine's past lives all involved humble circumstances, including poverty and even servitude. Thus they were by no means complimentary to her ego. Also, Dr. Weiss did not believe in reincarnation when he began hypnotherapy with Catherine, thus it can be argued that he did not initially induce her to concoct fanciful past lives by asking leading questions.

To Weiss, the most interesting feature of Catherine's story is that she would repeatedly describe intermediate states between incarna-tions that resemble the states reported in NDEs. Thus at the end of one past life account she said,

> I have left my body. I see a wonderful light. . . . There are people coming to help me. Wonderful people. . . . The soul . . . finds peace here. You leave all bodily pains behind you. Your soul is peaceful and serene. . . . The light is so brilliant! Everything comes from the light! Energy comes from this light. . . . (Weiss, 1988, pp. 82–83).

Catherine spoke of personalities called "Masters" who lived in the intermediate realm and provided wise advice to incarnating souls. Her testimony paints an overall picture of repeated rebirth as a learning process, a school of hard knocks in which souls gradually progress to higher spiritual destinations.

Judging from the number of popular books supporting this picture, it seems to be imbedded in the subconscious minds of many people. For example, Michael Newton has obtained many accounts of life between births through the use of hypnosis (Newton, 2000, 2002). These stories strongly support the idea that souls repeatedly incarnate in order to mature in spiritual knowledge. The stories elicited by Newton are strikingly consistent, and this suggests that they may partly result from the interaction between hypnotist and hypnotic subject. As direct evidence of life between births, their value is limited. However, they do show that many people have the idea of a school of repeated births.

9

STRANGE ENERGIES

"The world is not to be narrowed
till it will go into the understanding . . . ,
but the understanding to be expanded
and opened till it can take in
the image of the world as it is in fact."

—Sir Francis Bacon

In Chapters 6–8, the main emphasis has been on perception and communication. I have discussed extraordinary modes of awareness which seem to require sensory channels beyond those provided by the brain and nervous system. In a virtual reality model, these channels can be readily included in the interface software linking the virtual brain to the conscious perceiver.

This software must generate feedback affecting the virtual world itself. Thus in some cases, it appears that mental images can affect the body in ways that do not fully depend on the nervous system. Examples are stigmata and birth marks connected with possible past lives. In other cases, witnesses report imagery based on events that occur when their brains are apparently not functional—however, these events must later be recorded in the brain to generate the reports. In yet others, such as apparitions with multiple witnesses, it is unclear whether reported imagery originates in the mind or in the external world. Although feedback of images into the virtual world may be carried out by taking advantage of exponential amplification, the required feedback is so extensive and complex that this hypothesis becomes strained.

In a VR model, the imagery generated by the extended mind is ontologically similar to the imagery defining the virtual world. Both, of course, are simply software in such a model, but their similarity does not stop there. We have seen that the mind can generate realistic

3D models, and experience in the field of computer graphics suggests that this requires realistic physical modeling. Thus, realistic mental images may operate according to the laws of physics or similar laws.

At least for some images, the distinction between mental and physical is blurred, and the possibility is opened up that events in the virtual world may be directly and profoundly influenced by processes related to the extended mind and consciousness. This idea has radical consequences, but it seems to be backed up by abundant empirical data. It is now time for us to come face to face with some of this data.

POLTERGEISTS

One category of anomalous data is given by the so-called poltergeist cases, in which mysterious disturbances occur spontaneously in some household or place of business. The disturbances typically involve inexplicable sounds and raps, spontaneous movements of objects, unexplained fires, and, rarely, apparitions. Small objects are often said to fly through the air in unusual trajectories, and there may be "showers of stones" that mysteriously appear in rooms. Perhaps the most anomalous feature of poltergeist cases is that objects are often reported to appear or disappear, apparently without crossing space in the ordinary way.

Old tradition would attribute such phenomena to a "noisy ghost," or "poltergeist" in German. But modern parapsychologists have largely rejected the idea of literal ghosts, and they have preferred to replace poltergeist by the neutral term, "remote spontaneous psychokinesis," or RSPK. Poltergeist cases generally seem to revolve around a target person, who is the center of the disturbances. This person is now often called the "RSPK agent," on the hypothesis that he or she is responsible for the phenomena—either through normal or paranormal means.

The RSPK agent is often a child or adolescent who may suffer from emotional disturbance or poor health. The parapsychologist William Roll reported that in a set of 92 RSPK agents, 49 appeared to have serious medical or psychological problems. Of these, 22 suffered from seizures or were prone to dissociative states. Others suffered from lameness, dwarfed stature, terminal illness, kidney disease, hysteria, recurrent nightmares, somnambulism, neurasthenia, schizophrenia, nervous collapse, alcoholism, and rickets. In addition, some of these agents were children afflicted with hyperactivity, mental retardation, behavioral disorders, and tuberculosis.

An obvious explanation for RSPK cases is that the agents produce the seemingly paranormal effects by trickery. Such trickery has, indeed, been detected in many cases, but it is usually on a simple level appropriate for children. For example, a child or adolescent may surreptitiously throw stones or push furniture while no one is looking. It seems doubtful that these cases are often due to deceits practiced by skilled conjurors, although conjurors may be involved in some instances. On a statistical basis, it seems unlikely that skill in conjuring will be associated with childhood or with physical and psychological ill health. It also seems unlikely that skilled adult conjurors will often be motivated to fake paranormal effects in the vicinity of sick or disturbed children.

Quite violent movements of furniture and other large objects are frequently reported in poltergeist cases. For example, one case of RSPK in 1960 involved an 11-year-old girl in Sauchie, Scotland, named Virginia Campbell. She was visited by the Rev. T. W. Lund of Sauchie after unexplained knockings had occurred in her room for two days. Mr. Lund found Virginia lying in bed in a room filled with curious family members and neighbors. Loud knocking appeared to emanate from the bed-head, even though Virginia was not in a position to strike the bed-frame with her head or limbs. Lund reported that a 50-pound linen chest standing near the bed began rocking spasmodically and unevenly rising from the floor. Then it shifted sideways "with a jerky kind of motion through a distance of about 18 inches and back again" (Roll, 1977, p. 386).

Another RSPK case centered around an adult kitchen maid in a nursing home in Malvern, England. Miss Julia Clancey and four other witnesses signed the following statement:

> On the last week of January 1942, about 2:30 p.m. in good light, we, the undersigned, were present in the kitchen of Clarence Nursing Home, Graham Road, Malvern, Worcs. While we were all facing the kitchen range, the poker, suspended from a nail at the side of the range, detached itself from the nail, and passed over the suspended electric lamp. It struck the kitchen table point downwards near to Mrs. Collins, and made a clearly visible dent in the top of the table. It then fell down to the floor (Gauld, 1979, p. 261).

Conceivably, observations such as these could be due to misperception, accompanied by trickery. For example, while no one else was looking, someone may have grabbed the poker and tossed it into the air. The witnesses' attention was grabbed by the clatter of the poker as it fell on the table, and they simply imagined that they saw it fly up from the range. Their misperception may have been reinforced by agitated conversation after the event, in which they all became convinced they had really seen the poker take off on its own.

Studies of eyewitness testimony have shown that witnesses make many errors of perception and memory, and these findings are relevant to the evaluation of testimony in courts of law. The false memory syndrome, in particular, has recently been the center of a great deal of controversy. Psychologists have been accused of inducing people to falsely remember childhood sexual abuse, and these accusations have been based on a model of human memory as an imperfect and malleable process of reconstruction (Ofshe and Watters, 1993). There is much evidence that tends to support this model.

However, it is also a fact that people observe and remember many things correctly, and the day-to-day conduct of human affairs would be impossible without this. In addition, Ian Stevenson has given examples demonstrating that people may retain good memory of paranormal experiences over several years (Stevenson, 1971).

Poltergeist cases have been reported in all parts of America and Europe for at least four hundred years (Roll, 1977, pp. 383–84), and they are probably a worldwide phenomenon. It seems doubtful that people would repeatedly report spontaneous movements of large objects if such events actually never happen. One can always attribute such reports to malobservation, but to do this simply because the reported events seem impossible is certainly not scientific.

It could be argued that some people are motivated to see paranormal marvels, and therefore they are prone to imaginatively reconstruct them from their imperfect sense perceptions. However, witnesses of these events are not necessarily "true believers" of the paranormal. Stevenson reports that "many subjects also insist that prior to their experiences they had no settled convictions or knowledge about the experiences which parapsychology studies" (Stevenson, 1971, p. 111). It might, therefore, be worthwhile to see whether or not poltergeist phenomena display any lawful regularities that might tell us something about the workings of nature.

A CASE IN WALES

The psychologist David Fontana has reported on a poltergeist case in Wales that may illustrate some significant regularities of this kind (Fontana, 1991, 1992). The setting of the case is a small mechanical engineering repair shop located in a suburban shopping area in South Wales. The main witnesses were the proprietor of the shop, two men who worked for him, his wife, his wife's brother, and her brother's wife. Fontana characterized them as practical business people who were honest and reliable witnesses, and he pointed out that only one of them reported having any previous psychic experiences.

The reported phenomena consisted mainly of the inexplicable movement of small objects such as stones and coins, which would fly through the air and bang against walls, people, and objects in the rooms making up the shop. Large objects, such as planks of wood, were sometimes said to have been thrown with considerable violence. An apparition of a small boy was seen three times by one of the witnesses and was twice accompanied by the arrival of flying objects (Fontana, 1992). Frequent phone calls were also reported, in which the phone would be dead on answering or strange noises would be heard. There was no apparent target person in this case, and the witnesses all observed the strange phenomena either alone or in various combinations. The phenomena took place regularly during a period of over two years.

Fontana reported that he personally witnessed some of the phenomena, both in the presence of the other witnesses and when he was alone in the shop. He observed that if he or one of the other witnesses threw a stone into the "active corner" from which many phenomena seemed to emanate, then a stone would seem to be thrown back in return. It seemed as though an intelligent agency was reciprocating, and this impression was reinforced by other phenomena that appeared to occur in response to spoken comments. For example, Fontana notes that after the poltergeist was invited to "bring a pen," a pen seemed to mysteriously appear in a place that he had previously seen to be clear (Fontana, 1991, p. 394).

APPORTS

The appearance of the pen illustrates a curious phenomenon that has been reported in many poltergeist cases. This is the sudden appearance of objects within closed areas or their disappearance from those areas. These are generally called "apports," and their apparent paranormal transportation is called "teleportation." Another example is the report by one of the witnesses that stones were thrown at her while she was inside a closed toilet with the door locked on the inside. Yet another is the mysterious appearance of various keys. "These would appear in positions on a work-bench which moments before had been seen to be clear. The majority of the keys were of unknown origin" (Fontana, 1991, p. 393).

In one instance, an outside witness claimed that he saw 12 small engineering bolts fall from the ceiling when he was alone in the shop. Fontana relates that "From his position behind the counter he saw them, some 12 feet away and in his direct line of vision and in good light, apparently 'materialize' just below the ceiling, then fall normally to the floor" (Fontana, 1991, p. 393). Fontana characterized the witness as a reliable person who had recently retired from a responsible position.

Individually, mysterious appearances and disappearances can easily be put down to misperception. However, when they are consistently mentioned in case after case, they suggest that something real might be happening. In ordinary life, small objects are sometimes unexpectedly lost or found. But this does not seem to occur with the high frequency reported in RSPK cases, such as this one.

Many of the phenomena attributed to poltergeists are strongly in violation of the known laws of physics, and this is particularly true of apports. At first glance, it would seem that an apported object has been created out of nothing, thus drastically violating the principle of conservation of energy. On closer examination, one sees that the appearing objects were already in existence and were simply moved from one location to another, apparently without passing through the intervening space. This is not as bad as creation of matter, but it is nearly so.

The phenomenon of apports clearly calls for new physics, but this should not disturb us if we consider the revolutions in physics that have taken place in the 20th century. We are not in a position to define this new physics, but we can observe that apports seem to be connected with some intelligent agency. This agency is somehow able to modify an object so that it retains its shape, but is able to move without interacting with its surroundings.

HIGHER-DIMENSIONAL MOVEMENT?

An idea along these lines was introduced by the 19th-century German physicist, Johann Zöllner, who proposed that apports could be explained if objects could be moved in a fourth spatial dimension. The points defining a 3D object normally have three coordinates, x, y, and z. Suppose for the sake of argument, that we add a fourth coordinate, w, and we postulate that points can interact (or exert forces on one another) only if their w values are nearly the same. Suppose that the w coordinates of the points making up an object shift slightly, while their x, y, z coordinates remain the same. The object will then cease to interact with other objects that have not undergone a w shift, but it will retain the same 3D shape. It can then be moved to a new location in 3D space, and its w coordinates can be restored to their original values. It will seem that the object disappeared at one location and reappeared at another. If we assume a gradual change in interaction as w is shifted, we may be able to model the displacement of air that is implied by this kind of dimensional shift.

Zöllner proposed a number of interesting tests to verify this hypothesis, and he reported positive results, including the tying of knots in unbroken loops of cord (Zöllner, 1976, pp. 41–42). Unfortunately, however, he took the assistance of a notorious medium named Henry Slade and his findings were cast into doubt by bad association.

Nonetheless, similar phenomena continue to be reported. For example, the psychiatrist and psychical researcher Berthold Schwarz has recently reported on a number of experiments involving the linking of unbroken rings made of different substances. One series of experiments involved Joe A. Nuzum, a 32-year-old martial arts instructor and former foundry worker, who had developed a reputation for producing paranormal physical phenomena.

Schwarz gives the following account of a late-night session in July 1992, in his research room in Vero Beach, Florida. Nuzum was present, monitored by Schwarz and three television cameras. While Nuzum was in a trance-like state, a brass key spontaneously bent and a Ford automobile key linked through its hole to a ring on Nuzum's right fifth finger. At the same time, a fragment of the key's shaft broke off (Schwarz, 1994, p. 97).

Nuzum declared "This is killin' me," and the linked ring and key were removed from his hand with detergent. Schwarz reports that he took the linked ring and key to show his wife and, next morning, he placed them on top of a file cabinet in his office. That evening, he was shocked to find that the rings had unlinked. According to Schwarz's report, the ring and the key's hole (which is topologically another ring) were undamaged. At face value, we therefore have a case of matter passing through matter—a candidate for explanation by a dimensional shift. But unfortunately, the evidence in the form of linked objects did not persist for further study.

Schwarz reports that two rubber bands of different colors also linked during the same session, and these did remain linked indefinitely. They were inspected visually and with X-rays by Dr. Ruggieri of the Cleveland Foundation, and he found no evidence of cutting and splicing (Schwarz, 1994, p. 98). The question here is: Is there any way to mend a broken rubber band so that it seems unbroken under careful inspection?

On another occasion, Nuzum's wife videotaped the linking of a brass nut with a gold fraternity ring provided by Berthold Schwarz. This took place while the entranced Nuzum held the objects with his fingertips. Ray, a retired policeman, witnessed the action and remarked, "I examined them, the solid nut and ring . . . no way they should be linked together and yet they are" (Schwarz, 1994, p. 98). These items later unlinked, but they remained solid and unbroken. (This is reminiscent of the fairy gold of old tradition that later turns to ashes.)

These paranormal effects are backed up by photographs and videotapes, but it can always be argued that these could be faked. The value of Schwarz's report depends on his own integrity and on his ability to evaluate the honesty of people such as Joe Nuzum. As always, we can either consider that the reported phenomena may be real, or we can suppose some undetected hoax or delusion must be involved.

BACK TO PHYSICS

To account for apports, it is not enough to simply add a fourth coordinate of space to the familiar three. If such a coordinate existed, all objects would continually tend to drift off into another dimension. However, physicists have seriously considered theories that add extra dimensions to space, and they have devised ways of avoiding this problem. As they stand, these theories cannot accommodate Zöllner's alleged dimensional shift, but we will take a brief look at them, since they show the unanticipated ways in which physics can change.

The story begins with the famous Kaluza-Klein theory. In April of 1919, Albert Einstein received a letter from Theodor Kaluza, an obscure mathematician from the University of Konigsberg in Germany (Kaku, 1994, pp. 99–100). Kaluza presented a unified theory of gravity and electromagnetism based on the addition of an extra dimension of space to the four-dimensional space-time of Einstein's existing theory of general relativity. Thus, Kaluza's theory had four dimensions of space and one dimension of time.

When Kaluza wrote down Einstein's field equations in five-dimensional space-time, Einstein's original theory dropped out, along with Maxwell's equations of electromagnetism. Einstein's theory had explained gravity as a warping of four-dimensional space-time, and Kaluza's theory now explained light as a warping of five-dimensional space-time. Thus in one elegant stroke, Kaluza had unified gravity and electromagnetism. The only problem was that experience shows space to have three dimensions, not four.

Kaluza's solution to this problem was to propose that the extra spatial dimension was rolled up in a tiny circle so small that it could not be measured. In 1926, Oscar Klein calculated on the basis of quantum mechanics that the size of this circle should be 10^{-33} centimeters. This is the famous Planck length, which is 100 billion billion times smaller than an electron (Kaku, 1994, p. 106).

To see how this works, consider a hypothetical one-dimensional world inhabited by one-dimensional beings. If we add a second dimension to this world and roll it up in a circle, the world becomes a long, thin tube. If the radius of the tube is small enough, then it is indistinguishable from a one-dimensional line.

In recent years, the Kaluza-Klein theory has been generalized to the so-called superstring theories, with several (perhaps six) extra dimensions, all rolled up into a tiny compact space (Greene, 1999). The extra dimensions allow for the unified treatment of additional physical forces, and the rolling up explains why we don't see them. The proponents of these theories are hoping to formulate an ultimate "theory of everything" or TOE. However, this may be premature, especially if we consider the many anomalous phenomena that are reported in connection with consciousness.

Unfortunately, the rolled-up dimensions of the new theories cannot accommodate apports and interlinking of rings, since they were intended in the first place to keep space effectively three-dimensional. However, there may be other ways of reconciling an inherently multidimensional space with the three dimensions of ordinary experience. For example, the physicist Ronald Bryan has proposed that the extra dimensions needed to unify the forces of physics may extend to infinity. He speculates that "What keeps quarks and leptons (and us) from drifting off into the higher dimensions may be a local 'well' in space (a soliton) generated by the particles' field equations" (Bryan, 2000). A first stab at a theory of apports might involve intelligent manipulation of this well.

FALLING INTO MAYA

The paranormal researchers Don Elkins and Carla Rueckert related the following anecdote, which reveals the traditional Eastern understanding of apports:

> Baba Ram Dass, formerly Dr. Richard Alpert of the Dept. of Psychology at Harvard University, met Sai Baba in India and was given a small medallion by that guru. Sai Baba held out his hand, a glow appeared in his palm, and the glow slowly solidified into the medallion. Dr. Alpert was amazed and commented to one of Sai Baba's associates on this miracle of creation. "Oh don't be silly, he didn't create that," replied the devotee. "He has a whole warehouse full of those things. He just transported it here mentally" (Elkins and Rueckert, 1977, p. 23).

Elkins remarked that, "Sai Baba's own attitude toward this sort of thing is that all is illusion, or *maya*" (Elkins and Rueckert, 1977, p. 23). I may note that Sai Baba is famous for materializing objects, but he has also been accused of faking such materializations by sleight of hand. He may well be guilty of doing both. It is interesting to note that the Sanskrit word *maya* refers to the illusions created by magicians as well as to the idea that material existence is illusory.

I should also observe that although the virtual reality model does describe the physical world as illusion, it does not dismiss that illusion as a mere nothing, as the term *maya* may sometimes be thought to imply. As both magicians and computer artists know, it takes hard work to make a good illusion.

AN INDIAN POLTERGEIST

It is often possible to obtain a fresh perspective on anomalous phenomena by looking at cases occurring outside of the sphere of modern Western thinking. For example, here is a poltergeist case from India that was reported by the psychiatrist and parapsychologist Ian Stevenson (1972). This case involves apports, and it also illustrates some traditional Indian views regarding the paranormal.

It seems that a woman named Radhika from the village of Degaon, south of Mumbai (Bombay), had the reputation among her neighbors of being a sorceress. Mysterious disappearances of food were noted in the village, and people found that the missing food was turning up in Radhika's dwelling. They took it that she was stealing food by mystical means, and offered to provide her with food if she would stop.

Stevenson's informant, one Swami Krishnanand, decided to put Radhika's abilities to the test. In one instance, "Swami Krishnanand ... pointed to a *lota* [a small container] which he held in his hand and to a man who was milking a cow some distance away, and asked to have some of the milk put into the *lota*. Instantly the *lota* became filled with milk and at the same time the milker noticed that his own vessel had less, rather than more, milk in it. He looked up astonished" (Stevenson, 1972, p. 243).

On another occasion, Krishnanand asked Radhika to bring him some *puran puris* (a sweet, breadlike food) that were being cooked in a neighboring house about 100 feet away. "He then heard her mutter a few words and almost immediately saw two *puran puris* come flying through the air and land at his feet" (Stevenson, 1972, p. 242). This was first done outside his hut, and then in its interior, which the *puris* could reach only by following a torturous flight plan.

Radhika believed that these effects were due to a discarnate spirit that was allied with her, and Stevenson was inclined to favor this interpretation. In general, poltergeist reports coming from non-Western cultures tend to attribute reported paranormal effects to some kind of spirit being. Stevenson argued that, in some cases, it is more reasonable to interpret poltergeist effects in this way than it is to suppose that they are produced entirely by a living human agent. This would mean that the traditional term poltergeist might be more appropriate in some cases that the term RSPK, favored by parapsychologists. In non-Western cultures, it is also frequently assumed that when spirit beings trouble living people, they may be engaged in this activity by some other living person. This, of course, is commonly known as malefic witchcraft or sorcery, and it is a source of fear in many societies.

EUROPEAN WITCHCRAFT

Belief in witchcraft was widespread in Europe in the period from the late Middle Ages up to the scientific Enlightenment in the 18th century. For example, in 1682 a book entitled *Saducismus Triumphatus* was published in England by Joseph Glanvil, Chaplain in Ordinary to his Majesty and Fellow of the Royal Society (Glanvil, 1682). Glanvil defended the medieval Christian view of witchcraft, and he presented several case histories in an effort to show that witchcraft is real. His aim was to counter the views of people, called Saducees, who denied the existence of spirits.

One of his cases dealt with disturbances in the house of Mr. John Mompesson of Tedworth, beginning in 1661. In many respects, this was a typical poltergeist case. There were unexplained knockings and musical drumming sounds, as well as sounds of panting and scratching. Rooms were observed to become inexplicably hot and fill with offensive smells. Objects moved or flew through the air, doors opened and shut spontaneously, and strange lights were seen moving through the house. Apparitions were also seen, and Mr. Mompesson wrote Glanvil that "the house was several nights beset with seven or eight in the shape of Men, who, as soon as a Gun was discharged, would shuffle away together into an Arbour" (Glanvil, 1682, pp. 107–8).

As often happens in such cases, the disturbances seemed to focus on the children in the house. Glanvil testified that he and a friend entered the children's chamber during the disturbances and noticed a loud scratching sound that could not have been made by the two young girls who were lying in bed there. The sound would imitate scratches made by him, but it would move to a new location every time he tried to place his hand at the spot from which it seemed to come. He described a typical search for possible trickery:

> I searcht under and behind the Bed, turned up the cloths to the bed-cords, grasped the Bolster, sounded the Wall behind, and made all the search that possibly I could to find if there were any trick, contrivance, or common cause of it; the like did my friend, but we could discover nothing. So that I was verily persuaded, and am so still, that the noise was made by some Damon or Spirit (Glanvil, 1682, pp. 101–2).

The most curious feature of this case, from a modern point of view, is that a man was tried and convicted of causing the disturbances through witchcraft. Before the disturbances began, Mompesson had caused a vagrant drummer to be arrested and had confiscated the man's drum. The drummer had once been a soldier under Cromwell, and he "used to talk much of Gallant Books he had of an odd fellow, who was counted a Wizard" (Glanvil, 1682, p. 109). Later on, this man was arrested for stealing. While in jail, he boasted of causing the disturbances in Mompesson's house and declared that "I have plagued him . . . and he shall never be at quiet, till he hath made me satisfaction for taking away my drum." According to Glanvil, the man was tried for witchcraft at Sarum, and condemned to "Transportation" (hard labor at sea).

A case from the 1920s discussed by Ian Stevenson illustrates how fear of the supernatural may have been reinforced by personal experiences in traditional cultures (Stevenson, 1997, pp. 75–76). A woman named Eleonore Zugun was a focus for poltergeist disturbances during her early teens. These included the sudden appearance on her skin of lesions which resembled bites from teeth and punctures and scratches from needles. Investigators described the apparent tooth marks as follows:

> Then there appeared suddenly on her hands and forearms marks, which one could recognize only as bites. There were sharp teeth-marks, completely and unmistakably recognizable as such, exactly as though she [Eleonore] had been bitten by somebody. There would be from six to nine teeth above and below, the size of the oval varying, just as though this hypothetical mouth had been more or less widely open (Wassilko-Serecki, 1926, p. 595).

To Eleonore, the scratches and bites were plainly the work of *dracu*, Romanian for "the devil." One wonders whether she subconsciously created these marks as an RSPK agent, inspired by the power of her belief in traditional superstitions. During experiments in Berlin, investigators covered Eleonore's skin with a heavy layer of rouge in the areas where the bites and scratches tended to appear, and they saw these marks appearing on the rouge as well as on the underlying skin. If this is true, then RSPK—whatever its source may be—was evidently carrying out a remarkable simulation of a biting mouth.

SPIRITUALISM AND SCIENCE

In Europe and America, the Age of Enlightenment did much to dispel both the irrational fear of the supernatural and the very real fear of being tried and condemned for witchcraft. However, the apparent triumph of scientific reason had its down side, for it left people stranded in a soulless world of dead matter. As religion retreated before mechanistic science, spiritualism rose up in the mid-19th century to fill the gap on a popular level.

The basic idea behind spiritualism was that spirits of the dead could manifest themselves through the agency of certain gifted people, who became known as spirit mediums. These manifestations typically took place in so-called séances, where a number of people would sit around a table with a medium. Séances were often held in darkness or semi-darkness on the grounds that the spirits tended to shun bright lights.

The manifestations of spiritualism can be divided into two basic categories: spirit communications and physical phenomena. In the former, spirits of the dead ostensibly communicate with living people through the agency of the medium. Typically, the medium conveys messages from a departed relative or friend, either verbally or through some form of automatic writing (see Chapter 7).

The physical phenomena of spiritualism form a bizarre catalogue of apparently impossible oddities, many of which are familiar from our survey of poltergeist cases. They include (1) mysterious rappings and other sounds, (2) apparent shaking of the room, (3) levitation and movement of furniture and other objects, (4) levitation of the medium, (5) immunity to burning on the part of the medium and others, (6) appearance or disappearance of objects in closed containers, (7) touches, hugs, and pulls by invisible hands, (8) inexplicable cold breezes, (9) billowing of curtains and clothing, (10) luminous phenomena, (11) mysterious appearance of writing, (12) playing of untouched musical instruments, and (13) materialization of human figures or discon-nected hands or arms. The latter were often said to form from whitish "ectoplasm" streaming from the body of the medium.

Unfortunately, many of these phenomena can be readily simulated by legerdemain, especially in darkened rooms. The rise of spiritualism created a fertile field in which all manner of frauds and con artists rushed in to exploit credulous people. This was followed by exposures of fraud and the deliberate staging of false séances in an effort to immunize people against phony spirit mediums.

In the early 1880s, the Society for Psychical Research (SPR) was founded in England, and the prominent philosopher Henry Sidgwick became its first president. The psychologist William James became involved, and he subsequently played an active role in the American Society for Psychical Research, which was founded in 1895.

An impressive number of prominent scientists took a serious in-terest in psychical research in the late nineteenth and early twentieth centuries. These included the French astronomer Camille Flammarion and the English naturalist Alfred Russel Wallace, the co-inventor of Darwin's theory of evolution. Three Nobel laureates who devoted ex-tensive efforts to psychical research were the physicist Sir William Crookes, the physiologist Charles Richet, and the physicist Sir Oliver

Lodge. The Nobel-Prize-winning physicists J. J. Thomson and Lord Rayleigh also participated in this research, as did the physicists Wilhelm Weber and Sir W. F. Barrett (Kaku, 1994, pp. 50, 53). Even the famous Pierre and Marie Curie participated in psychical investigations.

THE FRAUD SQUAD

Some critics have argued that eminent scientists are not well equipped to detect fraud and trickery. They are naive about chicanery and legerdemain, and their intellectual pride tends to blind them to their limitations. According to these critics, only expert magicians are capable of seeing through the conjuring tricks used to simulate paranormal phenomena, and qualified magicians should always be present as fraud detectors in psychical investigations.

We might then ask whether or not qualified magicians have ever been convinced about the reality of the physical phenomena exhibited by mediums. The answer turns out to be yes.

For example, in the early 1900s, a controversy arose in the SPR regarding an Italian medium named Eusapia Palladino. Palladino had been caught cheating in tests arranged in Cambridge by the SPR in 1895, and the inclination of the Society's leaders was to dismiss her out of hand as a fake. However, she had been investigated by a number of prominent scientists, including Richet and Lodge, who were inclined to accept some of her phenomena as genuine. In an effort to settle the matter, the Society sent three skeptical experts in trickery to Naples in 1908 to put Eusapia to the test.

The three were the Hon. Everard Feilding, Hereward Carrington, and W. W. Baggally. Of these, Baggally was a skilled conjuror who had investigated many mediums in Britain without finding one that was genuine. Carrington was an amateur conjuror who had written a book on spiritualism containing an extensive analysis of fraudulent mediums. Feilding was supposed to be an arch-skeptic with extensive experience in detecting frauds.

Feilding was initially doubtful that anything positive would emerge from the Palladino investigation. However, he was impressed by the fact that many highly qualified scientists had accepted her as genuine. He remarked that

My own frame of mind, when starting on this investigation, was that, in view of the concurrent opinion of practically all the eminent men of science who have investigated Eusapia's phenomena, it was inconceivable that they could, in turn, have been deceived by the few petty tricks that have, from time to time, been detected, and that it was therefore probable that the phenomena were real. At the same time I could not believe in them. All my own experiments in physical mediumship had resulted in the discovery of the most childish frauds. Failure had followed upon failure. While, therefore, I tended to accept the general hypothesis that the facts of so-called spiritualistic physical manifestations must, on the evidence, be regarded as probably existent, my mental habit had become so profoundly skeptical, when it came to considering any given alleged instance of them, that I had ceased to have any expectation of finding it able to bear examination (Braude, 1991, p.137).

It turned out, however, that this investigation was an exception. Even though the eleven séances were held in good light, the investigations were treated to an onslaught of bizarre physical manifestations. The table levitated, they were poked and grabbed by mysterious hands, and they witnessed grotesque figures resembling crude stage props—such as a "black flat profile face" and a "cello like face on a warty nobbly body" (Braude, 1991, p. 138). Yet the experts in fraud detection could not see how the tricks (if they were tricks) were done.

Baggally declared that "Eusapia was not detected in fraud in any one of the 470 phenomena that took place at the eleven séances" (Braude, 1991, p. 140). He concluded:

Taking into consideration the manner of the control, that no mechanism was found on the medium's person, that no accomplice was present, and also that the three S.P.R. investigators were men who had been accustomed for years to the investigation of so-called physical phenomena of every variety, and who had detected fraud after fraud, I find it impossible to believe that Eusapia could have been able to practice trickery constantly during the many hours that the seances lasted and remain undetected" (Braude, 1991, p. 140).

One possibility is that an accomplice really was present, contrary to Baggally's assertion. Richard Wiseman has argued that an accomplice could have entered the curtained "cabinet" behind Eusapia through a false panel in a sealed door leading to an adjacent room (Wiseman, 1992). The cabinet was a right-triangle-shaped area in the corner of the room with sides formed by the walls of the room and the hypotenuse formed by the curtain. From behind the curtain, the accomplice could have produced some of the reported paranormal effects.

Consider, for example, the mysterious hands. Carrington remarked:

> That human hands—having all the peculiarities of hands, even to the presence of finger nails, should become visible and tangible during a séance—these hands not being Eusapia's nor any of the sitters'—this is so utterly at variance with common sense that one finds it next to impossible to believe it. And yet these hands are real, and by no possible means could they have been Eusapia's (Braude, 1991, p. 138).

According to Wiseman, these were the hands of an accomplice, who would reach through the curtain at opportune moments and molest the investigators. The accomplice's hands were visible and tangible, but one could argue that the experienced fraud detectors failed to understand that they were connected to a man standing behind the curtain.

None of the investigators ever felt sufficiently suspicious about the curtain to jump up and sweep it aside—an act that certainly would have embarrassed a lurking accomplice. However, they did occasionally look behind the curtain. For example, on one occasion, Carrington noted that "While I was looking at the small table in the cabinet (the curtains having been accidentally parted, allowing me to see the whole table) it made a series of little jumps in a direction away from the medium, and back into the cabinet. . . . The light was particularly good, at this time, and I could clearly see the whole of the table as it was moving" (Barrington, 1992, p. 330).

Wiseman's analysis provoked an extended debate in the pages of the *Journal of the Society for Psychical Research.* What emerges from this debate is that the three investigators were confident they had excluded the possibility of an accomplice, but they did not present any detailed discussion ruling out this possibility.

One alternative is that the investigators themselves were accomplices of Palladino, and the accusing finger has been pointed at Carrington, in particular. However, Wiseman remarked that there is little solid evidence to support this accusation (Wiseman, 1992, p. 135), and it seems a bit too convenient to suppose that expert fraud detectors must be conspirators simply because they fail to detect fraud.

If the accomplice theory is true, then the alleged expertise of the three investigators is worthless, and we have to conclude that even expert magicians cannot reliably avoid being fooled by cheap tricks. But if it is false, and the investigators themselves were honest, then we are confronted with some very puzzling phenomena.

BODILY EMANATIONS

One of most curious of these phenomena is the cold breeze that was said to emanate from a scar on Palladino's forehead—again in good light. To test this, "Baggally held a small paper flag to the medium's forehead—her nose and mouth, as well as our own, still being well covered. The flag blew right out several times, and then out so forcibly that it turned completely over and wrapped itself once around the flag-

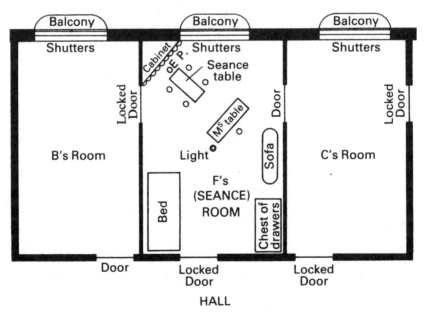

Figure 17. Floor plan of the Eusapia Pallidino séances held in Naples in 1908. The séances took place in the middle room, illuminated by electric lights hanging from the ceiling. The investigators sat with Eusapia Pallidino (EP) at the séance table. The stenographer Albert Meeson sat at M's table.

staff to which it was attached" (Barrington, 1992, p. 333).

It has been suggested that this breeze may have been projected from an India-rubber tube equipped with a squeeze-bulb. But after the flag experiment, the investigators report that they thoroughly searched Palladino's clothes and body without finding any concealed apparatus (Barrington, 1992, p. 333).

There are parallels to Palladino's cold breeze in the recent litera-ture on psychical research. For example, Berthold Schwarz reports that the 95-year-old psychic Jacques Romano possessed a curious "ray" that emanated from his finger and that he claimed to possess since childhood. The effect of this ray is that, when directed at a subject's skin, the subject experiences paresthesias (prickling sensations) or cool, breeze-like sensations. Schwarz observes that

> If the subject is blindfolded and has cotton stuffed in his ears, he will im-mediately and correctly localize the cool sensation to various parts of his body [struck by the "ray"] . . . When an unsuspecting three-year-old girl was blindfolded and merely instructed to "sit still for a little game" (in a room that was 70°F) she immediately commented, "It's cold in the kitchen. It's cold!" every time Romano applied his "ray" to parts of her face or hands (Schwarz, 1963, p. 114).

The ray could apparently produce its effects even when blocked by obstacles such as a telephone book, a flower pot, or thin sheets of metal. Schwarz also states that "On many occasions the 'ray' has transiently bent a candle flame, and this has also occurred when the candle was shielded with a glass chimney" (Schwarz, 1963, p. 114). This suggests that Romano's ray was not due to simple motion of air, even though the bending of the flame suggests the presence of a breeze.

Schwarz carried out double-blind experiments, in which Romano applied his ray to batches of sunflower seeds and hybrid corn seeds. There were no significant effects on the germination of these seeds or on the growth rate of the corn seeds. However, 1,400 sunflower seeds "radiated" by Romano grew 26.9% less than 1,400 nonradiated control seeds (Schwarz, 1963, p. 120). (Growth was evaluated by measuring total stems and roots in millimeters.) This result is highly significant, but it is not clear why the "ray" should affect sunflower plants and not corn. Schwarz tried zapping batches of seeds with his own "mock ray," but was unable to produce a significant effect.

A PARALLEL FROM MARTIAL ARTS

There is anecdotal evidence suggesting that energy apparently emanating from the body can exert powerful effects. For an example of this, I turn to the South Indian system of martial arts called Kala-rippayat. A man named Prakasan Gurukkal is said to be expert at the *choondu marmam* technique of this system. According to an article in *The Week,* dated March 26, 1993,

> When a hardy challenger lunges forward with a knife, it is time for *choondu marmam.* Prakasan thrusts his index finger with force at the attacker from a distance of five feet. The result is awe-inspiring. The man freezes for a moment and drops to the ground, goggle-eyed. An hour later, and he still had not regained his wits . . . On coming back to his senses, Babu, 33, the wiry Kalarippayat champion, confesses: "I really don't know what hit me. I just lost my balance and fell. I couldn't move my body at all" (Salim, 1993, p. 20).

Prakasan attributes his powers to the manipulation of the Life Force (Sanskrit *prana*) flowing in his body. He declares, "Believe me, I have no preternatural force. I strike at the seven marmams with my concentration. I can do it in a split second" (Salim, 1993, p. 21). Prakasan evidently believes that his powers are fully natural, perhaps without realizing that both his explanation and his alleged feats transgress known scientific laws. The *marmams* are traditional energy centers in the body having no obvious anatomical counterpart.

ECTOPLASM OR PROTOPLASM

On the evening of July 7, 1874, La Comtesse Caterina Lugano di Panigai sat in a séance with the celebrated spirit medium Daniel Dunglass Home and five others. The séance took place about 8 p.m. in a room of the hotel in Florence where Home was staying, and good light was provided by two candles and a petroleum lamp. Many unusual phenomena were reported, and after a particularly impressive spirit communication, the Comtesse thought to herself, "If you are really the spirit you claim to be, I ask you to take that rose from Henrietta, and bring it to me." She testified that

> The thought had hardly taken shape in my mind, when a hand, visible to everyone present, the large nervous hand of a man, grasped the rose, and disengaging it, brought it to me, and placed it in my fingers. This was not done in darkness or in a dim light. The room was well lit, the hands of every person present rested on the table, and there hovered in the air before us a hand as perfect in form as human hand can be (Home, 1879, p. 480).

Many of the physical phenomena connected with spirit mediums seem to be connected with some kind of energy emanating from the medium's body. One of the most peculiar of these is the so-called ectoplasm, a whitish fluid that is claimed to flow from the body of a medium and coalesce into well-defined forms such as hands, heads, or entire bodies. In some cases this fluid is said to be visible and to form bodies gradually. In other cases, such this one, the bodies seem to appear and disappear abruptly.

The French physiologist Charles Richet reported experiments in which ectoplasmic hands supposedly made molds in paraffin. Richet noted that he used paraffin that was chemically marked so that he could detect phony molds that might be substituted by sleight of hand. He pointed out that the molds he obtained were narrow at the wrist and thus they could not have been made by simply inserting a hand into the paraffin and pulling it out. A more elaborate procedure would be needed, in which the paraffin was allowed to partially solidify, and then it was sliced open by pulling on threads attached to the hand.

Richet's paraffin molds might be explained by Sir William Crookes' observation that materializing hands may disappear by apparently melting away into vapor. He testified that, "I have retained one of these hands in my own, firmly resolved not to let it escape. There was no struggle or effort made to get loose, but it gradually seemed to resolve itself into vapour, and faded in that manner from my grasp" (Braude, 1991, pp. 107–8).

Here we are reminded of the possibility, mentioned in Chapter 7, that an apparitional figure may be projected not into the virtual brains of the witnesses, but directly into virtual 3D space. Such a pro-

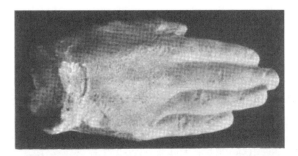
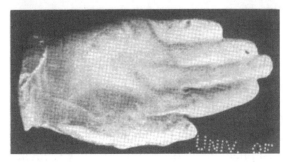

Figure 18. Plaster casts of materialized hands. Physiologist Charles Richet reported making paraffin molds of spectral hands. The paraffin was chemically marked to rule out the possibility of a substitution. He pointed out that the wrists were narrower than the hands, and therefore normal hands could not have been withdrawn from the molds. In this case, however, the hands "de-materialized," leaving the molds intact. Plaster casts, made from the paraffin molds, are shown here.

cess clearly involves manipulations of physical energy, resulting in effects such as pressure on Crookes' hand or displacement of paraffin. Since energy is presumably still conserved, this implies unknown reservoirs of energy and corresponding modifications of the laws of physics.

As always, all of these strange results can be attributed to trickery. However, both Richet and Crookes claimed that they took many precautions to rule out fraud, and they were convinced that they were observing real phenomena. Richet wrote,

> There is ample proof that experimental materialization (ectoplasmic) should take definite rank as a scientific fact. Assuredly we do not understand it. It is very absurd, if a truth can be absurd.
>
> Spiritualists have blamed me for using this word "absurd"; and they have not been able to understand that to admit the reality of these phenomena was for me an actual pain; but to ask a physiologist, a physicist, or a chemist to admit that a form that has circulation of the blood, warmth, and muscles, that exhales carbonic acid, has weight, speaks, and thinks, can issue from a human body is to ask him an intellectual effort that is really painful.
>
> Yes, it is absurd, but no matter; it is true (Mishlove, 1975, p. 85).

There are many reports of materializations of living, functioning human bodies. Here we give one taken from the literature on yoga, which rivals or surpasses psychical research as a source of such stories. This one is related by the famous Paramahamsa Yogananda, who wrote that his guru Sri Yukteswar appeared to him in physical form after his death. On asking him if he was truly in a physical body, Sri Yukteswar reportedly answered

> Yes, my child, I am the same. This is a flesh and blood body. Though I see it as ethereal, to your sight it is physical. From cosmic atoms I created an entirely new body, exactly like that cosmic-dream physical body which you laid beneath the dream-sands at Puri in your dream-world. I am in truth resurrected—not on earth but on an astral planet (Yogananda, 1981, p. 476).

It is interesting that Sri Yukteswar said that he saw his materialized body as ethereal, whereas to people in the earthly dream world it would seem physical. This is consistent with the virtual reality model, or with the idea of the dreamlike physical world as a display of *maya.*

Although the physical phenomena of spiritualism may seem absurd, it can be argued that this is a product of the collision of the Western mechanistic, scientific tradition with natural events that do not fit easily into a mechanistic paradigm. These phenomena seem capricious and difficult to control, but so is the weather. They offend our scientific sensibilities, but since time immemorial they have seemed perfectly normal (if sometimes disturbing) to people of non-Western cultures. They may, on the whole, be simply facts of nature.

From the standpoint of the virtual reality model, these phenomena suggest a common theme. They all seem to involve the transfer of structure and information from one virtual space to another. Thus an apport seems to require the shifting of a 3D object into another 3D continuum and back. An apparition may involve the impression of mental imagery on the physical continuum, and in the case of spectral emanations such as Richet's materializing hands, such impressions can apparently leave permanent effects.

The virtual reality model can accommodate many 3D spaces, and there is no problem in placing three-dimensional structures in these spaces. All of the spaces are simply represented by numbers (or abstract mathematical entities) whether they are defined to be mind-space, physical-space, or something presently unknown. The question is: How do we transfer 3D structure from one space to another? Such transfer involves issues such as (1) the displacement of air as the transfer is made and (2) the stresses and strains involved in a partially completed transfer. Energy accounts must be balanced, and it is possible that a net amount of energy will be transferred from one continuum to another. We must also consider the role of the extended mind in bringing about the transfer. It is clear that new physical laws are required. Physicists in recent years have sometimes lamented that they are approaching the end of fundamental discoveries in physics, but it appears that this worry is unnecessary.

10

HEALING

*"Miracles do not happen in contradiction
to nature, but only in contradiction to that
which is known to us in nature."*

—St. Augustine

Jack (also known as John) Traynor was born in Liverpool, England, of part Irish ancestry, and grew up in time to participate in the First World War. In the battle of Antwerp he received a head injury from shrapnel, but after three months in recovery, he rejoined his unit, which had been transferred to the Dardanelles. On May 8, 1915, he was injured again during the battle of Gallipoli. Two bullets passed through his chest, and another bullet severed the nerves of the brachial plexus, paralyzing his right arm (Fact sheet on Traynor).

In a hospital in Alexandria, an unsuccessful attempt was made to suture the nerves, and another operation was required on the hospital ship to England to stem post-operative hemorrhaging. At this time he began to have epileptic fits, which increased in frequency until he was having several seizures per day. Two more unsuccessful attempts to suture the nerves were made in 1915 and 1916, and he refused to allow his right arm to be amputated. He spent ten months in 1918 at Bromborough in a Center specializing in the treatment of epilepsy, and in 1919 he received electrical treatment and physiotherapy to his right arm in a hospital in Liverpool. During a cranial operation for epilepsy in 1920, a metal plate 2.5 cm in diameter was inserted to protect the right parietal region of the brain, which had been exposed by trepanation of the skull. He also developed double incontinence at this time. His physical condition seemed to be steadily deteriorating.

Yet a remarkable turning point occurred when Traynor made a pilgrimage to Lourdes in Southern France in 1923. Lourdes is the site where the Virgin Mary is said to have appeared in several visions to a peasant girl named Bernadette Soubirous in 1858. These visions took place in a grotto in a cliff called Massabieille near the river Gave. After one vision in particular, a spring began to flow in the grotto, and its water was soon reported to be responsible for miraculous cures. Today people from all over the world come to Lourdes to seek cures or to perform a religious pilgrimage. The estimated figures for 1948–49 are 15,000 to 20,000 sick people and some two to three million pilgrims, and the numbers have increased since then (Benor, 1992, p. 257).

In Lourdes, on July 24, a medical examination by Drs. Azurdia, Finn, and Marley confirmed that (1) Traynor had suffered from epileptic fits during the journey to Lourdes, (2) the radial, median, and ulnar nerves of his right hand were paralyzed, (3) there was atrophy of his pectoral and shoulder muscles, (5) he exhibited loss of voluntary movements of the legs and loss of sensation, and (6) he suffered from double incontinence. The metal plate in his skull was also noted.

The story goes that from the second day of bathing in the Piscenes, or bathes fed by sacred spring water, Traynor's epileptic fits ceased. While being bathed on July 28, his paralyzed legs trembled violently, and he tried to·stand up, motivated by the feeling that he would be able to do so. He was carried out on a stretcher, and when the Archbishop of Rheims blessed him, his right arm trembled violently, and the pain vanished. He was again examined by three doctors of the pilgrimage, who observed that Traynor could walk with some difficulty. Reflexes were present in the lower limbs, and he was able to move his legs voluntarily. He also was suffering from painful venous congestion of both feet.

In 1926, three years later, Jack Traynor was re-examined at the Medical Bureau at Lourdes, and his physical state was found to be perfectly normal, apart from a slight flexion contracture of the fingers of his right hand. His epilepsy was completely cured, and he had resumed his professional work. He died 20 years after his cure from unrelated causes (Fact sheet on Traynor).

What are we to make of a story like this? If we assume that the facts are as stated, we can see that various interpretations are possible. At one extreme, we can interpret this story as an example of a miraculous healing, brought about by divine intervention at the holy pilgrimage site at Lourdes. This is how Traynor himself viewed his experience, and it is said that every year after his pilgrimage he returned to Lourdes out of gratitude to voluntarily help the sick.

Another interpretation is that the nerves in Traynor's arms had regenerated naturally, but the shock of his injuries and his unsuccessful operations had induced a psychological complex, leading to apparent epileptic seizures and progressive paralysis. His faith in the healing potency of Lourdes enabled him to resume normal functioning, without the involvement of any supernatural or other-than-natural processes. This interpretation allows us to avoid invoking paranormal agencies, but we should be cautious about making special assumptions just for this purpose. In this case, we must assume that the doctors were mistaken about the condition of the nerves in Traynor's right arm. This is possible, but it may be that no one would have seriously proposed it if the remarkable cure had not happened.

THE PLACEBO EFFECT

Even if we accept that Traynor's paralysis and epilepsy were caused by physical harm to his brain and peripheral nerves, their cure can still be attributed to the action of Traynor's own mind, motivated by his strong faith in the healing potency of a sacred shrine. In Chapter 8, we observed some remarkable effects that the mind can induce in the physical body. For example, the memory of being painfully bound by ropes somehow caused realistic-looking, indented rope marks to appear on the arm of one patient. If the mind can cause skin cells to move and transform in such a way as to simulate the effects of pressure from tight ropes, then the mind might similarly be able to adjust the physical condition of neurons and their arrangement in space—at least if the neurons had not extensively degenerated.

The ability of the mind to cure bodily illness without medical intervention is known as the placebo effect. Ian Stevenson reports a study by a German gastroenterologist named Hans Rehder, which shows that this well-known phenomenon may be responsible for many cases of unusual healing that might otherwise be attributed to agencies outside the mind and body of the individual (Stevenson, 1996, pp. 300–301).

Rehder studied three female patients, all bedridden. One was in constant pain from chronic cholecystitus (inflammation of the gall bladder) with repeated attacks of biliary colic (pain from gallstones in the bile duct). The second patient was in almost continuous pain from intestinal obstructions caused by adhesions resulting from surgery, and she was unable to have normal bowel movements. She was emaciated and in a desperate condition. The third had widespread abdominal cancer stemming from an inoperable tumor in her uterus. She was severely anemic, and suffered from accumulation of fluid in her legs and abdomen.

Rehder was in contact with a spirit healer named Kurt Trampler, who claimed he could cure people from a distance by channeling the healing power of God. Trampler agreed to try to heal Rehder's patients from a distance, and Rehder was careful to tell them nothing about Trampler's efforts. At agreed upon dates and times, Trampler applied his distant healing technique to the three women, but their conditions remained unchanged.

Rehder then built up in his patients' minds a glowing picture of the wonders of miraculous healing, citing famous examples such as Lourdes. This was done separately for the three patients, who stayed in different rooms and did not communicate with one another. He gave them a pamphlet on healing by Trampler, and prepared them to expect complete healing. He then set exact dates and times when they were to receive distant healing from Trampler, but he made sure that Trampler would not be making his healing efforts at those times. Nonetheless, at the appointed times, all three women showed dramatic improvement and all three felt well enough to be discharged from the hospital. In the long term, the cancer patient died within a few months and the gallbladder patient eventually did require an operation. But the second patient remained well up to the time of Rehder's publication (Stevenson, 1996, pp. 300–301).

The term "psychosomatic illness" is normally taken to mean a kind of illusory condition, in which a person is deluded into thinking that he or she is sick but really isn't. The illnesses of the three women do not seem to be psychosomatic in this sense. It might be argued that the diseases were real, but the feeling of being cured was imaginary, as shown by the relapse of the cancer and gallbladder patients. However, one wonders what would have happened if Rehder's placebo healing trick could have been renewed regularly over a period of months. Would all three women have continued to function normally? Note that Traynor regularly performed service to the sick at Lourdes for the rest of his life, and so his faith was presumably continuously reinforced.

The placebo effect has been observed in a wide range of diseases, including angina pectoris, cancer, rheumatoid arthritis, warts, asthma, ulcers, migraine headaches, allergies, multiple sclerosis, diabetes, and psychiatric disorders. For example, a study of angina pectoris was conducted by Dr. Henry Beecher, in which patients scheduled for heart surgery to treat this disease were divided into two groups. One group got the full surgical treatment, and the patients in the second group were simply cut open and sewn back up. It turned out that both groups did equally well (O'Regan and Hirshberg, 1993, p. 40).

Here is another example of a placebo effect involving cancer.

> Dr. Philip West reported some years ago on the case of a man with severe cancer who begged to be given a dose of an experimental drug called Krebiozen, which was being touted as a "wonder drug." After one dose of this drug, the patient's tumor masses "melted like snowballs on a hot stove." The patient no longer needed an oxygen mask to breathe and even resumed piloting his own plane. When the man later read further reports that the drug was worthless, his cancer immediately began spreading again and he required hospitalization. He died a few days later (O'Regan and Hirshberg, 1993, p. 40).

In this case, Krebiozen served both as a positive placebo and as a negative one (a "nocebo"), depending on what the patient thought about it—a point that should be carefully considered by doctors when they give negative prognoses to their patients. Mental factors may have a great deal to do with so-called spontaneous remissions, in which serious diseases such as cancer are spontaneously cured or reversed in their course. Indeed, in a massive compilation of cases of spontaneous remission of various diseases, O'Regan and Hirshberg included numerous references to hypnosis, meditation, and "psychosocial," "psychosomatic," and "psychospiritual" factors as causes of remission or prolonged survival (O'Regan and Hirshberg, 1993).

Since the placebo effect may be involved in any curative process involving knowledge by the patient, it follows that any cure apparently brought about by a psychical or supernatural agency may actually be due to the mind of the individual involved. Yet this doesn't mean that the cure should be attributed solely to the action of the brain and the body's nervous and glandular system. As we saw in the case of the mentally induced rope marks, it may also involve direct interactions between the extended mind and the body. In addition, influences from outside the individual's mind cannot be ruled out, and combined effects involving both the individual mind and other minds are also possible.

MIRACULOUS SPIN DOCTORS

One factor in paranormal healing cases is that different accounts of the same case may convey different impressions. Thus far I have related the information on Jack Traynor listed in a rather dry and so-ber manner on a fact sheet issued from Lourdes. But if we turn to the popular book, *I Accept These Facts*, by Michel Agnellet, we obtain a different impression of Traynor's case. Agnellet presents Traynor's story in enthusiastic detail from a sympathetic viewpoint. He quotes him as saying that on the day after his first bath at Lourdes, "I literally jumped out of bed. I washed and shaved myself without any help and left the hospital on my own two feet," (Agnellet, 1958, p. 93). Agnellet also states that three surgeons who had been following Traynor's case examined him at Lourdes immediately after his cure and testified that there was no trace of epilepsy or paralysis, that the right arm was no longer atrophied and the pectoral and scapular muscles had been completely restored. He could use his right hand normally and the only sign left by the trepanation was a shallow depression in the bone which could be felt with the finger (Agnellet, 1958, p. 94).

The abrupt restoration of atrophied muscles is certainly not ex-pected in psychosomatic cases. One also wonders what became of the metal plate, which was observed in place in Traynor's skull during his examination on arrival at Lourdes.

Agnellet makes Traynor's cure seem substantially more miracu-lous than the bare list of data on the fact sheet. But if we set aside the sudden mending of the skull and muscles, we could still interpret the case as one of recovery from a psychosomatic condition, even though, in view of Traynor's reportedly grave condition, this interpretation does seem rather strained.

A very different impression of Lourdes healing cases is given in a critical review of Lourdes miracles by Dr. D. J. West (West, 1957). West argued that most of the 11 miracle cases he analyzed were susceptible to possible diagnoses overlooked by the doctors who had originally certified them as medically inexplicable. These diagnoses naturally tended to reduce the marvelous nature of the cures. West declared that the evidence for anything miraculous was exceedingly meager, and he pointed out that there were no cases in which a sudden structural change was confirmed by X-rays taken before and after the event. He did grudgingly concede, however, that there are cases of chronic, suppurating wounds at Lourdes that closed very rapidly and completely.

We can conclude that it is possible to sort out the evidence for inexplicable healings in various ways. Very little survives the gauntlet of the strictest conservative standards. At the same time, claims of marvelous events are plentiful, and these are not necessarily false simply because they cannot pass the closest critical scrutiny. For example, Traynor's case apparently was never put forward officially as a miracle, even though it was publicly declared inexplicable by the six doctors who were intimately involved in the case (Fact sheet on Traynor).

One important point regarding Lourdes is that the number of claimed miraculous cures is very small compared with the tens of thousands of sick people who seek healing there every year. One might therefore argue that out of so many people, one is bound to find a few unusual cures, simply by chance. However, for every reported cure there may be many that go unreported. Suppose, for the sake of argument, that out of a hundred sick people, one claims a cure. Suppose further that out of a hundred of these cures, one will have good documentation, and out of one hundred with good documentation, one will not be susceptible to any ordinary interpretation which undercuts its miraculous status. It follows that out of one million sick people, we may find one certifiably miraculous cure. Even then, we still have the option of saying that we just don't believe it and that it may be a fraud or an exaggeration.

INEXPLICABLE STRUCTURAL CHANGE

Although well-documented cases of healings with unusual structural change are hard to find, they do exist. An example is the story of Vittorio Micheli, who suffered from a bone cancer which totally destroyed the ball-and-socket joint on the left side of his hip (Salmon, 1972). This is the joint where the upper end of the femur articulates with the hip. Micheli's condition was well documented by medical doctors, who used X-rays and up-to-date medical tests in their diagnosis.

In 1963, Micheli visited Lourdes in the desperate hope of being cured. He testified that after being bathed in the sacred springs at the shrine, he experienced sensations of heat moving through his body, followed by an amazing resurgence of energy. Within two months, he was able to walk again, and physicians testified that his ball-and-socket joint had regrown. One physician commented,

> A remarkable reconstruction of the iliac bone and cavity has taken place. The X-rays made in 1964–5, –8 and –9 confirm categorically and without doubt that an unforeseen and even overwhelming bone re-construction has taken place of a type unknown in the annals of world medicine. We ourselves, during a university and hospital career of over 45 years spent largely in the study of tumors and neoplasms of all kinds of bone structures and having ourselves treated hundreds of such cases, have never encountered a single spontaneous bone reconstruction of such a nature (O'Regan, 1991, p. 51).

In this case we have no direct evidence that Micheli's cure was sudden. He was wearing a full body cast at the time of the healing, and this was not immediately removed. Thus we do not know how soon he could have walked. The interesting feature of this case, however, is that Micheli's hip joint underwent a reconstruction of a kind that happens in lower vertebrates such as amphibians, but is not known to occur in mammals. It is also noteworthy that, like Jack Traynor, Micheli reported unusual sensations at the time when he felt the healing take place.

Here is a case, not from Lourdes but similar to Traynor's case, in which severed nerves to a man's right arm were apparently restored over a period of months.

> A 42-year-old man had total paralysis of the right arm following a bullet wound in his neck, which cut through a major artery and irreparably severed

several nerves. A neurologist informed him that the arm would never move again. With three months' treatments (primarily consisting of magnetic passes), he regained some use of his arm and hand. Use of his thumb did not return until eight months later. The neurologist could not explain his recovery. "In fact, on his last medical visit, the patient was told there would be no charge because the neurologist had seen something he had not believed possible: movement not apparently prompted by neuronal connections" (Benor, 1992, p. 289).

This case was part of a study on the effectiveness in healing of "magnetic passes" (a form of alternative healing which needn't concern us here). The study involved 11 patients, of whom six were said to have shown sustained improvement, two had initial dramatic improvement, followed by relapse, and three did not respond. The remarkable feature of the case is that the neurologist apparently did not think that the severed nerves could have been restored (Benor, 1992, p. 290).

An example of a sudden cure is the story of Serge Perrin, who suffered from a chronic neurological disorder which culminated in frequent seizures, blindness in the left eye, and an inability to walk (Mouren, 1976). This condition was diagnosed by several physicians as organic rather than psychological, involving defects in the arteries supplying blood to the brain.

Perrin's condition had deteriorated steadily for several years, and by 1970 he was confined to a wheelchair and in need of constant care. During a visit to Lourdes in that year, Perrin reported feeling a sudden sensation of warmth in his lower limbs while attending a church ceremony. Within a few minutes he was able to walk. On leaving the church, he found that with his right eye covered he could read signs on the opposite side of the square with his left eye, even though that eye had been blind on entering the church. Medical examination showed that his neurological condition was completely cured, and he remained in good health for several years. Several medical doctors connected with Perrin's case noted that his cure was medically inexplicable. Of course, the sudden character of the cure depends heavily on the testimony of Perrin himself, who reported the abrupt restoration of sight in his left eye.

The story of Pierre de Rudder is another example of a sudden cure supported by medical testimony. De Rudder was a Belgian peasant whose leg was crushed by a falling tree in 1867, resulting in an open

fracture of the upper third of his left tibia and fibula. This never healed
due to an ongoing infection that destroyed newly formed bone and
prevented the damaged bones from consolidating (Fact sheet on de
Rudder). De Rudder repeatedly refused amputation, and after some
time his doctors abandoned him, regarding his case as hopeless.

Eight years after the accident, de Rudder made a pilgrimage to
Oostacker, a city near Ghent where a replica of the Lourdes grotto had
been constructed. While praying there in front of a statue of the Virgin
Mary, de Rudder felt a sudden change in his condition. He stood up
without his crutches and began to walk toward the statue. After returning home on his own two feet, he was examined by Dr. van
Hoestenberghe, who testified that

> Pierre is undoubtedly cured. I have seen him many times during the last eight
> years, and my medical knowledge tells me that such a cure is absolutely
> inexplicable. Again, he has been cured completely, suddenly, and instanta-
> neously, without any period of convalescence. Not only have the bones been
> suddenly united, but a portion of bone would seem to have been actually
> created to take the place of those fragments I myself have seen come out of
> the wound (Rogo, 1991, p. 294).

One may doubt that events transpired exactly as stated in the
stories about de Rudder. De Rudder's bones were exhumed after his
death in 1898, and they show clear signs of a healed fracture. (Replicas
are on display at the Medical Bureau at Lourdes.) Could it be that this
healing took place over an extended period and the story of sudden
restoration is simply a lie?

Here we are reminded of the philosopher David Hume, who
declared that "No testimony is sufficient to establish a miracle, unless
the testimony be of such a kind, that its falsehood would be more
miraculous, than the fact, which it endeavours to establish" (Hume,
1902, pp. 115–16). Of course, it is no miracle for testimony to be false,
and so we could use Hume's dictum to dismiss all alleged miracles
automatically.

MORE EXTREME CASES

There is certainly a great deal of testimony to dismiss. Here I will
list a few cases in which diagnosis by physicians is said to have been

involved. Like the others we have considered, these stories fall under the heading of anecdotal evidence, since we cannot be absolutely sure that they are true. Yet to drop such evidence from all consideration would be as unwise as to accept it blindly. The best course, therefore, is to consider extraordinary testimony tentatively, without becoming too attached to it one way or another.

Consider, for example, the healing of George Orr, who was blinded in his right eye in an iron foundry in 1927, when a bit of molten iron splashed into it. The vision in Orr's eye was reportedly restored during a service held by the faith healer Katherine Kuhlman in 1947, and the cure was verified by Orr's physician, Dr. C. E. Imbrie (Rogo, 1991, p. 276). This would not be expected from a medical standpoint, since the vision in Orr's eye had been blocked by scar tissue caused by the hot iron.

In another case, a man named Leo Parras was paralyzed from the waist down by back injuries sustained in an industrial accident. After 21 years in a wheelchair, he abruptly regained the ability to walk while being prayed over by Father DiOrio, another faith healer. It is said that Parras' family physician, Dr. Mitchell Tenerowicz, was astonished to find that he was able to walk, even though his leg muscles were still atrophied (Rogo, 1991, p. 281). This case can be contrasted with that of Jack Traynor, where it was claimed that atrophied muscles were suddenly restored.

We can compare this with the case of Gerard Baillie, who was blind from the age of two from a condition known as bilateral chorioretinitis, which involves deterioration of the optic nerves. He was cured at Lourdes at the age of eight, and an opthamologist certified that he could see, even though his optic nerves were still atrophied (Rogo, 1991, p. 289). This is similar to the case of Kelly Paquin, a girl who was born blind in one eye and was reportedly healed by Father DiOrio at the age of two. After the healing, Kelly's family physician expressed surprise that she could see through the eye, since it was still so scarred that this should not have been possible (Rogo, 1991, p. 282).

Although these healing miracles seem extraordinary, the same principles we have considered in previous chapters can explain them. In nearly all cases, we can model extreme healing effects by a process in which detailed information stored in the VR computer (or its equivalent in nature) is used to modify structures in virtual 3D space. Previously we have considered how mental images existing outside virtual space can impose patterns on the virtual brain and body. In miracles of healing, the relevant information may come from a universal storehouse of biological data. The process of healing involves using this information to regenerate the structures of the body, perhaps on a molecular level. If the placebo effect is involved, the process may be set in motion by the mind of the individual, but this implies that the individual mind can draw upon some higher source of information.

In a virtual reality model, this could all be programmed in suitable software. Damaged virtual bodies could be repaired, using a stored database of bodily blueprints. This requires physical laws governing the response of (virtual) physical matter to the structural patterns being imported from another virtual domain—in the case, the database. My basic argument is that if we can envision doing this in a man-made virtual reality, then the Ground Reality system underlying nature may already be doing it on a much more sophisticated level.

It is more difficult to explain cases where organs begin to work, even though they are still medically disfunctional. If this really happens in the case of vision, one wonders whether a form of out-of-body vision is involved, as described in Chapter 8. Much more data is required before we can form a judgement about this.

LABORATORY STUDIES

Nonphysical healing is generally associated with a religious shrine, with ceremonies performed by a revered religious personality, or by so-called psychical healers. The latter typically maintain a secular stance, but attribute their healing potency to agencies or energies unknown to modern science. Healers are usually portrayed as uniquely gifted or qualified individuals, but there are cases where ordinary people are said to exhibit a healing influence.

There have been many attempts to demonstrate the powers of psychical healers through controlled laboratory experiments. I will give several examples from a survey conducted by Dr. Daniel Benor, an American psychiatrist who studies paranormal healing in England.

A classical example is the pioneering experiment with mice carried out by Bernard Grad at McGill University in 1965. Ninety-six mice were wounded on their backs by removal of a one-half by one inch rectangle of skin. They were divided randomly into two groups. Oscar Estebany, a healer, held the cages of the mice in one group, and the other group was used as a control. After fourteen days, it was found that the treated group had healed significantly faster than the untreated group. This was rated with a probability of $p<0.001$ (Benor, 1992, p. 182). The experiment was repeated with 300 mice and careful controls, and significant results were also obtained. In yet another of Grad's experiments, a healer tried to slow down thyroid growth in mice treated with thiouracil, a goiter promoting drug. Significant results were also obtained, and it was also observed that cotton cuttings held by the healer exerted a healing effect when placed in the cages of the mice (Benor, 1992, pp. 182–83).

A number of experiments have been performed to test the influence of healers on cancer cells. For example Dr. John Kmetz described results of an experiment in which the psychic Mathew Manning tried to influence cultures of cervical cancer cells grown in specially prepared plastic flasks. These cells tend to adhere to the surface of flasks, but they can be dislodged by influences causing injury, death, or disturbances in metabolism. According to Kmetz,

> M.M. [Mathew Manning] was able to exert quite dramatic influences upon these cancer cell cultures, ranging in magnitude from 200 to 1,200 per cent changes, compared with appropriate controls. Most of these effects followed M.M. "laying on of hands" on the experimental flask for a 20 min period. ... However, strong effects also occurred when M.M. never touched the flasks, but attempted to influence the cultures at a distance, while confined in an electrically shielded room" (Benor, 1992, pp. 135–36).

In one experiment with a 38.02 percent deviation from chance expectation, the p-value used in statistical evaluations came to $p<0.00002$. This indicates that Manning's results were highly unlikely to have occurred by chance.

The destruction of cancer cells growing in flasks could easily be accomplished by some indiscriminant agency that would tend to kill all forms of life. However, for the healing of cancer, it is necessary for the healer to target a specific type of cell, while leaving all other cells in the body unharmed. The remarkable feature of psychic healing is that this apparently can be done, even though the healer does not possess detailed medical knowledge about different kinds of cells. Thus Daniel Benor remarks that "Healers feel that a native intelligence inheres in aspects of the healing process, so that the healer does not have to know such disciplines as biochemistry or anatomy in order to bring about physiological changes" (Benor, 1992, p. 129).

The ability of "ordinary" people to mentally influence biological systems was tested by William Braud. For each of 32 unselected subjects, red blood cells subjected to osmotic stress (hypotonic saline) were placed in 20 tubes. The subjects, who were not in the same room as the tubes, attempted to "protect" the cells in ten of the tubes, using visualization and intention strategies. The other ten tubes were left aside as controls. Protection, in this experiment, meant reducing the rate of hemolysis of the cells. Braud reported highly significant results, with $p < 0.000019$ (Benor, 1992, pp. 136–37). Here again, the subjects were able to bring about a desired influence without knowing the details of the biochemistry involved. Braud cautioned, however, that these laboratory results may not apply directly to hemolysis within the body, since the chemical environment of the body is much more complex than that of the test tubes.

Carroll B. Nash reported an experiment involving 52 "psychically ungifted volunteers," in which the aim was to influence the mutation of bacteria. Each subject was presented with nine tubes of mixed lac-negative and lac-positive *E. coli* bacteria and asked to mentally promote mutation of lac-negative to lac-positive in three of them and inhibit this mutation in another three. The remaining three tubes were set aside as controls. Careful blinds were used to prevent lab workers from knowing the identities of the tubes by any ordinary means.

Nash reports that "The mutant ratio of lac-positive to total bacteria was greater in the promoted than in the inhibited tubes, with . . . $p < 0.005$; less in the inhibited tubes than in the controls, with . . . $p < 0.02$; and greater in the promoted tubes than in the controls, although not significantly so" (Benor, 1992, p. 156).

Lac-negative *E. coli* bacteria are unable to metabolize lactose, and lac-positive bacteria have a single gene mutation that enables them to do this. The author points out that the experimental results may measure differential growth rates of the two strains and not mutation of one into the other. However, the results of the study do imply that the subjects were somehow able to discriminate between lac-negative and lac-positive bacteria, even though all they could see were test tubes containing fluid. This seems to require the existence of a process—somehow connected with the subjects—that analyzes each bacterial cell on a suitable biochemical basis.

These examples give a brief glimpse into the vast experimental literature on healing. Benor points out that in a survey of many controlled healing experiments, about two-thirds demonstrated positive effects, and although some were flawed, "there still remain a convincing number of excellent studies with significant results" (Benor, 1992, p. 252). Unlike cases of miraculous healing, experiments with animals, plants, and microbes cannot be explained by the placebo effect, unless we assume that these organisms can know experimenters' intentions and react to them mentally. This may actually be possible for some creatures (see Chapter 11). But even if it does happen, knowledge of human intentions is certainly not conveyed to subhuman organisms by normal means of communication. Some non-ordinary mode of influence must be involved.

ENCOUNTERS WITH SHINING BEINGS

The extreme cases of miraculous or medically inexplicable healing differ from the controlled experiments only in a matter of degree. Both require some agency that acts with knowledge on a detailed level. Consider hemolysis, for example. An agency that can manipulate molecules (perhaps in cell membranes) so as to keep a threatened blood corpuscle intact is hardly less remarkable than one that manipulates bone cells to heal a broken leg. The first agency works on a smaller scale than the second one, but both agencies require know-how as well as active potency.

It is possible that some medically inexplicable healings involve causal agencies in addition to the minds of the affected individuals. One theme that repeatedly comes up in these healings is that they involve a sentient being which is not manifest in gross bodily form and is often said to radiate divine luminosity. I will now turn to this topic.

Lourdes is famous as the site of reported apparitions of the Virgin

Mary, which took place in 1858. The Virgin Mary is typically described as brilliantly glowing and her appearances are often associated with miraculous cures. She is said to exhibit a beautiful human form to those who see her. However, she is typically visible only to selected persons, and she may appear or disappear abruptly. Generally, she is seen floating in midair. For example, Lucia dos Santos, one of the three children who experienced the famous Marian visions at Fatima, Portugal, in 1917, described the appearance of the Virgin Mary in the following words.

> She was more brilliant than the sun, and she radiated a sparkling light from her person, clearer and more intense than that of a crystal filled with glittering water and transpierced by the rays of the most burning sun (Johnston, 1979, pp. 27–28).

Many contemporary accounts of miraculous healings also involve shining beings who are not identified with a particular religious tradition. An example is the case of Hans Poulsen, a musician who was dying of cancer. Poulsen testified that he had the following experience during a ceremony performed by a healer.

> A timelessness seemed to just descend around me. It was the most powerful experience, I think, I've ever felt in my life. . . . Before me, out of this effulgent light, light was flooding the room from all around me, forming two radiant circles of gold, one within the other with light in colors flooding from them. A presence silent and serene was speaking to me. Much was said, only some of which I consciously remember. Yet I feel what was transferred still guides my life today. Yes, I was acknowledging: I do give you permission. Wave after wave of the most exquisite sensation poured in through the top of my head cascading through my body and out to the souls of my feet. The being spoke without words . . . (Poulsen, 1992).

After this experience, Poulsen was found by medical doctors to be free of the cancer. According to his own testimony, Poulsen's cure was connected with the resolution of emotional problems, including the bitterness caused by a divorce. Thus one could argue that, like the miraculous cures at Lourdes, his recovery may have been due to internal mental factors. But what is the significance of Poulsen's experience with the shining being at the time of his cure?

I raised this question with Dr. Daniel Benor. He commented that such beings are frequently associated with unusual cures. The patient may directly perceive the beings, or they may work through the healer. When asked whether he thought such beings were imaginary or real, Benor was quite open to the possibility that they are real.

There is an obvious parallel between Poulsen's effulgent presence and the beings of light reported in near death experiences. The latter are frequently reported to ask the NDEer to return to the physical body, and in some cases they are said to push the person back. If the experiencer is truly near death, this could also count as a kind of cure. To draw the parallel still closer, I note that Poulsen said that his healing experience seemed to take place in an out-of-body state.

AURAS AND CHAKRAS

There are some healers who claim to be able to perceive the human aura and interact with in the healing process. This aura is said to be a structured arrangement of energy fields surrounding and interpenetrating the human body. The energy is not an obvious manifestation of the energy fields known to physics, such as gravity or electromagnetism, and it is associated with emotions, feelings, and patterns of thought.

A particularly vivid description of the human aura is given by the healer Barbara Brenner, based to a large extent on her own "higher sense perception" (Brenner, 1988). Brenner explains in detail how she was gradually able to see human auras in greater and greater detail over a period of years in which she developed her healing abilities.

According to her, the aura has seven principle layers, each of which encloses and interpenetrates the layer before it. She identifies these as the etheric, emotional, and mental bodies, connected with the physical plane of existence, the astral body, and the etheric template, celestial body, and ketheric body, connected with the spiritual plane of existence. The astral body serves as a bridge between the spiritual and physical planes. She gives a detailed account of the colors, internal structure, and psychological roles of these layers (Brenner, 1988, pp. 49–54).

Connected with the layers of the aura are vortices of energy called chakras (from the Sanskrit word for wheel). There are seven major chakras, corresponding to the seven auric layers, and several minor ones. These are arranged along the spinal column, starting with the first or root chakra near the perenium, and ending with the seventh or crown chakra, located at the top of the head. These chakras, in ascending order, are said to be concerned with (1) physical functioning and sensation, (2) earthly emotions, (3) mental life, (4) love, (5) higher will, connected with the divine, (6) speech and responsibility, and (7) universal love (Brenner, 1988, p. 43).

To what extent are the aura fields and chakras real, and to what extent are they imaginary? Benor remarks that "One must be cautious in interpreting aura readings. In two pilot studies I ran with eight aura sensitives who simultaneously observed a series of four patients with known diagnoses, the divergence in aura observations and their interpretations were far greater than the overlaps. Yet the patients resonated with most of the readings, different as they were. It appears that sensitives may resonate with partial aspects of the people they observe" (Benor, 1992, p. 290).

Of course, the failings of some aura readers do not imply that no one can correctly perceive real structure in the human aura. From the standpoint of the virtual reality model, aura observations are reminiscent of the icons used to denote functions on a computer screen. An icon is a small design, meaningless in and of itself, which is associated with a particular function or program that can be carried out by the computer. It is not unique, and different icons could be used to access the same function. Similarly, different modes of perception of the aura and its various structures might refer to the same underlying reality.

The chakras are described in detail in the yoga system of India, and the chakra system described by Western healers and psychics is probably derived from this source. In traditional yoga, the chakras are perceived in practices of meditation. There are highly elaborate descriptions of the chakras in texts on yoga, and these are broadly similar to the system presented by Brenner, but different in many details (see, for example Goswami, 1999). The layers of the aura are not stressed in the Indian literature, but they may correspond to the five "sheaths" or *koshas* of Vedanta. These are (1) *anna-maya-kosha,* the physical body, (2) *prana-maya-kosha,* the etheric body, (3) *mano-maya-kosha,* the mind, (4) *vijnana-maya-kosha,* the higher understanding, and (5) *ananda-maya-kosha,* the sheath of bliss (Feuerstein, p. 178). It would be interesting know to whether or not a detailed study of the Western and Indian systems would reveal a shared empirical foundation.

GUIDES

Brenner remarks that "as soon as you open your perception to layers above the third you also begin to perceive people or beings who exist in those layers who do not have physical bodies" (Brenner, 1988, p. 51). Here the layers above the third are seen as higher planes or dimensions not restricted to a particular body. Their inhabitants include spirit guides—nonphysical beings who look after the welfare of the living.

Brenner describes many procedures that can be carried out by a healer. Mostly, these involve projecting energy through the hands in relation to perceived energy imbalances in the patient's aura. She also says that spirit guides connected with the patient or the healer may contribute to the healer's efforts. For example, while discussing the healing of a woman with a hiatal hernia, Brenner says

> You sense a presence behind you, maybe even more than one. Gently, ever so gently, the guides slip through your auric field. It feels very familiar, very comfortable, and most of all, it feels wonderful. You have been lifted to a state of angelic serenity. You are at peace with the universe. As you sit in surrender to your own higher creative power, you observe the guide's hands slipping into the body of your patient through your etheric hands. You watch them sewing up the hernia in the diaphragm. At first you are incredulous, but then it all seems so natural that you simply allow it to happen" (Brenner, 1988, p. 221).

From the standpoint of the virtual reality theory, one could model this by postulating a series of separately existing virtual "spaces," in addition to the 3D space of the virtual world. Each space has a projection operator that maps it down to the space "beneath" it in the series. The virtual "physical" body is manifest in the lowest space, and higher thought forms of various kinds are manifest in the higher spaces, including a space devoted to what I have called the extended mind.

In this scheme, spirits are conscious beings who have forms manifest in the higher spaces, but who lack a body on the physical level. Ordinary sense perception extends from consciousness down to the physical body, with no allowance for input of information on the intermediate levels. When such input is allowed, the result is "higher sense perception" to varying degrees. Thus the spirit beings become visible when higher sense perception is switched on, either by the conditioning of the individual or by the action of these beings on the higher levels.

SUMMING UP

The process of normal healing depends on organized systems within the body which protect it from external assaults and internal breakdown, and which enable damaged tissues to restore themselves. These processes involve stored information, and one obvious source of that information is the genome, where large amounts of data are encoded in DNA. Normal healing involves gradual processes of cell division and differentiation, controlled by genetic data.

In this chapter I have barely touched the vast ocean of evidence pertaining to paranormal or miraculous healing. The most striking implication of this evidence is that healing processes may influence the body in complex ways that cannot be fully explained on the basis of the body's own resources. It appears that nonphysical forms of information exist which can be called upon to repair or protect the body. The molecular systems of the body can be manipulated in a precise, controlled way by agencies outside the body's neural and glandular systems. These agencies may also bring about abrupt and complex reorganizations of tissue which are harmoniously integrated into the body as a whole, but which could not depend on ordinary cellular processes.

Such agencies evidently imply the existence of modes of physical action that deviate from the known laws of physics, but harmonize with them. The system of ideas connected with the human aura suggests that the physical body is maintained in its normal state of health by interactions with higher "bodies," existing in additional planes or dimensions of existence. In a virtual reality system, these higher bodies could be represented by informational patterns in "spaces" in addition to the 3D space of the virtual world. The laws or algorithms governing the higher spaces do not in any way conflict with the well-known laws governing action in ordinary 3D space. However, the interactions passing between physical space and higher spaces do require a modification of these familiar laws. I would expect these modifications to appear in the form of new types of energy or force. I note that healing researchers such as Glen Rein (1992) and Elmer Green (1990) have extensively considered the possible role of new forces in bodily phenomena. Clearly, much work is still required to fill in the details.

Processes of non-ordinary healing may depend on the mind of the individual, or on that mind plus inputs from other beings. The available evidence suggests that healing depends on the deepest levels of individual psychology, and on nonphysical sources of information defining bodily structures and their transformations. Thus the spirit

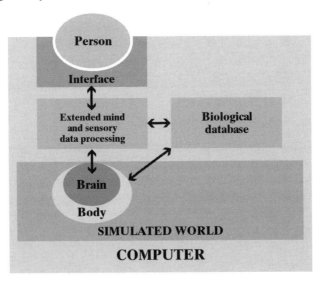

Figure 19. A virtual reality model of paranormal healing. Paranormal healing could be simulated in a virtual reality model by adding a database of biological information. The extended mind can access this database, which is assumed to contain both information and algorithms relevant to healing. These can be brought to bear on ailments in the virtual body. The arrows show one possible pathway of causation, in which the extended mind triggers software in the database to heal a particular bodily disorder.

beings involved in healings may be contributing both on the level of transformational wisdom and on the level of bodily engineering.

11

FROM CHANCE TO PURPOSE

*"There seems to be no more design
in the variability of organic beings, and in
the action of natural selection,
than in the course which the wind blows."*

—Charles Darwin

*"I would say that man, in his
bodily development, is a primate fetus
that has become sexually mature."*

—Louis Bolk

At first glance, the universe of modern cosmology resembles the dying embers left floating after an explosion of fireworks. There seems to be no design in the stars, nebulae, and galaxies that cannot be accounted for by simple physical processes. Yet this impression is misleading. Even though the argument for design has been banished from modern biology by the triumph of Darwin's theory, it still wins strong scientific support in the realm of cosmology.

First of all, there is the mysterious elegance of the laws of physics. Why should it be that these laws are comprehensible to human beings? This problem involves two remarkable facts that reach towards one another and meet in the middle. On one side, the laws of physics governing a good part of the natural world are simple enough to be grasped by a bright human graduate student. On the other side, it is remarkable that something as bright as a human graduate student has emerged from the dim-witted matrix of life on earth.

Consider the first side. The laws of physics are based on mathematical concepts that can be fully expounded in a few textbooks. But, in principle, these laws could be formidably complex. They could easily require hundreds or millions of textbooks to define. They might even be an indigestible morass of special cases and exceptions that could not be reduced to a rational system. There are many more ways to be complex than there are to be simple. The fact that the laws of physics are so simple and mathematically elegant has led many prominent scientists to conclude that God must be a mathematician.

The elegance of the laws of physics is also one of the conditions for the existence of life as we know it. Consider the fact that all electrons have exactly the same charge, and all protons have exactly the same opposite charge. This is essential for the stability of atoms and molecules. If these charges varied randomly from one particle to another, neutral atoms would not be possible, and biological molecules such as DNA could not function. It would seem that physics has been set up in such a way as to allow for life.

However, this argument should be qualified. If the charges of electrons and protons varied *very* slightly, this might not seriously interfere with chemistry. Yet we find that the properties of subatomic particles do not seem to vary in the slightest degree. So the elegance of physics goes beyond what would be required for life.

A UNIVERSE BUILT FOR US

If we examine the universe closely, we can find many features that would render life as we know it impossible if they were slightly changed. Here are a few examples pointed out by the astrophysicist Paul Davies (1992). First, the law of gravity and the thermodynamical and mechanical properties of hydrogen gas allow for the existence of stable stars. If gravity were much weaker, given the properties of hydrogen, then balls of gas big enough to trigger nuclear reactions would not form. If it were much stronger, stars would tend to collapse rapidly into black holes (Davies, 1992, p. 196).

According to astrophysics, heavy elements (above hydrogen on the periodic table) form in the nuclear furnaces of stars and are released into outer space by supernova explosions. If these explosions did not occur, the ingredients would not be available for the formation of terrestrial planets and the bodies of living organisms. However, supernovas depend crucially on the properties of neutrinos, ghostly subatomic particles that are difficult to detect because they interact very little with other matter. Thus neutrinos fortuitously have properties that allow for our existence (Davies, 1992, pp. 196–97).

Carbon nuclei are made in stars by a special nuclear reaction involving the simultaneous collision of three helium nuclei. The astrophysicist Fred Hoyle noticed that this reaction depends on a certain quantum mechanical effect (called a "resonance") that occurs at the energy level of helium nuclei in large stars. Without this effect, carbon would be a very rare element in the universe. After a detailed study, Hoyle found several other "coincidences" that were necessary for the production and preservation of carbon within stars. Observations such as these led Hoyle to finally adopt a theistic position, and he remarked that

> A common sense interpretation of the facts suggests that a superintellect has monkeyed with physics, as well as with chemistry and biology, and that there are no blind forces worth speaking about in nature. The numbers one calculates from the facts seem to me so overwhelming as to put this conclusion almost beyond question (Hoyle, 1982).

Many physical scientists have come to similar conclusions, based on their study of the universe and the laws of nature. These include astrophysicists Paul Davies, George Ellis, and Arthur Eddington, astronomers John O'Keefe, George Greenstein, and Alan Sandage, physicists Arno Penzias, Tony Rothman, Roger Penrose, and Vera Kistiakowsky, and many others (Kistiakowsky, 2000).

THE MONTE CARLO COSMOS

At the same time, many scientists resist the inference of design. Some dismiss the cosmic coincidences altogether by saying, "Of course these coincidences must be there, because, if they weren't, we wouldn't be here to talk about it." Others find this answer unsatisfying and seek a physical explanation for the observed cosmic fine-tuning.

One of these is Martin Rees, the British Astronomer Royal, who has developed an elegant model in which six numbers define the fundamental properties of the universe. Rees argues that each of these numbers must take on narrowly defined values in order for life to be possible (Rees, 1999). His numbers are (1) the strength of the force that holds atomic nuclei together, (2) the ratio between the strength of the forces holding atoms together and the force of gravity, (3) the average density of matter in the universe, (4) the cosmological constant, (5) the amplitude for forming seed galaxies in the early universe, and (6) the number (namely three) of spatial dimensions (Lemley, 2000, pp. 67–68).

If the first number were slightly larger than it is, nuclear fusion would have consumed all hydrogen in the Big Bang, leaving a universe with no fuel for stars and no water, among other things. If it were slightly smaller, a proton could not bind to a neutron, and the universe would consist only of hydrogen (Lemley, 2000, p. 66). Either way, it is hard to see how life in any form could arise.

Similar dire consequences follow from small variations in the other numbers. Yet it is extremely improbable for all six numbers to fall in the ranges required for life. The solution offered by Rees is his theory of the multiverse, or multiple universe. Suppose that there is some primordial substrate that continually generates universes like bubbles in fermenting beer. Suppose that each universe takes on a random set of values for the six numbers. Rees says that "If there are many universes, each governed by a differing set of numbers, there will be one where there is a particular set of numbers suitable to life. We are in that one" (Lemley, 2000, p. 66).

To account for one universe with life, this scheme requires us to posit a vast number of universes without life, as well as an underlying process that endlessly spawns universes. One could ask which theory carries more metaphysical baggage, this one, or the traditional idea of a cosmic designer.

Rees answers that metaphysical explanations cannot be tested, but his multiverse theory has the potential of being scientifically tested and confirmed. Cosmologists such as Stanford's Andrei Linde are investigating theoretical quantum processes that may amplify quantum fluctuations and cause new universes to continually sprout from old ones in a never-ending process (Lemley, 2000, p. 68). In Linde's theory, each universe may have different fundamental properties, and out of unlimited universes, at least one like ours is bound to show up.

It will not be possible to see one of these universes from another, since each is a separate, closed volume of space-time. This makes it hard to verify the theory. However, Rees hopes that "Some details of the fluctuations of ripples in the background radiation may help us determine the truth. Until then, the theory hangs on assumptions we must make about the physics of very dense states of matter" (Lemley, 2000, p. 69).

THE VIRTUAL UNIVERSE

It is interesting to compare the virtual reality model with Rees's theory. First of all, his theory is specifically intended to replace intelligent design with an unintelligent natural process. In contrast, the virtual reality model is based from the start on intelligence that ultimately emanates from the Ground Reality (or from the brains of the human programmers in a man-made VR).

However, the virtual reality system may make extensive use of iterated calculations to find solutions needed for guiding the virtual world. These iterative calculations are clearly analogous to Rees's scheme for generating multiple universes. They differ in that they are purely computational and they are controlled by the overall logic of the universal simulation. However, to find a universe suitable for a given form of the life, the virtual reality system might use iterative methods to find suitable values for Rees's fundamental constants.

It appears that Rees's theory may allow only a very tenuous form of observational verification, while leaving the major part of his multiverse as a mere inference. Likewise, we would not be able to distinguish between the "real" universe and a perfect simulation (by definition of "perfect"). However, the virtual reality model does allow for possible means of verification that may be much less expensive than the equipment used in astronomy and physics. A participant in a man-made VR can verify that he was in a virtual world by voluntarily taking off his interface gear and leaving the virtual world. The question arises of whether or not a participant could do this in the GR model.

This opens up an extensive topic of discussion that I will touch upon briefly in Chapter 12. For now, I note that the process of "taking off the interface gear" may involve several levels. If the senses of the conscious participant are channeled through several virtual realms, then by withdrawing the senses from one realm, one may be able to experience another realm. For example, this may be what happens in near death experiences. Withdrawing the senses from all realms would be equivalent to leaving the virtual reality altogether.

Apart from this, interactions between virtual realms should result in observable effects, and I have argued that these may include some of the so-called physical paranormal phenomena. One could also ask whether or not some of the "shining beings" mentioned in Chapter 10 may correspond to Tipler's "Turing-test passing interfaces" in a universe that is already simulated.

Since the virtual universe is intended to provide for life, the GR model predicts that life should be widespread throughout the universe. If it turned out that this were not so, that would be strong evidence against the model. This restriction should not be carried to an extreme, however. It does not rule out the existence of large masses of inanimate matter or long periods of preparation for habitable worlds. But it does militate against a universe with only one inhabited planet (the earth) or a universe predominated by vast, totally uninhabited galaxies.

BIOCHEMICAL MARVELS

Once the universe is manifest, with its stars, heavy elements, and planets, there is the possibility that life will arise under favorable conditions. At present, scientists do not know of any planet with life other than the earth, although many have speculated that the universe must contain vast numbers of inhabited worlds.

On earth, life began at an astonishingly early date. The earth dates back about 4.5 billion years, and it was in a molten state until about 3.8 billion years ago. Dickerson (1980) pointed out that simple, bacteria-like cells already flourished about 3.4 billion years ago, and Gould (1996, p. 176) pushed this back to 3.5–3.6 billion years ago. By 1.8–1.9 billion years ago, cells with more complex structure, called eukaryotes, had come into being. As recently as 580 million years ago, the first multicellular animals appeared in the fossil record.

In the 1920s, the Russian scientist A. I. Oparin proposed that life must have originated on the early earth by purely physical processes in a "primordial soup" of disorganized molecules (Oparin, 1938). This idea has remained popular ever since the chemist Stanley Miller ran sparks through a simulated primordial atmosphere and produced amino acids, the building blocks of proteins (Crick, 1981, pp. 77–78).

Given a warm soup of suitable molecules, how would life arise? It is not likely that a living cell of the modern type could assemble spontaneously from a combination of simple chemical compounds. Even the simplest modern cell is an incredibly complex molecular machine, and to throw it together in one fell swoop is extremely improbable. Some intermediate steps are needed, forming a chain leading from simple molecules to organized life. To obtain some idea of the requirements this chain must meet, it is instructive to work backwards from existing cells and try to assess the nature of the most recent links.

Modern cells depend on protein molecules, which are precisely specified chains of up to hundreds of amino acid sub-units. Each protein molecule performs many functions in the cell, and it is manufactured by a process called protein biosynthesis, in which genetic information encoded in DNA is translated into identical information in messenger RNA. The messenger RNA is then processed though cellular factories called ribosomes, which build proteins out of amino acid sub-units according to the RNA coding. This process runs in a circle, since every step depends crucially on the action of proteins that were made previously by the same process.

Woese (1965) proposed that on the early earth, precursors of modern cells must have had a very inaccurate system for translating genetic messages into amino acid sequences of proteins. They must therefore have depended on "statistical proteins" with amino acid sequences that varied substantially from one molecule to the next. Such molecules would not act in a very precise way. According to Martynas Ycǎs, such a crude metabolic system would have only a few genes, but the statistical proteins manufactured according to these genes could carry out many different metabolic functions (Ycǎs, 1974). However, the high-precision interactions that take place in modern cells wouldn't have been possible for these crude, early proteins.

Many theories have been proposed as to how the earthly biochemical system first got started. Some start with RNA and bring in proteins later (Gesteland and Atkins, 1993), while many others begin with proteins and somehow link them to RNA and DNA. Whatever theory we adopt, it remains true that if modern high-precision cells gradually evolved, then they must have been preceded by cruder prototypes. But would a crude cell work? To see why this might be problematic, consider some of the molecular mechanisms that are essential for modern cells.

For example, the process of protein biosynthesis requires amino acid molecules to be attached to so-called transfer RNA molecules (tRNA). There are twenty kinds of amino acids, and an amino acid of a given type has to be attached to a tRNA molecule that "codes" for that type. Otherwise, a mistake will occur in the assembly of amino acids into proteins.

An amino acid molecule is connected to the right tRNA by a protein called aminoacyl-tRNA synthetase. For example, a molecule of the amino acid isoleucine should be attached to isoleucyl-tRNA. According to Fersht (1977, p. 280), the two amino acids valine and isoleucine are so similar chemically that isoleucyl-tRNA synthetase could favor the direct binding of isoleucine over valine to the isoleucyl-tRNA by at most a factor of 20–40 in a living cell (the bacterium *E. coli*). This means that there is a good chance that a mistake will be made.

The actual factor of 3,000 is achieved by an editing mechanism, which acts to eliminate valine once it binds with the isoleucyl-tRNA synthetase molecule. A similar editing mechanism is used by the valyl-tRNA synthetase to eliminate threonine, which may bind to this molecule in place of valine. These editing mechanisms seem to require a great deal of precise structural detail on the part of the aminoacyl-synthetase molecules.

Without them, and others like them, it seems that the mechanism of protein biosynthesis would indeed produce "statistical" proteins, including "statistical" aminoacyl-synthetase molecules. The question is, would aminoacyl-synthetase molecules with errors be even less likely to attach amino acids to the right tRNAs? If so, we could be confronted with an "error catastrophe," resulting in a complete breakdown into chaos and dissolution.

It is not clear that a highly error-prone cell would be able to consistently reproduce and evolve into something higher. But suppose we have a crude cell that can somehow get by on error-ridden proteins, and suppose we add a couple of editing mechanisms to enhance the precision of protein biosynthesis. If other important editing mechanisms are still missing, there will still be many mistakes in the proteins produced, including the proteins that embody the new editing mechanisms. So the new mechanisms probably won't work very well, if at all. To bootstrap up to effective high precision, it would seem that all of the necessary editing mechanisms would have to be added at once—a leap that is highly improbable.

There are many theories of the origin of life, and I will not try to review them here. All face the task of explaining how a low precision proto-cell would work, even though all known living cells depend on high precision mechanisms. They also must explain how a low precision cell can attain high precision step-by-step when known high-precision mechanisms have to be built by a complete high-precision system of manufacture.

Could it be that life did not arise on the earth by physical processes? One possibility considered by a few scientists is that life may have been seeded on the earth from elsewhere (e.g. Crick and Orgel, 1973 and Hoyle, 1981). If 15 billion years have elapsed since the big bang, then life had billions of years to originate somewhere in our cosmic neighborhood and billions of years to travel to the earth. However, this theory merely puts off the problem of life's origins to an earlier time.

THE VIRTUAL ORIGIN OF LIFE

The virtual reality model starts with consciousness, but this does not mean that life in a virtual world must spring up, fully formed, in the very beginning. It is possible to envision evolutionary experiments carried out within a virtual world. These might make use of Darwinian trial and error in phases of the simulation which involve evolution of consciousness. At the same time, Darwinian iterative processes could be assisted from time to time by pure computer calculations (also iterative) that were designed to solve fundamental engineering problems. For example, in a man-made VR, we might want to explore the development of consciousness in dolphin bodies. We would use "off line" CAD calculations to design our dolphin models, and then we would run extensive trials in which human subjects occupied the models in a virtual marine environment.

Similarly, one can speculate that some features of living organisms in nature were actually designed with the aid of "off line" calculations outside the virtual world. This might include such features as the protein biosynthesis system in cells. At the same time, the overall process of biological evolution on the earth may be a vast experiment in the evolution of consciousness—made possible by its timeless nature (see Chapter 3).

Of course, the virtual reality model puts off the ultimate origin of life to an earlier stage. The identity of the virtual reality "programmer" must be sought in the Ground Reality itself. What is the nature of the Ground Reality, and how does it come to generate such elaborate and marvelous phenomena? I will touch on this topic in the last chapter. For now let us continue to look at the history of life on earth.

THE FOSSIL RECORD

The modern scientific history of life on earth is not a matter of evolutionary theory. Rather, it is based on empirical evidence collected in the science of paleontology, the study of fossil organisms. This field of study was first systematically developed in the 19th century, when geologists began to study the strata of the earth and give them relative dates based on the superposition of one stratum over another. Their shocking realization was that different strata contain different types of fossils and only the most recent layers contain remains of familiar life forms. This, more than anything else, shattered the ancient conviction that life has remained unchanged since its inception.

According to paleontologists, for billions of years life on earth consisted of little more than algal mats and slurries of bacterial cells. Gradually, cells became more complex, and about 600 million years ago, multicellular organisms arose. After some mysterious precursors in the Vendian Period, numerous remarkable forms of multicellular life seemed to spring into being abruptly within a time span as short as a few million years (Nash, 1995). This is the famous Cambrian explosion, which introduced nearly all of the basic body plans of subsequent earthly creatures.

After the introduction of multicellular organisms, the fossil record seems to reveal a long period in which various forms of life succeeded one another. From time to time, new forms were introduced which, from our point of view, represent an advance in organization. In the Devonian Period, about 360 to 400 million years ago, fishes became prominent and plant and animal life first emerged from the seas and began to occupy the margins of the land. In the subsequent Carboniferous Period, primitive alligator-shaped amphibians crawled through the archaic vegetation of vast coal swamps.

By the Permian Period, reptiles and the precursors of mammals had appeared. This era was terminated by the worst of several mass extinctions of life, in which it is estimated that up to 96% of all living species perished for unknown reasons (Gould, 1980, p. 43). After the Permian, the world famous dinosaurs dominated the earth for about 150 million years, until they mysteriously met their end in another mass extinction about 65 million years ago. In the dinosaur era, birds and flowering plants made their first appearance. Small mammals flourished throughout this period, but the proliferation of large mammals had to wait for the disappearance of the dinosaurs.

Finally, a few hundred thousand years ago, primitive *Homo sapiens* appeared on the scene. Human civilization first arose a few thousand years ago, within the last 0.0017% of the entire period since the Cambrian explosion of multicellular life.

Although many doubts can be raised about this picture of life's earthly history, it seems to be basically correct. A careful study of the evidence for ancient human life indicates that the human body plan and the stone-age level of human culture may extend back for millions rather than just for hundreds of thousands of years (Cremo and Thompson, 1993). However, radical though this finding may be, it changes only the details and not the overall pattern of the fossil record.

PLANET OF MOLLUSKS

The fossil record seems, on the whole, to reveal the progressive introduction of life forms with increasingly advanced bodily organization. This progression is irregular and frequently interrupted. It proceeds from unicellular organisms to marine invertebrates and simple marine plants, and from there to primitive vertebrates, fish, amphibians and terrestrial vegetation, reptiles, birds and flowering plants, advanced mammals, and finally human beings. In the vertebrates the brain and nervous system tend to become progressively more advanced, culminating in the human condition.

At the same time, it must be observed that this apparent progress was extremely slow until very recent times, and as new stages of organization have been added, the previous stages have remained prominent. Thus bacteria are still the most common and widespread organisms on the earth. Invertebrate life in tidal pools goes on in much the same way as it has since the Cambrian Period, and insects are doing essentially the same things they did in the days of the gigantic Carboniferous dragon flies and roaches.

This observation gave Charles Darwin the gut feeling that, contrary to the teachings of his religious upbringing, there could be no divine hand in the evolution of life. After marveling about the grand view of nature evolving under the action of physical law, he reflected in his notes on the unsatisfactory nature of the traditional religious view:

> How far grander than idea from cramped imagination that God created (warring against those very laws he established in all organic nature) the Rhinoceros of Java & Sumatra, that since the time of the Silurian he has made a long succession of vile molluscous animals. How beneath the dignity of him, who is supposed to have said let there be light & there was light . . . —bad taste" (Darwin, 1960, p. 132).

Today, of course, scientists explain the succession of life forms in the fossil record by the neo-Darwinian theory of evolution. In this theory, evolutionary developments are attributed to random variation sifted by natural selection. This theory can create plausible explanations of many observed features of the biological world, and it is reasonable to suppose that the Darwinian mechanism of evolution does function in nature. However, it is far from clear that this mechanism is the last word. Organs of high perfection and complexity, such as the eagle's eye or the human speech center, are notoriously difficult to explain by mutation and natural selection. In addition, many features of the fossil record can be placed in the Darwinian framework only by an act of faith.

There has been intense controversy over Darwin's theory. The Harvard evolutionist Steven Jay Gould has stressed that Darwin led us into a world where matter is everything and "mind, spirit, and God as well, are just words that express the wondrous results of neuronal complexity" (Gould, 1977b, p. 13). This stance has met with strong resistance from Christians, with their tradition of divine creation. On the Christian side, scientists such as physicist Gerald Schroeder and biochemist Michael Behe have framed a scientific case against Darwinism, citing evidence of design in nature (Schroeder, 1997; Behe, 1996). On the Darwinian side, scientists including Gould and Oxford zoologist Richard Dawkins have taken up the cudgels for Darwinism (Dawkins, 1986).

The arguments in this controversy are highly complex and detailed, and I will not try to review them here. Rather, I will restrict myself to making a simple observation. If we leave aside Darwin's materialistic philosophy and focus on the scientific content of his theory, we see that it is not so much a theory as a framework that can accommodate many theoretical elements. Darwin's basic proposal is that genetic variation and natural selection account for the origin of species, given some initial, primitive organisms. Darwin saw natural variation as random, in the sense of being unrelated to final results or goals. Nonetheless, whatever process produces variation in organisms is grist for the Darwinian mill. As new processes are discovered, they can be added to Darwin's framework without disrupting it or displacing what it already contains.

For example, Darwin had a very undeveloped understanding of variation and inheritance, but later on this deficiency was remedied by introducing Mendelian genetics and knowledge of DNA into the Darwinian theoretical framework. Once these additions were well established, it looked as though all variation in species was due to random editing of the genetic information encoded in DNA.

Then the biologist Lynn Margulis threw a monkey wrench into this tidy picture. She argued persuasively that the organelles in higher cells (called eukaryotes) are the descendants of symbiotic bacteria that lived inside the ancestors of these cells (Gould, 1977b, p. 115). The organelles include the cellular powerhouses called mitochondria, the chloroplasts, which extract energy from sunlight in plants, and cilia, which allow cells to swim or create currents in their surrounding fluid. One might have thought that Darwin's theory required these organelles to arise through a hard-to-imagine, mutation-driven sequence of intermediate forms. But suddenly, Darwinism was relived of this unwelcome burden. The organelles apparently originated in a completely different way—by a new form of variation.

Now consider the virtual reality model. I have argued for the existence of a Ground Reality consisting of consciousness and various functions that I have compared with computer software. Some of these functions impinge on living organisms and allow them to be influenced by information originating outside the virtual 3D space.

Suppose, for the sake of argument, that we actually live in such a virtual reality. In that case, these additional functions will inevitably have some effect on both the genetic variation and the survival of organisms. They are simply additions to the Darwinian framework, and everything that is already there in that framework can remain.

The higher functions of the virtual reality model have presumably been in existence throughout the history of the universe. They are not bound to any particular location in virtual space, and they are certainly are not limited to the tiny speck of cosmic dust known as the planet earth. If the universe is 15 billion years old, then consciousness probably interacted with physical life on many planets billions of years ago. It is therefore not surprising if it has interacted with life on earth from its very inception.

This picture of evolution introduces an element of purpose and conscious intention that conflicts with Darwin's materialistic outlook, but it does not disrupt his theoretical framework. In this scheme, we needn't put God to work fashioning each vile molluscous creature, but neither do we have to suppose that life has no purpose in a broader scheme of things.

INCREASING YOUR EQ

Once the basic molluscan body plan was established, the many subsequent variations on this theme—mostly involving shapes and sizes of shells—can easily be seen as blind products of natural forces. The same holds true for many types of organisms. However, if we look at the higher vertebrates, a group comprising a tiny fraction of the earth's living population, we do seem to see evidence for direction and purpose.

Consider the mystery of human beings, who combine the instincts of mollusks with the insights of philosophers. The physicist Paul Davies remarked that

> We have cracked part of the cosmic code. Why this should be, just why Homo sapiens should carry the spark of rationality that provides the key to the universe, is a deep enigma. We, who are children of the universe—animated stardust—can nevertheless reflect on the nature of the same universe, even to the extent of glimpsing the rules on which it runs (Davies, 1992, p. 232).

To get some insight into this from the evolutionary perspective, we can begin by looking at the history of vertebrate brains. Brain size depends partly on body weight, but this dependency can be factored out to give us an "encephalization quotient" (EQ) that tells us whether an animal's brain is large or small for its size (Gould, 1977b, p. 187). When this is done, cold-blooded vertebrates are found to have consistently smaller EQs than their warm-blooded counterparts (Gould, 1977b, p. 188). An exception can be made for sharks, and certain small, predatory dinosaurs, such as the *Velociraptor* (assuming it was cold-blooded). The brains of the cold-blooded fish, amphibians, and reptiles have always tended to remain more-or-less the same. However, since the beginning of the Age of Mammals (following the demise of the dinosaurs), mammalian brains have tended to consistently increase in EQ, with the brains of carnivores maintaining a steady lead over those of herbivores (Gould, 1977b, p. 189).

The evolutionist Stephen Jay Gould gives a Darwinian explanation for the increase in mammalian EQs. The idea is that by developing bigger brains, some carnivores got smarter, got more to eat, and produced more young. Therefore they outnumbered and soon replaced their small-brained cousins. At the same time, some herbivores outsmarted the carnivores by developing bigger brains and they also prevailed in the struggle for survival. The carnivores and herbivores engaged in a cephalic arms race, developing larger and larger brains throughout the Age of Mammals.

Gould points out, however, that until the rise of the Isthmus of

Panama, South America was a refugium for small brained marsupial mammals. The marsupial carnivores and herbivores maintained small brains until larger-brained carnivores from North America crossed the isthmus and wiped them out (Gould, 1977b, p. 190). But why didn't the marsupial carnivores and herbivores engage in their own cephalic arms race? All one can do is make the rather unenlightening observation that natural selection just didn't work that way for South American marsupials.

Gould raises a related point. He notes that the oldest brain cast of a primate dates back 55 million years, close to the beginning of the Age of Mammals. The owner of the cast, called *Tetonius homunculus*, had the largest brain for its size of any animal of its time—three times as big as that of the average contemporary mammal. Gould asks why this should be so in a small tree-dwelling mammal similar to small-brained rats and shrews. It seems that the primate family, which includes human beings, has been consistently large-brained from its very beginning. Why this should be is unknown, but it is the starting point of an even greater mystery, to which I now turn.

PRE-EVOLVED HUMANS

If we glance at an infant chimpanzee we are immediately struck by the fact that it looks much more like a human being than an adult chimp, with its massive teeth and protruding jaw (Figure 20). In a series of papers in the early 20th century, the Dutch anatomist Louis Bolk expanded on this observation by arguing that human beings evolved by retaining the juvenile or embryonic features of their ancestors. In effect, the human being was pre-evolved in the form of the primate fetus long before the actual appearance of humans on the earth. As Bolk put it, "Our ancestor already possessed all primary specific characteristics of contemporary man, but only during a short phase of its individual development" (Gould, 1977a, p. 360).

Bolk was an evolutionist, but not a Darwinist. He believed that the human form arose through a gradual and coordinated retardation of development, controlled by adjustments of the endocrine glands. This would imply that many key features of human anatomy have not been chosen by a process of natural selection, acting on random genetic variations. They have simply come about as inevitable consequences of an overall shift in glandular function.

Stephen Jay Gould rejected Bolk's non-Darwinian approach to evolution, while endorsing his overall theory of fetalization. Gould favors a Darwinian theory of piece-by-piece, or "mosaic" evolution, in which many different features of human anatomy were more-or-less independently chosen by natural selection as a consequence of their adaptive value. Curiously enough, however, the chosen features are overwhelmingly characterized by a retardation of development and a prolongation of fetal modes of growth. In technical terms, human anatomy is "paedomorphic," which means having childlike form, and it is a product of "neoteny," or retention of juvenile traits.

One surprising paedomorphic feature of humans is their upright stance and bipedal mode of locomotion. The long, strong legs that are

so useful for walking can be attributed to a tendency for fetal organs to start small at the tail end of the body and then catch up later (Gould, 1977a, p. 383). By prolonging this tendency,

Figure 20. Baby and adult chimpanzee. The head of a baby chimpanzee has human proportions, its neck is erect and centered beneath the head, and its torso is human in form. In contrast, the adult chimp has a massively protruding jaw and a small cranium. Its head is slung forward from its neck and supported by powerful muscles.

the human legs become much longer than those of other primates. This process will not account for the extremely long arms and short legs of the Great Apes, since the arms are closer to the head than the legs. Thus the condition of the apes must be regarded as a specialization—presumably for brachiation in trees—that adds something new and different to the fetal growth pattern.

It is often thought that the human foot is highly specialized for walking. However, its features also turn out to be paedomorphic. In the early embryonic stage of all primates, the big toe is lined up with the other toes, just as it is in human adults. In humans this condition is retained, but in other primates, the big toe gradually rotates for effective opposability. Fortuitously, this neotenous feature of the human foot is well adapted for human plantigrade locomotion (Gould, 1977a, p. 375).

The vertebral column is more centrally positioned in humans than in apes or monkeys. This feature represents an extension of a developmental trend found in primate embryos, but it is also an important component of the upright human posture (Gould, 1977a, p. 383). The foramen magnum, where the spine connects with the skull, is at the back of the skull in adult apes and monkeys. However, in humans and in infant apes and monkeys, it is at the bottom of the skull. This configuration is useful for upright posture, but at the same time it is neotenous. As Bolk put it, "Bipedal walk found in primitive, fetal, central position of the foramen magnum a lucky condition, sympathetic to its trend" (Gould, 1977a, p. 397).

Gould points out that human anatomy does have some specialized features, such as several aspects of pelvic shape and the bending of the spinal column in the lumbo-sacral region (Gould, 1977a, pp. 383–84). (The latter, of course, is famous for backaches and seems less than optimal in design.) In contrast, many of the distinguishing features of the Great Apes are specializations that deviate from the basic primate pattern (Gould, 1977a, p. 384).

The most obvious feature of human fetalization is the expanded brain, which Gould attributes to a prolongation of fetal growth rates. Some authorities have argued that the reduction of the human facial skeleton is a consequence of the expansion of the brain, but Gould points out that this is an independent paedomorphic feature (Gould, 1977a, p. 393). The late closing of the human cranial sutures is yet another independent paedomorphic feature, since it takes place well after the brain has finished growing (Gould, 1977a, pp. 372–73).

Even the protruding human chin and nose can be accounted for as consequences of neoteny (Gould, 1977a, pp. 381–82). These developments depend on the reduction of the face, but other neotonous features, such as hair reduction and the orientation of the female genital tract seem to be independent expressions of an overall fetalization process.

The enlarged brain is accompanied by prolonged infancy and childhood, which allows for the transmission of culture through education. The life-long human persistence of curiosity and playfulness is a kind of "behavioral neoteny" that parallels morphological neoteny (Gould, 1977a, p. 402). The human upright stance frees the hands for manipulation of objects and allows the burgeoning human intellect to develop technology. Gould notes that the larger human brain may account for the extended human life span (unusual for mammals of human size), which allows for prolonged individual learning. He also cites an argument contending that the ability of neurons in the adult human brain to readily form new connections "is a continuation of growth processes that are much more pronounced in embryos" (Gould, 1977a, p. 401).

This evolutionary picture presents human beings as an expression of pre-existing fetal features. As Gould put it, "The availability of these features as transient stages in juvenile ancestors and the existence of a mechanism (retarded development) for their transfer to adult descendants establishes their preadaptive value" (Gould, 1977a, p. 397). "Preadaptive" means that the features were there in latent form before natural selection could choose them on the basis of their adaptive value.

So why did such a convenient suite of features exist? From a neo-Darwinian perspective, they can be regarded at most as adaptations for life in the womb. For example, it is advantageous for the embryonic brain to be spherical since a sphere fits the largest mass into the smallest space (Gould, 1977a, p. 397). However, such arguments amount to saying that the human form was pre-evolved by chance and then simply unveiled by Darwinian processes. Since so many features are involved, the chance that they will all pop up simultaneously is very small, and we are justified in looking for a different explanation.

PLATFORMS FOR HIGHER CONSCIOUSNESS

The evidence seems to point to the human being as a novel element in the world of earthly life—a walking platform for the manifestation of mind and consciousness, based on plans dating back to the earliest primates. If the fetalization theory is correct, the human brain is simply an expanded version of the basic mammalian brain, brought about by changes in growth rates. But for such a brain to perform marvelous new functions allowing for human civilization, it needs more than extra neurons. It also requires the equivalent of new software, and such software can be provided through the virtual link to the extended mind. Thus one can hypothesize that humans are a result of two levels of planned transformation, a visible one that created the childlike but adaptable human body, and an invisible one that upgraded the interface between brain and consciousness.

Gould muses that "The evolution of consciousness can scarcely be matched as a momentous event in the history of life; yet I doubt that its efficient cause required much more than a heterochronic extension of fetal growth rates and patterns of cell proliferation" (Gould, 1977a, p. 409). To bring about consciousness by a mere adjustment of growth rates is a tall order. But by increasing the number of neurons in the brain, retaining their fetal adaptability, and providing a setting conducive to education, such adjustments may facilitate the expression of consciousness through matter.

MIND IN ANIIMALS

If human bodies are connected to consciousness through a complex system of mental functions, then it is natural to ask when and how this state of affairs arose. It is not possible to give a detailed answer to this question, but it is interesting to note that there is some evidence that higher mammals are capable of telepathic or clairvoyant perception.

For example, Rupert Sheldrake and Pamela Smart conducted a study of a dog named Jaytee that seemed to know in advance when his owner (Pam Smart) was due to return home (Sheldrake and Smart, 2000). Smart and Sheldrake conducted more than 100 experiments in which Smart would travel for several kilometers and return home, while the place near a window where the dog usually waited for her was videotaped continuously. The videotapes were time coded and were scored blind. The investigators report that "In experiments in which P.S. [Pamela Smart] returned at randomly selected times, Jaytee was at the window 4% of the time during the main period of her absence and 55% of the time when she was returning ($p < .0001$)" (Sheldrake and Smart, 2000, p. 233). The dog showed similar behavior in other experiments in which Smart returned at times of her own choosing.

Sheldrake and Smart argue that there were no sensory cues available to inform the dog that its owner was returning. Smart's parents were sometimes at home with the dog, but care was taken to make sure that they did not know when Smart was coming back. On fifty occasions, Jaytee was left on his own and these trials also yielded significant results. Sheldrake and Smith also discuss an independent study by Wiseman, Smith, and Milton (1998, 2000) that purportedly refuted the dog's alleged abilities. They argue that the data collected by these authors actually confirm their own findings.

Sheldrake and Smart conclude that Jaytee's return-anticipating behavior may have depended on telepathic influence from its owner. If this conclusion is valid, it suggests that dogs may share with human beings some of the extended mental functions discussed in previous chapters.

In the virtual reality model, such functions involve organized systems that are not part of the virtual body. As such, they could not arise solely through the Darwinian mechanism, which is limited to modifying the body's genome. It would interesting to know how widespread paranormal abilities may be among living species.

THE GREAT CHAIN OF BEING

In both Western and Eastern traditions, people used to see the world as a more-or-less static hierarchy, extending from God on the top, down to orders of spiritual or angelic beings, to humans, to animals and plants, and finally to matter. Within an individual, this hierarchy could be seen as spirit, mind, body, and matter.

This Great Chain of Being was linked together in two ways. First of all, there was a top-down relationship of superiority and control.

Secondly, there was a bottom-up sequence of successively higher levels of consciousness. Some schools of thought included the idea of a process of transmigration, in which conscious beings could rise through the hierarchy from the vegetative level to the levels of animals, humans, and beyond. Spiritual practices were provided that would assist humans in this process of elevation.

It has often been observed that in the 19th century, the theory of evolution turned the Great Chain of Being on its side, converting it into a temporal sequence of purely material evolutionary stages. These stages are widely seen as progressive: Matter spontaneously formed primitive living organisms, and these organisms gradually passed through higher and higher stages of organization, culminating in the human species. Given this idea, it stands to reason that evolution may continue up the chain and ultimately produce God. Of course, this is Tipler's idea.

To a strict Darwinist, this is wrong, for there is no directing force within evolution. If organisms have in some cases increased in sensory or mental power, that is simply because natural selection happened to favor this under the prevailing circumstances. Selection could just as well have favored increased thickness of the skull and a smaller brain. Nonetheless, if we can identify a progressive directing force, we are free to add it to Darwin's theory without detracting from the theory's existing scientific content.

The naturalist Alfred Russel Wallace tried to do this back in the 19th century. In 1858, Wallace became famous by sending Charles Darwin a paper on evolution and innocently asking for Darwin's comments. The paper shocked Darwin, because it outlined the main points of his own evolutionary theory, which he had been secretly developing for some 20 years. Darwin responded by publishing his *Origin of Species*, and Wallace allowed him to take priority.

Wallace accepted Darwinism (or "Wallacism," as Darwin once put it), but he was troubled by phenomena that Darwinism couldn't readily explain. For example, he pointed out that, "Natural selection could only have endowed savage man with a brain a few degrees superior to that of an ape, whereas he actually possesses one very little inferior to that of a philosopher" (Wallace, 1895, p. 202). If a child from a primitive tribe is given a modern education, he or she is as likely to excel in science and mathematics as any other person in modern society. Yet the child's ancestors presumably never had contact with mathematics beyond simple counting. One might well ask why advanced technical intelligence evolved in societies in which it had no application.

After his pioneering work on evolution, Wallace became convinced of some of the paranormal phenomena described in Chapter 9, and he came to accept the reality of spirits. This provided a new element in his picture of nature and a possible new cause of evolutionary change. To Darwin's dismay, Wallace boldly added spirit intervention to evolutionary theory. Forty years later, at the end of his life, Wallace continued on his heretical path, but he maintained that "I still uphold, as I have always done, the essential teachings of Darwinism" (Wallace, 1911, p. 333).

Wallace argued that intervention by higher beings could account for the direction that he saw in the history of life. In his last book he wrote

> I now uphold the doctrine that not man alone, but the whole World of Life, in almost all its varied manifestations, leads us to the same conclusion—that to afford any rational explanation of its phenomena, we require to postulate the continuous action and guidance of higher intelligences; and further, that these have probably been working towards a single end, the development of intellectual, moral, and spiritual beings (Wallace, 1911, p. 316).

To Wallace the motivating force for the temporal chain of being is the continuing presence of the atemporal chain. Intellectual, moral, and spiritual beings developed on the earthly plane because they already existed in a different form on higher planes of being. Although this may seem to be begging the question, it is a consistent way of reconciling evolution with traditional views.

In the virtual reality model, we also have the equivalent of the Great Chain of Being. Here the chain consists of various mental functions that bridge the gap between consciousness and the virtual brain. These functions include processes that could be used to modify virtual bodies and bring about a directed series of bodily forms.

Yet many questions remain. If complex, nonphysical processes are guiding evolution, then how did they arise? If the manifestation of embodied intelligence was planned, what is its purpose? Finally, what can we say about this mysterious element of consciousness that I frequently refer to but never explain? We will turn to these questions in the final chapter.

12

THE ONE AND THE MANY

*"The Absolute Truth is simultaneously,
inconceivably divided and undivided."*

—Chaitanya Mahaprabhu

Thus far, I have treated consciousness as an unknown while elaborating the details of the virtual world. To study consciousness itself we need a reliable source of information about it. Unfortunately, modern scientific disciplines, including psychology, have relatively little to offer in this regard. At present, the main available sources of information on consciousness are the contemplative traditions, including yoga and different schools of meditation.

Although these traditions are not generally viewed as scientific, they have always placed a heavy emphasis on empirical observation of states of consciousness. Typically, they are framed as elaborate philosophical systems intended to explain the results of introspective processes. These systems are similar to scientific theories, which sum up our understanding of large amounts of empirical data. Like such theories, contemplative traditions often try to be universal in scope, even though their real strength lies in a specialized area. Thus the contemplative traditions may teach ancient forms of physics or astronomy, while at the same time offering many valuable insights into the nature of consciousness.

THE ONE

Many old spiritual traditions refer to the Supreme Being as one, undivided entity. When we ask what this means, we find at once that we are confronted with a paradox (a statement pointing beyond, *para*, thought, *dokein*). Although the One is undivided, it also contains

243

parts, including everything that exists.

It is not possible to formulate this idea in rigorous, rational terms, but various metaphors are traditionally given that point to it intuitively. The example is often given of a vast net of countless jewels, in which each jewel reflects in each of the other jewels in the net and is, in fact, one with it (Rinpoche, 1993, p. 37). Of course, reflection does not really create oneness, but the suggestion is made of an entity with infinitely many parts, each of which is somehow the same as the whole entity.

One way to look at this is to say that each part of the whole contains some representation of the whole, or some significant marks of influence from all other parts of the whole. Although this defines a kind of oneness, the oneness of the One is something much stronger than this. It is an actual identity of all parts of the whole, which nonetheless remain distinct. Perhaps the most explicit statement of this paradoxical state of affairs was given by the 15th-century Indian mystic Chaitanya, who declared that the Absolute Truth is simultaneously, inconceivably divided and undivided (Prabhupada, 1974, p. 119). Here the word "inconceivable" (*acintya* in Sanskrit) rules out perfectly conceivable arrangements, in which diverse parts are simply connected together by mutual relationships.

Being conscious, the One is a subject, not an object. For consciousness to register an image, it must have parts, just as the image does. But if the process of perception can be reduced to parts, it becomes mechanical and the unified nature of consciousness is lost. This is precisely the point of thought experiments such as John Searle's Chinese room (discussed in Chapter 1), in which the power of a computer to be conscious is repudiated by breaking the computer down into parts. Intuitively, we experience consciousness as unified, even though the objects of our consciousness are diverse. This is the paradoxical state of affairs mentioned by Chaitanya, and it is the reason why rational philosophy cannot grasp consciousness.

An analytic philosopher might reply to this by saying, "So much the worse for consciousness. It is a meaningless concept." However, another feature of the One is that individual consciousness can rise to higher levels of perception in which the intuitive appreciation of oneness becomes overwhelmingly persuasive. This, of course, is the conclusion all schools of meditation and yoga. It is a case where empiricism refutes philosophical argumentation.

THE MANY

How does individual consciousness relate to the One consciousness? The most obvious feature of human life is that individual consciousness is normally limited to the physical body and senses. If consciousness were totally unified, then the mental images in the minds of several people would be as much integrated together as the parts of a single image perceived by one person. However, this is certainly not generally reported. Even in cases of paranormal cognition, we do not see a merging of two personalities, so that the memories, thoughts, and sense perceptions of two persons are seen from one conscious perspective.

Ordinary experience tells us that there are individual psyches or centers of consciousness, each with its own mind and senses. Yet a prominent tradition of Hindu thought holds that the individual psyche (*jiva* in Sanskrit) is inherently identical with the supreme consciousness. This idea dates back at least as far as the ancient *Upanishads*, which are famous for statements such as "Everything is only the Absolute. There is no other. I am that" (Feuerstein, 1998a, p. 341). One understanding of this is that the individual existence of the psyche is illusory. Thus the Advaya-Taraka-Upanishad says that "Realizing the psyche (*jiva*) and the Lord (*ishvara*) to be illusory, and abandoning all differentiation as 'not this, not that' (*neti neti*)—that which remains is the nondual Absolute" (Feuerstein, 1998a, p. 427). This philosophy is generally known as *advaita-vada*, or nondualism.

Of course, one may ask, if individual existence is illusory, what suffers from the illusion? It could not be the nondual Absolute itself, since this is said to eternally exist in full bliss and knowledge. One answer is that a small part of the absolute consciousness falls under illusion due to the influence of *maya*, just as a small part of the atmosphere is divided from the whole by a pot. On the face of it, this analogy works because (1) the atmosphere is inherently divisible, and (2) the pot is something distinct from the atmosphere. We can try to mend the dualism in (2) by supposing that the "pot" emanates from the atmosphere and is one with it. In this case we obtain a picture in which the Absolute is capable of multiple modes of consciousness, and the Absolute puts itself partly into illusion by exercising its own energy (the pot, or *maya*).

Another answer is that the nondual Absolute contains subdivisions that are inherently one with it (so that it can be nondual), but which may fall into the illusion of being separate from it. This differs from the first answer in that it posits subdivisions that are susceptible to illusion, rather than subdivisions that are caused by the power of illusion.

The Vaishnava School of Hinduism has what appears to be the most explicit expression of this idea. The term Vaishnava refers to the worshipers of Vishnu (the All-pervading). This community developed several different responses to the doctrine of *advaita-vada* in the period from roughly the 10th to the 15th centuries. These include *vishishta-*

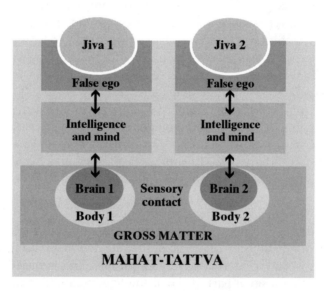

Figure 21. The virtual reality model from the standpoint of *sankhya* philosophy. From the standpoint of *sankhya,* one of the six schools of traditional Indian philosophy, the computer of the virtual reality model corresponds to the *mahat-tattva*—the total material realm (see Figure 3). The interface equipment corresponds to the false ego (*ahankara*), and the sensory data processing is carried out by intelligence and mind (*buddhi* and *manas*).

advaita or specific monism (Ramanuja), *shuddha-dvaita* or purified dualism (Madhva), *shuddha-advaita* or purified nondualism (Vishnu-swami), *dvaita-advaita* or dualism and monism (Nimbarka), and Chaitanya's *acintya-bheda-abheda*. Ramanuja, in particular, taught that "although all the energies of the Lord are one, each keeps its individuality *(vaishishtya)*" (Prabhupada, 1973, p. 117). These philosophies range in emphasis from strong dualism to nondualism tempered by some form of individualized consciousness. They all grapple with the problem of reconciling the experience of illusion with the oneness of the Absolute consciousness.

In one prominent formulation of the Vaishnava teachings, there are three secondary emanations from the energy of the Supreme Being, namely *cit* or spiritual substance, *jiva*, or individualized consciousness, and *maya*, the energy manifesting the material world (Dasa, 1999, p. 180). The *jivas* are pure conscious subdivisions of the Supreme, and by nature they live in the *cit* world in full harmony with the supreme conscious source. However, they are capable of becoming bound to the illusory world of *maya* by identification with a virtual ego, intelligence, mind, and body. In this state, the *jiva* and its ego, intelligence, and mind transmigrate from one physical body to another, impelled by attachments arising from bodily activity, or *karma*.

The material realm is also known in India's *sankhya* philosophy as the *mahat-tattva*, and it is broken down into a number of categories, including false ego *(ahankara)*, intelligence *(buddhi)*, mind *(manas)*, and the gross material elements. (Sankhya is one of the six traditional schools of Indian philosophy.) Figure 21 shows the virtual reality model recast in these terms, and it can be compared with Figure 3 in Chapter 1. The self *(atma)* manifests many individual selves, or *jivas*, and we have seen that different schools of Hinduism have different views as to whether these divisions are permanent or temporary. False ego is considered to be the point of contact between the conscious self and the material energy. Intelligence and mind are considered to be subtle elements which can function independently of the gross physical body. The various functions that I assigned to "extended mind" in previous chapters fall into these *sankhya* categories. Finally, the virtual world corresponds to gross matter, which *sankhya* breaks down into broad categories of earth, water, fire, air, and ether (space).

While the Vaishnava theology posits structure within consciousness itself, Buddhism explicitly teaches that consciousness is divided by the influence of the mind, which is seen as an ever-changing network of actions and reactions. In Buddhism there is no soul (or *jiva*), but the individual mind is repeatedly reborn by—in effect—downloading itself into new bodies. Liberation is attained when the individual recognizes that consciousness is one and thereby ceases to identify with the phenomena continually arising within consciousness. Here too the implication is that the one consciousness is capable of many conscious points of view.

In contrast, the Western Christian tradition gradually became firmly wedded to the idea that the self is the physical body. By the Fourth Lateran Council in 1215, heretics were required to assent to the doctrine that "all rise again with their own individual bodies, that is, the bodies which they now wear" (Murphy, 1992, p. 202). Although this may seem absurd, a passage in the New Testament clarifies what Christian theologians may have originally had in mind:

> All flesh is not the same flesh: but there is one kind of flesh of men, another flesh of beasts, and another of fishes, and another of birds. There are also celestial bodies, and bodies terrestrial: but the glory of the celestial is one, and the glory of the terrestrial is another. . . . So also is the resurrection of the dead. It is sown in corruption; it is raised in incorruption: It is sown in dishonor; it is raised in glory: It is sown in weakness; it is raised in power: It is sown a natural body; it is raised a spiritual body (I Corinthians 15:39–44).

It seems clear from this that the resurrected body was once thought to be of a different nature than the ordinary human body. Nonetheless, some scientists, such as John Polkinghorne and Frank Tipler, have tied the Christian doctrine of bodily resurrection to the scientific theory that life and consciousness are reducible to material patterns (see Chapter 5). The Buddhist doctrine of mind as a stream of actions and reactions is also susceptible to this kind of interpretation. Thus the philosopher John Searle has ribbed scientists who dream of downloading themselves into computers by accusing them of being "closet Buddhists" (Searle, 1990).

THE MIND IN BUDDHISM

However, matters are not so simple. In the virtual reality model, reality is divided into two parts: the virtual world, where everything can be reduced to bits (i.e. the binary units of calculation), and consciousness, which is irreducible. The question is, on what side of this divide do we place various entities, qualities, and features? We can obtain some useful insights by looking at Buddhist doctrine from the standpoint of this question. I will refer specifically to Tibetan Buddhist doctrine, which is presented with great clarity by the Buddhist teacher Sogyal Rinpoche (1993).

First of all, Buddhism regards all objects and phenomena as temporary and empty, or devoid of essence. This concept applies well to matter, as it is understood by modern science. All material objects are composed of swarms of subatomic particles that are in a continual state of transformation. Even though physics grants these particles some inherent qualities (such as charge and mass), these are so rudimentary and so foreign to our experience that it is reasonable to view matter as devoid of essence. This has inspired many people with a deep sense of cosmic alienation and meaninglessness. Thus the physicist Steven Weinberg lamented that, "The more the universe seems comprehensible, the more it also seems pointless" (Weinberg, 1977, p. 144).

Yet Sogyal looks at this from another perspective. He says that by contemplating change and impermanence, "we come slowly to find ourselves face to face, in gratitude and joy, with the truth of the changeless, with the truth of the deathless, unending nature of mind!" (Rinpoche, 1993, p. 40). Here "mind" refers not to the individual mind, but to the universal consciousness, which Sogyal calls "Rigpa" in Tibetan. He says that this is "a primordial, pure, pristine awareness that is at once intelligent, cognizant, radiant, and always awake. It could be said to be the knowledge of knowledge itself" (Rinpoche, 1993, p. 47). By seeing the meaninglessness of material nature, we can be freed from attachment to it, and this opens the gateway to a realization of our true nature.

We see then that consciousness, as Rigpa, stands on the other side of the reducibility divide. It is not temporary or devoid of essence. Rather, it has timeless qualities of intelligence and radiant clarity.

Sogyal identifies it with the Supreme Being of major world religions. "It is in fact the nature of everything," and "to realize the nature of mind is to realize the nature of all things" (Rinpoche, 1993, p. 47).

The Rigpa is clearly an active agency. First of all, it runs the process of reincarnation. Reincarnation is said to show "some kind of ultimate justice in the universe" (Rinpoche, 1993, p. 94). As such, it must be directed by an agency with an "ultimate," or essential sense of justice. Secondly, it is responsible for the total display of empty phenomena. For example, all "risings" of thoughts within the individual mind are "none other than this Rigpa's self-radiance" (Rinpoche, 1993, p. 161).

Tibetan Buddhism asserts the existence of six different realms of being—the worlds of the gods, demigods, humans, animals, hungry ghosts, and the hellish worlds (Rinpoche, 1993, p. 112). Except for the human one, these realms are a bit embarrassing in the modern context, and they are often dismissed as mere symbolism or superstition. However, the human realm is no more real or unreal than the other five in Buddhist doctrine. Sogyal says that these worlds "may in fact exist beyond the range of perception of our karmic vision" (Rinpoche, 1993, p. 112). While appealing for support to modern scientific theories of parallel universes, he points out that "the great Buddhist teachings speak of innumerable worlds in different dimensions" (Rinpoche, 1993, p. 113).

I have pointed out in earlier chapters that it takes hard work to produce a good illusion. In the virtual reality model, innumerable parallel worlds could be manifested, along with protocols for communication between worlds. However, this would require the existence of highly sophisticated software—or its equivalent—supported by the hypothetical Ground Reality. The same point can be made about the Rigpa. To sustain complex, inhabited worlds, the Rigpa must be endowed with vast capacities to direct and manipulate information. Even though the shifting patterns of information are empty and evanescent, there must exist something permanent in the background that is capable of producing them.

Tibetan Buddhist cosmology also includes enlightened beings in various categories, including many buddhas. Sogyal explains these beings as follows:

The five masculine buddhas are the pure aspect of the five aggregates of ego. Their five wisdoms are the pure aspects of the five negative emotions. The five female buddhas are the pure elemental qualities of mind, which we experience as the impure elements of our physical body and environment. The eight bodhisattvas are the pure aspect of the different types of consciousness, and their female counterparts are the objects of these consciousnesses (Rinpoche, 1993, p. 280).

All of these deities are "in the mind," but not in the finite, discursive mind of the individual. Rather, they are aspects of the universal mind. Here we seem to have a philosophy similar to Plato's, with the buddhas serving as the pure, ideal counterparts of imperfect earthly emotions and states of ego.

Sogyal points out that spiritual realization is to recognize one's true identity with the universal mind. While this is not attained, the deities appear to be external to the individual, and Sogyal speculates that for Christians, they might take the form of Christ or the Virgin Mary (Rinpoche, 1993, p. 284). When realization is achieved, these distinctions vanish and the practitioner "realizes that the mind that perceives the deity and the deity itself are not separate" (Rinpoche, 1993, p. 285). This, however, does not diminish the reality or greatness of the deity, which is part of the universal mind and not part of the limited mind of the individual.

One medieval Tibetan Buddhist named Dombipa apparently argued that emptiness applies only to material reality. According to Buddhist scholar Robin Kornman, Dombipa held that, "whereas a critique from the point of view of emptiness seems to erase the conventional world from existence, further contemplation will show that there is an extraordinary world left over after the critique, a sacred world full of nonconventional beings and things—buddhas and their infinite qualities" (Kornman, 2001, p. 77).

In addition to buddhas, Tibetan tradition also includes many enlightened masters, such as Padmasambhava, who established Buddhism in Tibet in the eighth century. It is said that Padmasambhava "has appeared countless times to the masters of Tibet, and these meetings and visions have been precisely recorded: the date, the place, and manner in which they occurred, along with the teachings and prophecies Padmasambhava gave" (Rinpoche, 1993, p. 145). Padmasambhava once walked the earth as a man, but tradition maintains that he continues to live today.

This implies that the universal mind must provide a suitable vehicle for an enlightened being who continues to exist in individual form beyond the physical plane of existence. In summary, the universal mind must be endowed with many inherent qualities and capacities needed to manifest worlds of conscious life. Here I am extracting an account of these qualities and capacities from an old tradition by logical analysis. But the possibility is there that one might acquire direct knowledge of these topics by immediate experience and that such experience may have contributed substantially to the creation of the tradition.

THE ABSOLUTE, WITH FORM AND WITHOUT

In Hinduism there are conceptions of the Absolute Consciousness that closely parallel the teachings of Buddhism. Even the nomenclature is similar. Thus Sogyal refers to the Ground Luminosity, or Clear Light, as an unveiling of the universal mind which occurs naturally at the moment of death. This parallels the Sanskrit term Brahmajyoti, where Brahma denotes the ultimate source and *jyoti* means light.

The Brahman or Brahmajyoti is described as *nirguna*, or devoid of qualities. However, this refers to material qualities pertaining to the realm of *maya*. The material qualities are by nature illusory, and temporary, but by no means nonexistent. In the virtual reality model, they correspond to the vast streams of ever changing information defining the virtual world. As such, they are accessible to rational analysis, which is itself simply a kind of data processing.

In contrast, the qualities of the Absolute resist rational analysis, and they are often described in terms of negation and paradox. Thus it will be said that whatever you can think of, the Absolute is not that. This means that the Absolute is "no thing," but it is far from being "nothing." The Absolute is also described in terms of opposites. Thus it has form and is formless, and it is both one and divided. These contradictory statements are intended to point to a reality that we can appreciate intuitively, even though it cannot be grasped by finite processes of symbol manipulation.

Saying that the Absolute is formless may be taken to imply that it has no form, but this applies only to material structure. A material form is made of little parts, such as atoms distributed in space or binary bits arranged in data structures. The Absolute is said to have a transcendental form in which each part is equivalent to the whole and can perform the functions of all the other parts.

The paradoxical nature of transcendental form is illustrated by a story about the childhood of the divine avatar Krishna. It is said that Krishna had been naughty and His mother Yasoda wanted to tie Him up with a rope as punishment. To her dismay, no matter how much she extended her rope by tying extra sections to it, it wouldn't stretch around Krishna's body until, finally, He allowed this to happen (*Bhagavatam*, 10.9.14–18). This, of course is impossible for a physical body, and the story points to a kind of form that is paradoxical. Significantly, it begins by saying that the Godhead "has no beginning and no end, no exterior and no interior, no front and no rear" (*Bhagavatam*, 10.9.14).

In some branches of Hinduism, it is taught that the Supreme is both personal and impersonal. For example, in the *Bhagavata Purana* it is said that "Learned transcendentalists who know the Absolute Truth call this nondual substance Brahman, Paramatma or Bhagavan" (*Bhagavatam*, 1.2.11). Here the term "nondual" (Sanskrit *advayam*) means that the Absolute is One. At the same time, it has three features: the all-pervasive consciousness (Brahman), the higher Self within the heart (Paramatma), and the Personality of Godhead (Bhagavan). Like the Father, Son, and Holy Spirit of the Christian Trinity, these three aspects are understood to be simultaneously one and different.

Here "personality" does not refer to the pattern of information defining the psychology of an embodied individual. The latter is actually a kind of persona, or dramatic representation, which hides the true personality both from itself and from others. Rather, "personality" refers to the underlying active subjectivity that turns these transforming patterns of information into a conscious being, and not a mere machine.

THE THEORY OF EVOLUTION

The idea that species are produced through gradual physical transmutation, starting with primitive life forms, is apparently a creation of modern European thinking, dating back no further than the 18th century in well developed form. One of the main incentives for this development was the rising awareness that the earth dates back much further than the celebrated Biblical creation date of 4004 B.C., calculated by Archbishop Ussher in 1654. As naturalists pushed back the age of the earth, the Biblical story of a recent creation in six days seemed more and more untenable. The layered strata of the earth seemed to point to great age, and the fossils pointed to a succession of forms of life. Evolution by physical processes appeared as a rational alternative that could be accepted by scientists schooled in Newtonian mechanistic thinking.

It is ironic that traditional Hindu chronology posits vast, cosmic time cycles, ranging from the divine *yuga* of 4,320,000 years to the day of Brahma, 1,000 times as long. Yet the idea of a progressive transmutation of species apparently does not appear in traditional Indian thought. Life forms, numbering 8,400,000, are said to be created and annihilated repeatedly in the course of cyclic time, but they are declared to be always the same as the species inhabiting the earth today.

In the East, nearly all of the old contemplative traditions take a cyclic or steady-state view of history. However, these traditional systems do generally contain the idea of a progressive evolution of consciousness from lower to higher states.

The Hindu text known as the *Padma Purana* provides an example of the idea of evolving consciousness. This traditional text posits a gradual evolution of souls by transmigration through 8,400,000 different forms of life. This process is generally progressive, although reversals are admitted. Remarkably, the evolutionary succession is given as aquatics, plants, insects and reptiles, birds, beasts, and human beings (Prabhupada, 1970). This parallels the paleontological succession of marine life, terrestrial plants, insects and amphibians, reptiles, birds, advanced mammals, and finally humans. The parallelism is so close that the modern Vaishnava teacher Bhaktivedanta Swami Prabhupada saw the *Padma Purana* as anticipating Darwin's theory of evolution (Prabhupada, 1972a). However, he personally adhered to the traditional doctrine of evolution through transmigration.

Prabhupada's predecessor, Bhaktivinod Thakur (1838–1914), made a similar conservative rapprochement with evolution. Bhaktivinod was a Vaishnava theologian who worked as a magistrate in the British Raj and was greatly concerned with the impact of Western ideas on traditional Indian thought. In a work composed in 1879, he interpreted the traditional ten incarnations (avatars) of Vishnu in an evolutionary sense. Thus he remarked that

> When the *jiva* takes the form of a fish, Bhagavan becomes the Matsya *avatara*. A fish is spineless, but when the spineless state gradually becomes the hardshell state, the Kurma *avatara* appears. When the hard-shell state gradually becomes a spine, the Boar (Varaha) incarnation appears (Dasa, 1999, p. 131).

Bhaktivinod is clearly taking "fish" (*matsya*) to mean an invertebrate marine creature. He says that the historical succession of ten avatars lines up with a matching succession of life forms, beginning with invertebrates and culminating in fully conscious man. Although this is a significant departure from traditional thinking, it appears that Bhaktivinod never systematically developed his evolutionary ideas or gave very great stress to them.

A more radical approach to evolution was taken by the Indian yogi and revolutionary, Sri Aurobindo. Aurobindo accepted the physical evolution of species and interpreted it as a steady progression toward ever-higher forms of consciousness, powered by the Supermind (Feuerstein, 1998a, p. 76). This is the solution I mentioned in Chapter 11, in which the temporal chain of being is directed by the atemporal chain, which has existed all along. Aurobindo followed this solution to its natural conclusion by arguing that

> If a spiritual unfolding on earth is the hidden truth of our birth into Matter, if it is fundamentally an evolution of consciousness that has been taking place in Nature, then man as he is cannot be the last term of that evolution: he is too imperfect an expression of the spirit, mind itself a too limited form and instrumentation. . . . If, then, man is incapable of exceeding mentality, he must be surpassed and supermind and superman must manifest and take the lead of the creation. (Aurobindo, 1949, p. 292).

Aurobindo devoted his life to the understanding of how humanity might evolve to a higher stage, in which the body becomes "concentrated energy which obeys the will," rather than "a little soul carrying corpse" (Govindan, 1991, p. 143). In recent years, Michael Murphy of Esalen has taken up Aurobindo's idea of evolution and made it the motivation for an extensive investigation of human potential (Murphy, 1992).

AN EVOLUTIONARY DILEMMA

Although he accepted evolution, Aurobindo did not base his ideas on the Darwinian mechanism of evolution. Rather, he agreed with Alfred Russel Wallace in seeing evolution as an unfolding within nature of an existing divine order. This involves taking the hierarchical levels of an atemporal Chain of Being as the stages of a temporal evolutionary sequence. Superman should follow man because superman already exists, either in manifest or potentially manifest form.

This view of evolution has been elaborated by the contemporary philosopher Ken Wilber. He describes the Chain of Being as follows:

> Involution is the prior (but also timeless) movement whereby spirit goes out of itself to create soul, which goes out of itself to create mind, which goes out of itself to create body (*prana*), which goes out of itself to create matter. Each junior level is a restriction, manifestation, or stepped down expression of its senior dimension . . . but each lower wave 'forgets' its senior dimension (amnesia), so the end product is the world of matter, lying around all by itself and wondering how it got there (Wilber, 2001, p. 368).

Given this hierarchy stretching from spirit to matter, "Evolution then proceeds to unfold and remember that which was enfolded and forgotten: out of matter arises life; out of life evolves mind; out of mind emerges soul; out of soul emerges spirit, which is both the Ground and the Goal of the entire sequence" (Wilber, 2001, p. 368).

Here one can interpret the sequence of matter, body, mind, soul, and spirit to refer to different levels or modes of conscious functioning, ranging from the most restricted up to the most expansive. Thus "matter," in the context of the virtual reality model, means consciousness identifying with the virtual world in a very limited way and "spirit" means consciousness situated in its own glory, whether connected with a virtual body or not.

The word "evolution" is actually based on Latin words meaning "out-rolling" or unfolding. But one may presume that this process of unfolding is flexible, and that it can even be influenced by Darwinian natural selection. Thus we do not have to suppose that the rhinoceros of Sumatra and Java must be contained in the hierarchy of involution in order to be manifested in time. But the basic ideal forms of the hierarchy are there as templates for evolutionary development.

Wilber's theory applies on both the microcosmic and macrocosmic levels. On the former, it allows for the development human consciousness within one lifetime. From a scientific standpoint, it may seem that the development of consciousness simply reduces to the organization of matter in the brain. However, in Wilber's model, the higher levels of the chain are not reducible to the lower levels. Thus the lower levels cannot generate the higher levels. Rather, development is a matter of activating higher levels of consciousness and allowing them to create effects on lower levels. Put simply, self realization requires a self to realize, and when realization occurs, the physical body is also transformed.

In the virtual reality model, this translates into a requirement for transformation within consciousness. Involution is the process by which the One generates many within itself (while remaining one). The virtual world is then a playground in which various transformed modes of consciousness can be tried out in a simulated environment. For this to be worth doing, one can surmise that conscious entities will learn something from the experience that wouldn't have emerged if the One simply remained undifferentiated.

On the macroscopic level, this scheme becomes a theory of the origin of species. Its alternatives seem to be (1) strict Darwinism, (2) a single creation as in Christian teachings, (3) multiple creations and annihilations as in Hinduism, or (4) a steady state with no beginning as in Buddhism. However, in one sense this theory does not contradict the old notions of cyclic or steady-state chronology. If evolution can repeatedly unfold on the microcosmic level, it can also do so on the macrocosmic scale. Given the billions of years during which the universe has existed and the vast numbers of habitable planets that may exist, the unfolding of systems of species may be a commonplace affair.

This looks like a plausible evolutionary scenario which accommodates the scientific data on evolution while at the same time incorporating spiritual hope and progress. However, from a scientific perspective it confronts us with a serious problem. Human and superhuman stages of development are included in the atemporal chain, and thus they and the higher spirit above them antedate the evolutionary process. Putting it bluntly, does God have a human body, or does human nature somehow pre-exist in the Absolute?

If by human body we mean an arrangement of intestines, blood vessels, and other plumbing, then the answer is clearly no. These are details that might be worked out in a variety of other ways. However, the essence of human nature must be there in the timeless involutional hierarchy for this scheme of evolution to work. The Absolute must be as anthropomorphic, in an idealized sense, as it was ever thought to be in traditional religious systems. In addition, although particular bodily details may not be indispensable, these details may represent a solution to a problem based on absolute goals. For example, I argued in Chapter 11 that the human body as we know it may be a pre-evolved platform for the manifestation of higher consciousness. In other words, the human body may be a particular solution to the problem of how to manifest higher stages of consciousness in the context of earthly mammalian life.

SUMMING UP

We began this chapter with the aim of learning something about the "Ground Reality" of consciousness that plays a key role in the metaphorical virtual reality model. What seems to emerge is a model that melds together several different elements in a paradoxical way. These elements include consciousness itself, which remains as inexplicable as ever. In addition, there is active power that is capable of processing data on a vast scale. This corresponds to *maya*, the power of illusion in traditional Indian thought. Finally, there is built-in information that makes the Ground Reality specific. In the computer analogy, this corresponds to the difference between an unprogrammed universal computer, which could do anything but does nothing in particular, and a programmed computer that carries out particular applications. All three of these features exist together in a paradoxical undivided unity.

The built-in information does not have to literally consist of strings of bits, as the computer metaphor suggests. It may consist of Platonic ideal forms (whatever they are) or ideal functions that cannot be reduced to mere abstractions or concepts. In Buddhism, the built-in information corresponds to the various Buddhas and the ideal principles that they embody or represent. In Vaishnava thought, it corresponds to the primordial couples, Radha-Krishna or Lakshmi-Narayan, that are the original templates for all individualized beings. This aspect of the Ground Reality is perhaps the most difficult to accept from a modern standpoint, since it makes the Absolute appear to be anthropomorphic. But it is this aspect that defines the Chain of Being and allows it to drive an evolutionary process that manifests progressively higher expressions of consciousness.

WHY?

While reflecting on the possibility of a unified theory of the universe, Stephen Hawking noted that such a theory is just a collection of rules and equations. So he asked, "What is it that breathes fire into the equations and makes a universe for them to describe?" (Hawking, 1988, p. 174). One could say that the rules selected for the universal virtual reality are the ones that came alive and had a universe to describe. But why create a virtual universe in the first place?

Consider the history of life on the earth. According to paleontology and archeology, life on earth began with billions of years of bacteria and blue-green algae. Gradually the pace of change picked up. There have been marine invertebrates for about 600 million years, reptiles for half as long, and advanced mammals for about 60 million years. Human civilization seems to date back no more than some 10 thousand years, and advanced science and technology go back three or four centuries at most. It is natural to ask why this exponentially accelerating development has taken place, and where it is headed.

By introducing a timeless hierarchy of being and turning it on its side, we can give a tentative answer to this question that may have some intuitive appeal. This directed model of evolution may explain some features of the past. It may also predict an interesting future in which extraordinary features of consciousness that are now rarely seen gradually become systematically manifest. These include the paranormal abilities discussed in Chapters 6–10 and the higher modes of consciousness exhibited by perfected beings.

We are still faced with the important question of why beings must struggle in ignorance, if the absolute consciousness has always existed in perfection. Why must consciousness gradually progress through hundreds of millions of years of lowly creatures, before flowering into advanced spiritual beings? Some schools of thought have attributed this to a fall from grace, and others have simply started with the reality of ignorance and sought to annul it by attaining enlightenment.

It would appear that the original One Being differentiates through emanations and eventually expands consciousness into the lowest levels of the chain of being. From there consciousness gradually rises up and returns to its original source. Is this simply an expression of divine overflowingness, or is there a deep purpose behind it? We may wonder whether the great experiment in virtual reality is simply an unfolding of what was always potentially there, or whether it will bring back something truly new to the universal consciousness.

BIBLIOGRAPHY

Agnellet, Michel, 1958, *I Accept These Facts*, London: Max Parrish.

Almeder, Robert, 1997, "A Critique of Arguments Offered Against Reincarnation," *Journal of Scientific Exploration*, Vol. 11, No. 4, pp. 499–526.

Aspect, A. and Grangier, P., 1986, "Experiments on Einstein-Podolsky-Rosen-type correlations with pairs of visible photons," in *Quantum Concepts in Space and Time*, R. Penrose and J. C. Isham, eds., Oxford: Oxford University Press.

Aurobindo Ghose, Sri, 1949, *The Human Cycle*, Pondichery, India 605002: Sri Aurobindo Ashram Press.

Barrington, Mary Rose, July 1992, "Palladino and the Invisible Man Who Never Was," *Journal of the Society for Psychical Research,* Vol. 58, No. 828, pp. 324–40.

Begley, Sharon, 2001, "Searching for the God Within," *Newsweek*, Jan. 29, 2001.

Behe, Michael, 1996, *Darwin's Black Box*, New York: The Free Press.

Benor, Daniel J., *Healing Research*, Vol. 1, Deddington, UK: Helix Editions, Ltd.

Bhagavatam, Srimad, 1972–82, translation and commentary by A. C. Bhaktivedanta Swami Prabhupada, Los Angeles: Bhaktivedanta Book Trust.

Bohm, David and Hiley, B. J., 1984, "Measurement Understood Through the Quantum Potential Approach," *Foundations of Physics,* Vol. 14, No. 3, pp. 255–74.

Bower, B., Dec. 2, 1995, "Brain scans set sights on mind's eye," *Science News,* Vol. 148, No. 23, p. 372.

Braude, Stephen, 1991, *The Limits of Influence*, London: Routledge.

Brenner, Barbara Ann, 1988, *Hands of Light*, Toronto: Bantam Books.

Bryan, Ronald A., 2000, "What Can Elementary Particles Tell Us About the World in Which We Live?", *Journal of Scientific Exploration,* Vol. 14, No. 2.

Copleston, Frederick, 1964, *A History of Philosophy*, Vol. 5, Garden City, New York: Image Books.

Costa de Beauregard, Olivier, 1979, "The Expanding Paradigm of the Einstein Paradox," in *The Iceland Papers,* ed., Andrija Puharich, Amherst, Wisconsin: Essentia Research Associates.

Cremo, Michael and Thompson, Richard, 1993, *Forbidden Archeology*, Los Angeles: Bhaktivedanta Book Publishing, Inc.

261

Crick, Francis and Orgel, Leslie, 1973, *Icarus*, Vol. 19, p. 341.

Crick, Francis, 1981, *Life Itself,* New York: Simon and Schuster.

Crick, Francis, 1994, *The Astonishing Hypothesis,* New York: Simon and Schuster.

Cvitanovic, Predrag, ed., 1984, *Universality in Chaos*, Bristol, UK: Adam Hilger Ltd.

Darwin, Charles, 1896, *The Life and Letters of Charles Darwin*, ed. Francis Darwin, Vol. 1, New York: Appleton.

Darwin, Charles, 1960, "Darwin's Notebooks on Transmutation of Species. Part 3. Third Notebook" (July 15th 1838–October 2nd 1838), Sir Gavin de Beer (ed.), *Bulletin of the British Museum (Natural History) Historical Series*, Vol. 2, No. 4., London.

Dasa, Shukavak N., 1999, *Hindu Encounter with Modernity*, Los Angeles: SRI.

Davies, P. C. W., 1992, *The Mind of God,* New York: Simon and Schuster.

Davies, P. C. W. and Brown, J. R., eds., 1986, *The Ghost in the Atom,* Cambridge: Cambridge Univ. Press.

Dawkins, Richard, 1986, *The Blind Watchmaker*, W. W. Norton & Co.

Dennett, Daniel, 1981, "Where Am I?", in *The Mind's I,* D. R. Hofstadter and D. C. Dennett, eds., Toronto: Bantam Books.

Dennett, Daniel, 1991, *Consciousness Explained*, Boston: Little, Brown and Co.

Dennett, Daniel, 1996, "Commentary on Chalmers," *Journal of Consciousness Studies*, Vol. 3, No. 1, pp. 4–6.

Dennett, Daniel, Oct. 4, 2000, "A friendly alert to Jaron Lanier," www.edge.org, Deutsch, David and Lockwood, Michael, March, 1994, "The Quantum Physics of Time Travel," *Scientific American,* Vol. 270, No. 3.

Dewitt, Bryce S. and Graham, Neill, eds., 1973, *The Many-Worlds Interpretation of Quantum Mechanics,* Princeton, NJ: Princeton University Press

Dickerson, R. E., 1980, "Cytochrome c and the evolution of energy metabolism," *Scientific American*, 242, No. 3, pp. 137–53.

Ditto, W. L., Rauseo, S. N., and Spano, M. L., Dec. 24, 1990, "Experimental Control of Chaos," *Physical Review Letters,* Vol. 65, No. 26, pp. 3211–3214.

Dunne, B. J., Jahn, R. J., and Nelson, R. D., 1983, *Precognitive Remote Perception,* Engineering Anomalies Research Laboratory, School of Engineering/Applied Science, Princeton University.

Dunne, B. J., Jahn, R. J., and Nelson, R. D., 1985, *Princeton Engineering Anomalies Research,* Engineering Anomalies Research Laboratory, School of Engineering/Applied Science, Princeton University.

Dyson, Freeman, July 1979a, "Time without end: Physics and biology in an open universe," *Reviews of Modern Physics,* Vol. 51, No. 3, pp. 447–60.

Dyson, Freeman, 1979b, *Disturbing the Universe,* New York: Harper and Row.

Eliade, Mircea, 1964, *Shamanism: Archaic Techniques of Ecstasy,* Princeton: Princeton University Press.

Elkins, Don and Rueckert, Carla, 1977, *Secrets of the UFO,* Louisville, KY: L/L Research.

Everett, Hugh III, July, 1957, "'Relative State' Formulation of Quantum Mechanics," *Reviews of Modern Physics,* Vol. 29, No. 3, pp. 454–462.

Fact sheet on de Rudder, published at Lourdes: Imprimerie de la Grotte.

Fact sheet on Traynor, published at Lourdes: Imprimerie de la Grotte.

Fersht, A., 1977, *Enzyme Structure and Mechanism,* San Francisco: W. H. Freeman.

Feuerstein, Georg, 1998a, *The Yoga Tradition,* Prescott, Arizona: Hohm Press.

Feuerstein, Georg, 1998b, *Tantra,* Boston: Shambala.

Feynman, Richard, December 29, 1959, "There's Plenty of Room at the Bottom," lecture given at the annual meeting of the American Physical Society.

Feynman, Richard, 1985, *QED,* Princeton: Princeton University Press.

Fishman, Steve, September 1990, "The Dean of Psi," *Omni,* Vol. 12, No. 12.

Fjermedal, Grant, 1986, *The Tomorrow Makers,* New York: Macmillan.

Folger, Tim, Dec. 2000, "From Here to Eternity," *Discover,* Vol. 21, No. 12.

Fontana, David, April, 1991, "A Responsive Poltergeist: A Case from South Wales," *Journal of the Society for Psychical Research,* Vol. 57, No. 823, pp. 385–402.

Fontana, David, April, 1992, "The Responsive South Wales Poltergeist: A Follow-up Report," *Journal of the Society for Psychical Research,* Vol. 58, No. 827, pp. 225–31.

Gauld, Alan, 1983, *Mediumship and Survival,* London: Paladin Books, Granada Publishing Ltd.

Gauld, Alan, and Cornell, A. D., 1979, *Poltergeists,* London: Routledge & Kegan Paul.

Gell-Mann, Murray and Hartle, James B., 1990, "Quantum Mechanics in the Light of Quantum Cosmology," in *Complexity, Entropy, and the Physics of Information,* Vol. 8, ed. W. H. Zurek, Redwood City, California: Addison-Wesley Pub. Co., pp. 425–58.

Gesteland, R. F. and Atkins, J. F., eds., 1993, *The RNA World,* Cold Spring Harbor, NY: Cold Spring Harbor Laboratory Press.

Glanvil, Joseph, 1682, *Saducismus Triumphatus,* London: printed by Tho.

Newcomb, for S. Lownds at his Shop by the Savoy Gate.

Goldberger, A. L., Rigney, D. R., and West, B. J., Feb. 1990, "Chaos and Fractals in Human Physiology," *Scientific American,* pp. 42–49.

Goldstein, Alvin G., 1976, "Hallucinatory Experience: A Personal Account," *Journal of Abnormal Psychology,* Vol. 85, pp. 423–29.

Goswami, Shyam Sundar, 1999, *Layayoga: The Definitive Guide to the Chakras and Kundalini,* Rochester, Vermont: Inner Traditions.

Gould, Stephen Jay, 1977a, *Ontogeny and Phylogeny,* Cambridge: Harvard University Press.

Gould, Stephen Jay, 1977b, *Ever Since Darwin,* New York: W.W. Norton & Co.

Gould, Stephen Jay, 1980, "Chance Riches," *Natural History,* Vol. 89, No. 11.

Gould, Stephen Jay, 1996, *Full House,* New York: Three Rivers Press.

Govindan, Marshall, 1991, *Babaji and the 18 Siddha Kriya Yoga Tradition,* Montreal: Kriya Yoga Publications.

Green, Elmer, Nov. 21, 1990, *Consciousness, Psychophysiology and Psychophysics: An Overview,* Topeka, Kansas: The Menninger Clinic.

Greene, Brian, 1999, *The Elegant Universe,* New York: Vintage Books.

Gribben, John, 1984, *In Search of Schrödinger's Cat,* London: Wildwood House.

Gurney, Edmund, Myers, Frederick W. H., and Podmore, Frank, 1886, *Phantasms of the Living,* Vol. 2, Gainesville, Florida: Scholars' Facsimilies and Reprints, 1970.

Hahn, Roger, 1967, *Laplace as a Newtonian Scientist,* Los Angeles: Univ. of California.

Hansel, C. E. M., 1966, *ESP: A Scientific Evaluation,* New York: Charles Scribner's Sons.

Hawking, Stephen, 1988, *A Brief History of Time,* Toronto: Bantam Books.

Hawking, Stephen, 1993, *Black Holes and Baby Universes,* New York: Bantam Books.

Henon, M., 1976, "A Two-dimensional Mapping with a Strange Attractor," *Communications in Mathematical Physics,* Vol. 50, pp. 69–77.

Home, Daniel Dunglass, 1879, *Lights and Shadows of Spiritualism,* New York: G. W. Carleton & Co.

Honorton, Charles and Ferrari, Diane C., December, 1989, "'Future Telling': A Meta-Analasis of Forced-Choice Precognition Experiments, 1935–1987," *Journal of Parapsychology,* Vol. 53.

Hoyle, Fred, 1982, "The Universe: Past and Present Reflections," *Annual Review of Astronomy and Astrophysics*: 20:16

Hoyle, Fred and Wickramasinghe, Chandra, 1981, *Evolution from Space,* London: J. M. Dent and Sons.

Hume, David, 1902, *An Inquiry Concerning Human Understanding,* in *Enquiries Concerning Human Understanding and Concerning the Principles of Morals,* 2nd edition, ed. L. A. Selby-Bigge, Oxford.

Irwin, H. J., 1987, "Out-of-body experiences in the blind," *Jour. of Near-Death Studies,* 6, pp. 53–60.

Johnston, Francis, 1979, *Fatima,* Rockford, Ill.: Tan Books.

Jung, C. G., 1973, *Synchronicity, An Acausal Connecting Principle,* Princeton: Princeton University Press.

Kaku, Michio, 1994, *Hyperspace,* New York: Oxford University Press.

Kistiakowsky, Vera, 2000, "Quotes from Scientists Regarding Design of the Universe," posted on the world wide web, last updated 5/3/2000.

Kornman, Robin, March 2001, "On This You Can Rely (As Time Goes By)," *Shambhala Sun,* Vol. 9, No. 4, pp. 77–79.

Krippner, Stanley, September, 1994, "Waking Life, Dream Life, and the Construction of Reality," *Anthropology of Consciousness,* Vol. 5, No. 3, pp. 17–23.

Kurzweil, Ray, 1999, *The Age of Spiritual Machines,* New York: Viking.

La Mettrie, Julien Offroy de, 1747, *L'homme machine.*

Lanier, Jaron, 2000, "One Half of a Manifesto," www.edge.org.

Lemley, Brad, Nov. 2000, "Why Is There Life?", *Discover,* Vol. 21, No. 11.

Leibniz, Gottfried, 1714, *The Monadology.*

Libit, Benjamin, December 1985, "Unconscious cerebral initiative and the role of conscious will in voluntary action," *The Behavioral and Brain Sciences,* Vol. 8, No. 4.

Lorenz, Edward, 1963, "Deterministic Nonperiodic Flow," *Journal of the Atmospheric Sciences,* Vol. 20, pp. 130–41.

Macy, Mark, Spring 1993, "When Dimensions Cross," *Noetic Sciences Review,* No. 25, pp. 17–20.

Mattuck, Richard D. and Walker, Evan Harris, 1979, "The Action of Consciousness on Matter: A Quantum Mechanical Theory of Psychokinesis," in *The Iceland Papers,* ed., Andrija Puharich, Amherst, Wisconson: Essentia Research Associates.

McGreevy, Michael, 1989, "Personal Simulators and Planetary Exploration," NASA Ames Research Center.

Mishlove, Jeffrey, 1975, *The Roots of Consciousness,* New York: Random House.

Moody, Raymond, 1993, *Reunions,* New York: Ivy Books.

Moravec, Hans, 1989, "Human Culture: A Genetic Takeover Underway," in *Artificial Life,* Santa Fe Institute Studies in the Sciences of Complexity, Vol. 6, ed. C. Langton, Redwood City, California: Addison-Wesley Publishing Co.

Mouren, Pierre, 1976, *The Cure of Serge Perrin,* Lourdes: Imprimerie de La
    Grotte.
Murphy, Michael, 1992, *The Future of the Body,* Los Angeles: Jeremy P.
    Tarcher, Inc.
Nash, Madeleine, Dec. 4, 1995, "When Life Exploded," *Time.*
Neelakantan, V. T., 1952, *Mysticism Unlocked*, 9, Surammal Lane, Egmore,
    Madras-8, India: V. T. Neelakantan and S. A. A. Ramaiah, publishers.
Nelson, R. D., Dunne, B. J., and Jahn, R. G., 1988, "Operator Related
    Anomalies in a Random Mechanical Cascade Experiment," Princeton:
    Princeton Engineering Anomalies Research, Princeton University.
Newberg, Andrew and D'Aquili, Eugene, 2001, *Why God Won't Go Away*,
    New York: Ballintine Books.
Newton, Isaac, January 17, 1692/3, Letter to Richard Bentley in *The Corre-
    spondence of Isaac Newton*, Vol. III, 1688–1694, ed. H.W. Turnbull,
    Cambridge University Press, 1961.
Newton, Michael, 2000, *Destiny of Souls*, St. Paul, Minn.: Llewellyn Publica-
    tions.
Newton, Michael, 2000, *Journey of Souls*, St. Paul, Minn.: Llewellyn Publica-
    tions.
Ofshe, Richard and Watters, Ethan, March/April 1993, "Making Monsters,"
    Society, Vol. 30, No. 3, pp. 4–16.
Oparin, A. I., 1938, *The Origin of Life*, trans. Sergius Morgulis, second ed.,
    1953, by New York: Dover Publications, Inc.
O'Regan, Brendan, 1991, "Healing, Remission, and Miracle Cures," *in
    Noetic Sciences Collection*, eds., B. McNeill and C. Guion, Sausalito, Ca.:
    Institute for Noetic Sciences.
O'Regan, Brendan and Hirshberg, Caryle, 1993, *Spontaneous Remission*,
    Sausalito, CA: Institute of Noetic Sciences.
Ostoma, Tom and Trushyk, Mike, July 7, 1999, "Cellular Automata Theory
    and Physics," internet document, emqg@rogerswave.ca.
Pasricha, Satwant, 1990, *Claims of Reincarnation*, Harman Publishing House.
Pasricha, Satwant and Stevenson, Ian, 1986, "Near-Death Experiences in
    India," *The Journal of Nervous and Mental Disease*, The Williams &
    Wilkens Co., pp. 165–70.
Pattee, H. H., 1989, "Simulations, Realizations, and Theories of Life," in
    Artificial Life, Santa Fe Institute Studies in the Sciences of Complexity,
    Vol. 6, ed. C. Langton, Redwood City, California: Addison-Wesley
    Publishing Co.
Penrose, Roger, 1989, *The Emperor's New Mind,* New York: Oxford
    University Press.
Pfleegor, R. L. and Mandel, L., July 25, 1967, "Interference of Independent

Photon Beams," *Physical Review*, Vol. 159, No. 5, pp. 1084–88.

Polkinghorne, 1986, *One World*, London: SPCK.

Popper, Karl R. and Eccles, John C., 1977, *The Self and Its Brain*, New York: Springer International.

Poulsen, Hans, June 26–30, 1992, Lecture in Panel on Medical Anomalies, ISSSEEM 2nd Annual Conference, Bridging the Paradigms Through Clinical Practice, Research & Theory.

Prabhupada, A. C. Bhaktivedanta Swami, 1970, Letter to Hayagriva, dated March 9, 1970.

Prabhupada, A. C. Bhaktivedanta Swami, 1972a, Lecture in Bombay, Nov. 19, 1972.

Prabhupada, A. C. Bhaktivedanta Swami, 1972b, Letter to Madhudvisa, May 16, 1972.

Prabhupada, A. C. Bhaktivedanta Swami, 1973, *Sri Caitanya-caritamrta of Krishnadasa Kaviraja Gosvami, Adi-lila*, Vol. 2, Los Angeles: Bhaktivedanta Book Trust.

Prabhupada, A. C. Bhaktivedanta Swami, 1974, *Sri Caitanya-caritamrta of Krishnadasa Kaviraja Gosvami, Adi-lila*, Vol. 1, Los Angeles: Bhaktivedanta Book Trust.

Prabhupada, A. C. Bhaktivedanta Swami, 1975, *Sri Caitanya-caritamrta of Krishnadasa Kaviraja Gosvami, Madhya-lila*, Vol. 2, Los Angeles: Bhaktivedanta Book Trust.

Prabhupada, A. C. Bhaktivedanta Swami, 1986, *Bhagavad-gita As It Is*, Los Angeles: Bhaktivedanta Book Trust.

Pribram, Karl, 1982, "What the Fuss is All About," in *The Holographic Paradigm,* ed. Ken Wilber, Boulder and London: Shambala.

Prigogine, Ilya, 1980, *From Being to Becoming*, San Francisco: W. H. Freeman and Co.

Puthoff, Harold and Targ, Russell, March, 1976, "A Perceptual Channel for Information Transfer over Kilometer Distances: Historical Perspective and Recent Research," *Proceedings of the IEEE,* Vol. 64, No. 3, pp. 329–54.

Radin, Dean and Nelson, Roger, 1989, "Consciousness-related effects in random physical systems," *Foundations of Physics,* Vol. 19, pp. 1499–1514.

Raghavan, V., 1956, "Yantras or Mechanical Contrivances in Ancient India," Transaction No. 10, Bangalore: The Indian Institute of Culture.

Rees, Martin, 1999, *Just Six Numbers*, Weidenfeld & Nicolson.

Rein, Glen, 1992, *Quantum Biology: Healing with Subtle Energy*, Palo Alto, CA: Quantum Biology Research Labs.

Ramachandran, V. S., and Blakeslee, Sandra, 1998, *Phantoms in the Brain*, New York: William and Morrow.

Restak, Richard, 1994, *The Modular Brain,* New York: Simon and Schuster.

Rheingold, Howard, 1991, *Virtual Reality*, New York: Simon and Schuster.

Rhine, J. B., 1974, "A New Case of Experimenter Unreliability," *Journal of Parapsychology,* Vol. 38, pp. 215–25.

Rhine, J. B., 1977, "History of Experimental Studies," in *Handbook of Parapsychology,* B. Wolman, ed., New York: Van Nostrand Rheinhold Co.

Rhine, Louisa, 1961, *Hidden Channels of the Mind,* New York: William Sloan Associates.

Ring, Kenneth, 1985, *Heading Toward Omega,* New York: Quill.

Ring, Kenneth and Cooper, Sharon, 1997, "Near-Death and Out-of-Body Experiences in the Blind: A Study of Apparent Eyeless Vision," *Journal of Near-Death Studies*, 16(2) Winter 1997.

Rinpoche, Sogyal, 1993, *The Tibetan Book of Living and Dying*, San Francisco: Harper.

Rogo, D. Scott, 1991, *Miracles: A Scientific Exploration of Wonderous Phenomena*, London: The Aquarian Press.

Roll, William G., 1977, "Poltergeists," in Benjamin B. Wolman, ed., *Handbook of Parapsychology*, New York: Van Nostrand Reinhold Co.

Rosen, Steven, 1991, *The Lives of the Vaishnava Saints, Shrinivas Acharya, Narottam Das Thakur, Shyamananda Pandit*, Brooklyn, New York: Folk Books.

Rostand, Jean, 1960, *Error and Deception in Science*, New York: Basic Books.

Rucker, Rudy, 1983, *Infinity and the Mind,* New York: Bantam Books.

Sabom, Michael, 1982, *Recollections of Death,* New York: Harper & Row.

Sabom, Michael, 1998, *Light and Death*, Grand Rapids, MI: Zondervan Publishing House.

Salim, Saslin, Mar. 26, 1993, "Finger Fighter," *The Week,* pp. 20–21.

Salmon, Michel-Marie, May 3, 1972, "La Gu'erison Extraordinaire de Vittorio Micheli, 'Sacome du Bassin'," Comite Medical International de Lourdes.

Schatzman, Morton, 1980, *New Scientist,* Vol. 87, pp. 935–37.

Schmidt, Helmut, 1970a, "Quantum-Mechanical Random-Number Generator," *Journal of Applied Physics,* Vol. 41, pp. 462–68.

Schmidt, Helmut, 1970b, "A PK Test with Electronic Equipment," *Journal of Parapsychology,* Vol. 34, No. 3, pp. 175–81.

Schmidt, Helmut, 1974a, "Comparison of PK action on two different random number generators," *Journal of Parapsychology,* Vol. 38, No. 1, pp. 47–55.

Schmidt, Helmut, 1974b, "Psychokinesis," in J. White, ed., *Psychic Exploration: A Challenge for Science,* New York: Perigree Books.

Schmidt, Helmut, 1975, "Toward a mathematical theory of psi," *Journal of the American Society for Psychical Research,* Vol. 69, pp. 301–19.

Schmidt, Helmut, 1976, "PK effect on pre-recorded targets," *Journal of the American Society for Psychical Research,* Vol. 70, pp. 267–92.

Schroeder, Gerald, 1977, *The Science of God,* New York: The Free Press.

Schwartz, Gary, 2002, *The Afterlife Experiments,* New York: Pocket Books.

Schwarz, Berthold, 1963–64, "Human Presumed Mitogenic Effect," *The Indian Journal of Parapsychology,* Vol. 5, No. 3, pp. 113–37.

Schwarz, Berthold, 1994, "Presumed Paranormal Linkage of Rings," *International Journal of Psychosomatics,* Vol. 41, Nos. 1–4, pp. 95–99.

Searle, John, 1981, "Minds, Brains, and Programs," in *The Mind's I,* D. R. Hofstadter and D. C. Dennett, eds., New York: Bantam Books.

Searle, John, 1990, "What is Wrong with the Philosophy of Mind," lecture delivered at the First International Conference on the Study of Consciousness within Science, held at University of California at San Francisco.

Shannon, Claude, July 1948, "A Mathematical Theory of Communication," *Bell System Technical Journal,* Vol. 27, pp. 379–423.

Sharp, Kimberly Clark, 1995, *After the Light,* New York: William and Morrow & Co., Inc.

Sheldrake, Rupert and Smart, Pamela, 2000, "A Dog That Seems to Know When His Owner Is Coming Home: Videotaped Experiments and Observations," *Journal of Scientific Exploration,* Vol. 14, No. 2.

Silk, Joseph, July 1995, "Road to Nowhere," *Scientific American,* Vol. 273, No. 1.

Skarda, C. A. and Freeman, W. J., 1987, "How brains make chaos in order to make sense of the world," *Behavioral and Brain Sciences,* 10:2, pp. 161–73.

Stapp, Henry, 1993, *Mind, Matter, and Quantum Mechanics,* Berlin: Springer-Verlag.

Stevenson, Ian, 1966, *Twenty Cases Suggestive of Reincarnation,* New York: American Society for Psychical Research.

Stevenson, Ian, 1971, "The Substantiality of Spontaneous Cases," in W. G. Roll, ed., *Proceedings of the Parapsychological Association,* No. 5, Duke Station, Durham, North Carolina.

Stevenson, Ian, July, 1972, "Are Poltergeists Living or Are They Dead?" *The Journal of the American Society for Psychical Research,* Vol. 66, No. 3.

Stevenson, Ian, 1996, "On the Necessity of Medical Documents in Claims of Paranormal Phenomena in Diseases," *Journal of Scientific Exploration,* Vol. 10, No. 2.

Stevenson, Ian, 1997, *Reincarnation and Biology,* Westport, Connecticut: Praeger.

Stevenson, Ian, 2000, "*The Truth in the Light* by Peter Fenwick and *Light and Death* by Michael Sabom*," Journal of Scientific Exploration*, Vol. 14, No. 1.

Stevenson, Ian and Greyson, Bruce, July 20, 1979, "Near-Death Experiences: Relevance to the Question of Survival After Death," *JAMA*, Vol. 242, No. 3.

Stevenson, I. and Pasricha, S., 1980, "A Preliminary Report on an Unusual Case of the Reincarnation Type with Xenoglossy," *The Journal of the American Society for Psychical Research*, 74, pp. 331–48.

Stevenson, Ian and Samaratne, Godwin, 1988, "Three New Cases of the Reincarnation Type in Sri Lanka With Written Records Made Before Verifications," *Journal of Scientific Exploration*, Vol. 2, No. 2, pp. 217–38.

Talbot, Michael, 1991, *The Holographic Universe,* Harper Perennial.

Targ, Russell, 1996, "Remote Viewing at Stanford Research Institute in the 1970s: A Memoir," *Journal of Scientific Exploration*, Vol. 10, No. 1, pp. 77–88.

Thompson, Richard, 1981, *Mechanistic and Nonmechanistic Science,* Los Angeles: Bhaktivedanta Book Trust.

Tipler, Frank, 1994, *The Physics of Immortality,* New York: Doubleday.

Toffoli, Tommaso, 1984, "Cellular Automata as an Alternative to (Rather than an Approximation of) Differential Equations in Modeling Physics," *Physica 10D,* pp. 117–27.

Turing, Alan, 1950, "Computing Machinery and Intelligence," *Mind,* Vol. LIX, No. 236.

von Neumann, John, 1949, "Fifth Lecture: Re-evaluation of the Problems of Complicated Automata—Problems of Hierarchy and Evolution," reproduced in *Theory of Self-Reproducing Automata*, ed. Author Burks, Urbana and London: Univ. of Illinois Press, 1966.

von Neumann, John, 1955, *Mathematical Foundations of Quantum Mechanics*, Princeton: Princeton University Press.

Wallace, Alfred Russel, 1895, *Natural Selection and Tropical Nature.*

Wallace, Alfred Russel, 1911, *The World of Life*, New York: Moffat, Yard, and Co.

Wassilko-Serecki, Z., 1926, "Obervations on Eleonore Zugun," *Journal of the American Society for Psychical Research*, 20:513–23, 593–603.

Weinberg, Steven, 1977, *The First Three Minutes*, New York: Bantam Books.

Weinberg, Steven, 1992, *Dreams of a Final Theory,* New York: Pantheon Books.

Weiss, Brian, 1988, *Many Lives, Many Masters*, New York: Simon and Schuster.

West, D. J., 1957, *Eleven Lourdes Miracles*, London: Gerald Duckworth.

Wheeler, John A., January 1988, "World as system self-synthesized by quantum networking," *IBM Journal of Research and Development*, Vol. 32, No. 1.

Wheeler, John A., September 1991, "Sakharov Revisited: It from Bit," manuscript.

Wheeler, John A., 1994, *At Home in the Universe*, New York: American Institute of Physics, p. 293.

Wigner, Eugene, 1960, "The Unreasonable Effectiveness of Mathematics in the Natural Sciences," *Communications in Pure and Applied Mathematics*, Vol. 13.

Wigner, Eugene, 1962, "Remarks on the Mind-Body Question," in *The Scientist Speculates*, ed. I. J. Good, New York: Basic Books.

Wigner, Eugene, 1964, "Two Kinds of Reality," *The Monist*, Vol. 48, pp. 248–64.

Wigner, Eugene, 1970, "Physics and the Explanation of Life," *Foundations of Physics*, Vol. 1, No. 1, pp. 35–45.

Wilber, Ken, 1996, *A Brief History of Everything*, Boston: Shambala.

Wilber, Ken, 2001, *The Eye of Spirit*, Boston: Shambala.

Wiseman, Richard, January, 1992, "The Feilding Report: A Reconsideration," *Journal of the Society for Psychical Research*, Vol. 58, No. 826, pp. 129–52.

Wiseman, R., Smith, M., and Milton, J., 1998, "Can animals detect when their owners are returning home? An experimental test of the 'psychic pet' phenomenon," *British Journal of Psychology*, 89, pp. 453–62.

Wiseman, R., Smith, M., and Milton, J., 2000, "The 'psychic pet' phenomenon: A reply to Rupert Sheldrake," *Journal of the Society for Psychical Research*, 64, pp. 46–49.

Woese, C. R., 1965, "On the evolution of the genetic code," *Proceedings of the National Academy of Sciences, USA*, 54, pp. 1546–51.

Wolfram, Stephen, 2001, "Publications by Stephen Wolfram—Random Sequence Generation by Cellular Automata," stephenwolfram.com.

Xu Jing-hua and Li Wei, 1986, "The Dynamics of Large Scale Neuroglia Network and Its Relation to the Brain Functions," *Communications in Theoretical Physics* (Beijing, China), Vol. 5, No. 4, pp. 339–346.

Ycăs, M., 1974, "On the earlier states of the biochemical system," *Journal of Theoretical Biology*, 44, pp. 145–60.

Yogananda, Paramahamsa, 1981, *Autobiography of a Yogi*, Los Angeles: Self-Realization Fellowship.

Zöllner, Johann, 1976, *Transcendental Physics,* reprint of the 1888 edition, New York: Arno Press.

INDEX

273